WHY WARRIORS
LIE DOWN & DIE

Towards an understanding of why the Aboriginal people
of Arnhem Land face the greatest crisis in health and
education since European contact.

DJAMBATJ MALA

By Richard Trudgen

Aboriginal Resource and Development
Services Inc. Darwin

Photographs

Front Cover: Witiyana Marika (taken by Bob Cross, 2000).
                    Witiyana is one of the founding members of the Youth Yindi band.
                    He is using the *bilma* (clapsticks) which have many uses from providing rythmn
                    for song cycles to being used by the political leaders to call the people together.

Rear Cover: Yolŋu men looking for barramundi in the Glyde River at the site where stockmen
                    crossed the river to attack the Yolŋu clans on the eastern side during the pastoral
                    wars from 1895 onwards (taken by Richard Trudgen, 1975).

Spine: Witiyana Marika (taken by Bob Cross, 2000)

Trudgen, R.I. (Richard Ian), 1950 -
Why Warriors Lie Down and Die

ISBN 0 646 39587 4

First Published in Australia in August 2000 by
Aboriginal Resource and Development Services Inc.,
First Floor, Uniting House,
191 Stuart Highway, Parap,
Northern Territory 0820

Second Printing: October 2000
Third Printing (with corrections):   March 2001
Fourth Printing (with corrections):   September 2001

© Richard Ian Trudgen, 2000

Cover Design by: Nick Brenner of NBFILMS

Typeset and Printed by
Openbook Publishers
205 Halifax St
Adelaide, South Australia, 5000

Aboriginal Resource and Development Services Inc.
www.ards.com.au

All proceeds from the sale of this book will go to
Aboriginal Resource & Development Services Inc.
for community development and community education work.

CONTENTS

ACKNOWLEDGEMENTS

Many people have contributed in one way or another to this book. First I must thank the Rev Dr Djiniyini Gondarra, my boss, for giving me this project and the support it required over three long years. Then for the support I received from all my colleagues at Aboriginal Resource and Development Services during the many exacting hours we all put in over this period. Thanks, guys, for arguing the arguments and for putting up with me when my brain couldn't take any more.

To my wife/friend Hazel and my children/friends, thanks for letting me be preoccupied every weekend and exhausted when I dropped into your 'time zone'—home.

To my Yolŋu friends, thanks for not giving up on me. I know at times you thought I'd caught the white fella disease of having to write a book instead of dealing with the crisis in front of us. My hope is that, in some strange way, this book will help relieve the crises that you face daily.

Thanks also to Rob and Ann Duffy for helping me to believe I could ever write anything and for introducing me to a word processor. And thanks, Ann, for doing so much of the original editing and helping me to find what I was really wanting to say.

Thanks to the scores of people who sent and introduced me to papers, books and other material that had to be ploughed through for referencing.

This would not have all gelled together without the expertise of my editor, Owen Salter. Thanks, Owen, for straightening up my rough work, yet allowing my style and arguments to flow freely.

Last but not least, I thank everyone who has influenced my thinking through debate and ideas in any way. Although these people are many, I still take full responsibility for all I have written within these pages.

GLOSSARY

Balanda is used to refer generally to non-Aboriginal or European people. It comes from the word 'Hollander' or 'Ballander'. When Aboriginal people from Arnhem Land first met white people in Sulawesi, Macassar (Ujung Pandang or Makassar), they saw the 'Ballanders', so the word for white person became Balanda. Balanda in the people's language has both a singular and plural sense like the English word 'sheep'.

Bäpurru is the patrilineal descent group, or clan, who find their corporate identity in the ownership of *yirralka* (traditional estates covering both land and water). It is the *bäpurru* or its members who own collectively all the surface resources of that estate. It is around the *bäpurru* that inter-clan trade is organised.

Djambatj is the term applied to a good hunter, the one who gets his quarry with a single shot. These people display a high level of mastery not only in the actual hunt, but also in the manufacture and use of weapons, an intimate knowledge of their environment and a great knowledge of the inner thinking and ability of their quarry. They have the great strength, skill and discipline of a *warrior*.

Mala is the term used to describe a group. *Djambatj mala* speaks of the great past deeds and abilities of the Yolŋu of Arnhem Land and of their potential for the future. This sub-heading will make more sense to Yolŋu than to most people who read this book as the term *djambatj* is a much-coveted title.

Riŋgitj is an alliance of *bäpurru* of the same moiety—a nation of clans. Up to six clans can make up one of these nation alliances. These nations can be spread over a great distance with other clans of other *riŋgitj* located in between them. This means that the clans of one nation do not have a common boundary with the other clans of the same nation. It is the *riŋgitj* that collectively owns the subsurface of all the clan estates within that alliance. In the whole of north-east Arnhem Land there are approximately sixteen nation groups. Each nation of land-owning clans shares a common constitution/law base. Each of the nations also has a common army for protection of each *bäpurru* estate within that nation.

Wämut is the *mälk* (skin name) which most Yolŋu use to refer to the author. There are sixteen such names that operate within the Yolŋu kinship system. Each person has only one skin name and it is used as a 'calling name' for everyday use.

Yolŋu is a word used specifically in this book to identify Aboriginal people in north-east Arnhem Land. In local languages it is the equivalent of 'person' or 'people', but it is now used to identify Aboriginal people as opposed to non-Aboriginal. Across Australia a number of words are used to identify different groups of Aboriginal people: *Koori* in the south, *Murri* in Queensland and so on. The term in north-east Arnhem Land is Yolŋu.

Yolŋu Matha, literally means 'Yolŋu tongue' and is the common term used by Yolŋu to refer to the range of traditional languages spoken by persons of different Yolŋu clans in the north-east Arnhem region. Each clan has its own particular language, but all Yolŋu can speak several (often many) languages because they are born into multilingual households. Some of the more commonly used languages, such as *Djambarrpuyŋu*, *Gupapuyŋu* and *Gumatj*, are fairly well understood throughout the north-east Arnhem region by each of the different clans.

Notes

ARDS is the Aboriginal Resource and Development Services Incorporated, a community development/community education organisation that has a twenty-five year history of working with Yolŋu. The ARDS organisation is my employer.

Dominant culture is used to refer to all who come from the dominant Australian cultural group, whatever their racial or ethnic background. People in this group usually speak English as a first language and would agree on most of the common core values that contemporary Australian people hold to. These values differ from those of the traditional indigenous people who speak their traditional languages, still live by their traditional laws, and for whom English is a second or subsequent language. Throughout the book I will use the term 'dominant culture', except in cases where I am quoting Yolŋu who use the more specific term like Balanda.

Moiety is the word used to describe the two halves of society. The Yolŋu names for these are *Dhuwa* and *Yirritja*. At creation, Yolŋu society came into being in two halves. All creation, including humans, is either *Dhuwa* or *Yirritja*. The only other well-known equivalent to *Dhuwa Yirritja* is the Chinese Yin Yang, although there are a number of differences between these two systems.

Translation form

Most comments from Yolŋu speakers in this book have been translated into modern English, using a meaning-based translation method. Some words or short phrases have been left in Yolŋu Matha with the English translation in brackets alongside. These translations also use the meaning-based method unless a literal translation is necessary to demonstrate a point.

A pronunciation guide for Yolŋu Matha words is located on page 252

ARNHEM LAND AND ENVIRONS

Scale: 10mm = 35km

Cape Wessel

Wessel Islands

The English Company's Is

Cape Arnhem

Nhulunbuy
Yirrkala
Gove Peninsula

Port Bradshaw

Caledon Bay

Trial Bay

Gulf of Carpentaria

Arnhem Bay

Buckingham Bay

Raymangirr
Gapuwiyak

Biranybirany

Gangan

Isle Woodah

Blue Mud Bay

Umbakumba
Groote Eylandt
Alyangula
Angurugu

Elcho Is

NW Crocodile Is

Galiwin'ku

Nangalala

Arafura Swamp

Koolatong River

Numbulwar

Crocodile Is

Milingimbi

Glyde River

Goyder River

Port Roper

Arafura Sea

Ramingining

Murwangi

Rose River

Roper River

Blyth River

Maningrida

ARNHEM LAND

Wilton River

Ngukurr (Roper River Mission)

Roper River

Liverpool River

Roper Bar

Nth Goulburn Is
Sth Goulburn Is
Warrawi

Roper River

Croker Is
Minjilang

Oenpelli

East Alligator River

Jabiru

Coburg Peninsula

Victoria
(1838-49)

Van Diemen Gulf

Sth Alligator River

West Alligator River

Pine Creek

Area Enlarged

Darwin

AUSTRALIA

-iv-

THE YOLŊU REGION OF ARNHEM LAND

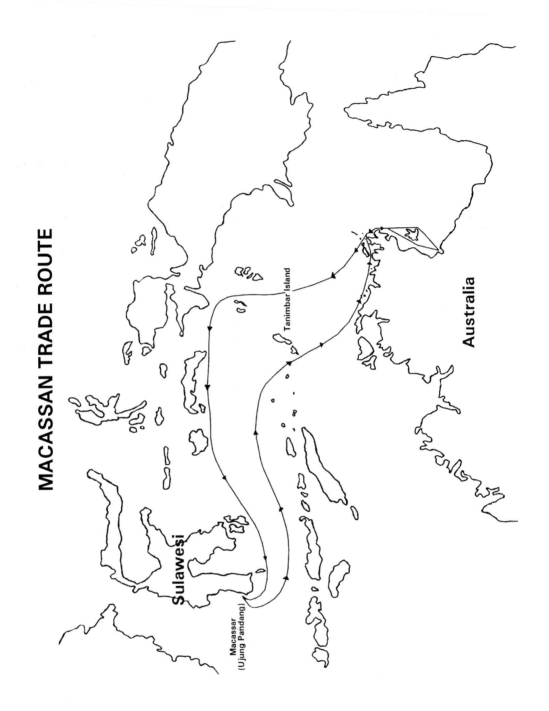

MACASSAN TRADE ROUTE

Sulawesi

Macassar
(Ujung Pandang)

Tanimbar Island

Australia

FOREWORD

I met *Wämut* (Richard Trudgen) when he first came to Arnhem Land. He came from the Balanda (non-Aboriginal) world and I grew up with my people, the Yolŋu of Arnhem Land. When I left school I did my apprenticeship as a fitter and turner in the mission workshop at Galiwin'ku on Elcho Island. I continued my education working as a lay pastor to my people at Galiwin'ku when *Wämut* arrived at Milingimbi. He was also a fitter and turner.

Like me, *Wämut* was more interested in people than just fixing machines, and when the opportunity came he changed over to community work so he could spend more time working beside and training Yolŋu. By the time I left Arnhem Land to continue my formal education in the Balanda world, he had started to learn our language, history and law.

In his new training role, however, *Wämut* ran into problems. He used the old style of training at first, but it just did not work. No matter how hard he tried, the people did not seem to understand. He would get very frustrated not knowing what was wrong.

Despite these frustrations, *Wämut's* role of community worker opened up a lot of new ways and opportunities for him to see things from the people's perspective and to try and understand why the methods he was using did not work. It gave him a chance to spend a lot of time with the old people and clan leaders on their homelands, in the community councils and in family groups. At the same time he had to work with the many government departments involved in homeland centre development, along with the local community councils and other Yolŋu associations and industries.

Through all this *Wämut* started to see that Yolŋu were *märr-dhumbal'yun* (confused, mystified) about the Balanda world. This confusion was very deep and very hard for people who have never experienced it to understand. Yolŋu have been conquered in many different ways. After the Balanda fought wars against us and destroyed our ancient trade with the Macassans, we ended up on missions just to survive. At this time the Yolŋu leaders gave up. They said, 'It is no good fighting Balanda because they have some sort of supernatural power. Maybe the only way we can survive is get this power.' So our minds were conquered along with our lands.

No matter how hard we fought and applied ourselves, however, the Balanda always won. Their strange, lawless ways and advanced, powerful technologies always defeated us. The missions and the government welfare department used powerful leaders (superintendents) who acted like dictators over both other Balanda and us. This left the old people thinking, 'Maybe this new way, "schooling", is the path to getting this Balanda power'. So they sent their children to the mission schools in the hope of getting this power from the Balanda.

We believed then that if we just went to the Balanda schools and returned home at the end of high school with *djorra'* (papers/certificates) then that *djorra'* would bring us Balanda luck and power. We thought it was the certificate that would get you a vehicle, make you rich and give you Balanda power and authority. This authority we thought would be like the power the superintendent had and the power the Balanda used to push us off our lands. But when the young ones went through that education, it did not work. They got the certificates but they did not seem to be effective. In fact, they were more confused about the Balanda world than before. Many were so confused they started drinking or just dropped out. Others went mad trying to understand the strange mysteries of the Balanda.

This confusion still exists today and is killing our people. We are confused about why so many Yolŋu are dying in this modern era when we now live like Balanda. We always feel we have been deceived when it comes to discussion about our lands and resources. This confusion is so great that it affects our families and the way we work and live. Many Yolŋu, especially those with Balanda education, just give up. 'It's no use,' they say, 'we will never understand Balanda. Maybe they are hiding the real truth and power from us.'

Wämut saw this confusion and how it led to a lot of conflict between Balanda and Yolŋu when they did not really understand each other. Yet at the same time he saw that when Yolŋu worked within our own law, knowledge and social structure, things worked very well. We learnt quickly and the people were very productive.

As *Wämut* listened to the clan elders, training Yolŋu for all sorts of jobs and positions and helping others return to their homelands, he saw that basic elements were missing in many of the programs set up to educate and help the people. The same things were missing from both the mission and welfare approaches of the past and also from the government approach that started in the 1970s. He saw that these programs did not fit into where the people were at, so the people were not really learning and the confusion increased. This became a turning point in his life as he started challenging the mission and government authorities, pointing out to them where they were failing to meet the real needs of the people.

What he said seemed strange to many Balanda and even to some of us mission-educated Yolŋu because we did not see our own confusion. We had come to believe, even though we could speak English well, that the Balanda world really did have some strange supernatural power and did not operate on tangible things that we could understand. Only the old men *Wämut* worked with understood him. Many Balanda considered he was *bawa'mirr* (mad). They attacked him saying, 'I don't think you're right; you're not understanding it properly. There must be something wrong with you.' Others said, 'I've known Yolŋu for a long time and I've never heard them say they're confused or don't understand the Balanda world.' From all this pressure, *Wämut* became very sick and in 1983 left Arnhem Land after eleven years.

The next few years were a very hard time for me, because I too found the programs and methodologies I was using were not working. It was a time when I was looking at my own approach. What was the best way to do education, and what programs could really help Yolŋu people experience real dignity and pride? How could we stand as equals with Balanda instead of always agreeing, in almost a begging way, to anything they said to us because we were so confused and in awe of them? Of course, this feeling within us would sometimes burst out and we would become very angry because we believed we were human and capable of knowing too. I was tired of the confusion and confrontation, always fighting, fighting, fighting. There seemed to be no way to solve it. I remember talking to my father about it. He would say, 'There is another way. In the old way of our people, our elders would sit down and talk through and analyse problems together, even if it took a long time. This way we would find ways of solving problems together.' So I started looking for that way of doing things.

Then in the late 1980s I met *Wämut* again and we started to talk once more about how to meet the needs of the Yolŋu in Arnhem Land. Was there a way in which Balanda and Yolŋu could together solve the problems we faced, through a *mägaya dhukarr* (peaceful way/path)? In the early 1980s I used to hear some of the things *Wämut* said and, like the others who criticised him, I too thought he was *bawa'mirr*. But now I knew he was not. What he was saying was right. So I invited him to come and work with me.

When *Wämut* returned to ARDS, he started practising his different methodology of education within ARDS itself, on our leaders and on me. This education, aimed at overcoming the confusion, excited me and I called it 'discovery education' because we could discover the answers we wanted to the problems that faced us in a way that made good sense to us. Rather than Balanda telling us in a foreign language and style what they thought we should know, this education was in our language, and it was built on how we saw things from within our own cultural framework. Through this new process I started to see that we could really understand the Balanda world in the same way we understood our Yolŋu world.

From *Wämut's* influence and the dialogue that occurred, ARDS moved away from political confrontation into education through dialogue. We started concentrating on finding ways to educate and train Yolŋu so that they could really understand the strange world of the Balanda and participate as equals.

That is why I asked *Wämut* to write this book. Many books and papers have been written about the Yolŋu of Arnhem Land. This one is very different. It is written out of the pain experienced by living with the suffering that is everyday life for Yolŋu. But *Wämut* has not stopped there. Out of this pain has grown something very valuable in the form of new understandings and a new way for Yolŋu to learn about the foreign Balanda world.

I wanted *Wämut* to speak to Balanda about the real situation we face in our lives every day, a reality that is hard for people of another culture to imagine. I wanted him to show Balanda the important role they have in helping Yolŋu break through the confusion that confronts us. In doing it, *Wämut* has used many stories told by the people over the years. He has used health and education as main themes to talk about how communication breaks down and why government programs fail. He then brings together what others have found across the world to show this is not just a Yolŋu or Aboriginal problem, but a problem that exists whenever cultures and languages collide. Then he shares some insights about the way forward.

So I invite you to read this book. In that way we can walk together for a while and discover a more common path to solve the problems we face.

Rev. Dr. Djiniyini Gondarra OAM

Political leader of the Golumala clan

Chief Executive Officer of Aboriginal Resource and Development Services Inc. (ARDS)

Member of the Council for Aboriginal Reconciliation.

INTRODUCTION

Some people reading this book will only know Arnhem Land as the home of a few prominent Yolŋu, people such as the Yothu Yindi rock band, the previous chairman of ATSIC and the two Yunupiŋu brothers, who have been honoured as past recipients of the Australian of the Year award. The profile of these people has given Australian citizens a rose-coloured view of Arnhem Land and its people. The true-life situation on the ground is very different.

My own experience of Arnhem Land began in January 1973 when I arrived at Milingimbi mission just off the north-central Arnhem Land coast. I spent three months at Milingimbi and then moved to the mainland to help in the development of the new township of Ramingining. The Ramingining experience lasted for over a decade. During those years I had many different jobs, moving in 1975 from the position of mechanic/fitter to that of community worker, where I was trained in the whole area of community development/community education. Then in 1982 I contracted a 'golden staph' infection and in the end had to leave Arnhem Land in September 1983.

In those eleven years, I lived with a unique group of people. They taught me more than I was ever able to teach or share with them. They became friends and adopted relatives. I owed them much and it hurt me deeply to leave. But there were no options—I had to rebuild my health.

It was September 1991 when the Rev Dr Djiniyini Goṉḏarra asked me to return and work regionally with a wider group of Yolŋu. Two others, the chairman of Aboriginal Resource and Development Services Inc. (ARDS) and the director of ARDS, also approached me about coming back. The three of them, all Yolŋu men and leaders in their own right, spoke to me separately and gave me different reasons why they wanted me back.

Djiniyini said: 'When the mission and government talked about self-determination and self-management in the 1970s and early 1980s, Yolŋu were excited and took up the challenge. But what has happened has shocked us. It is like the wider church took a big bowl of water and washed their hands of us, leaving us confused and struggling to survive. That is why I am asking you, *Wämut*, to come back and work with us, because you know our culture, law and language and you know the way we think.'

The next week the chairman met me in one of the communities. He asked if Djiniyini had spoken to me. I said he had and that I was thinking about it. He went on: 'We want Balanda (white people) like you to come back and work with us because the new Balanda do not understand us and we don't understand them. *Nhe maryngi napurruŋgalaŋuw ŋayaŋuw, ga napurr maryngi ŋayaŋuw nhokalaŋuw* (You know the deep inner-being of Yolŋu people and we know your deep inner-being). We need people like you so we can learn how to get control over our communities again.'

I met the director of ARDS the next day. He sat with me and pleaded with me to come back and work for the organisation. Again I asked why. He said: 'There are so many things I am confused about in Balanda law. At the moment some government departments are thinking of cutting all the funding to ARDS and I can't understand why. The pressure to administer ARDS is just too much,' he went on. 'I want to run away from it all the time, yet I believe community development is the only way we can help our people.'

Once again I told him I would think about coming back and let him know when I had a clear answer.

A week later I rang the director to say that I would take up the position of consultant to the executive officer of ARDS. Immediately he started outlining more of the problems he had. He was confused about how the government got money and why it was strictly controlled, and about why communication between Yolŋu and Balanda nearly always ended in conflict. I spoke with him on the phone that day for a long time, ending by saying, 'I can explain everything better when we are sitting face-to-face after I get there next year.'

The plan was that my family and I would arrive back in the north the following January after finalising my business affairs down south. As I spoke to the director on the phone that day I thought everything would be okay. I said as much to him. But in the following fortnight, the director had a massive heart attack, the latest in a string of heart attacks he had suffered over his seven years in Darwin as director of ARDS. This time it was terminal. He was only forty-seven years old.

So my return to work with the Yolŋu after eight years away was marked by the stark reality of what had become 'normal' life in Arnhem Land. The people were dying at a horrific rate, more than five times the national average.[1] And they were dying of diseases that they had not seen before, diseases that were considered to be those of affluent society: heart attack, strokes, diabetes, cancer.

Alongside this I discovered that the communities in Arnhem Land had changed. The people's freedom to direct their own lives had been almost completely eroded. A large number of short-term 'outside' staff had come and gone, each one needing to be 'broken-in' and orientated to the cultural context. This process placed huge pressures on Yolŋu community members as they tried to teach the newcomers about the Yolŋu way of life. Most of these staff members left before the process really started, then someone new would come in and the Yolŋu leaders would have to begin all over again.

This stressful experience meant that many Yolŋu leaders who had functioned well during the early 1980s were burnt out or dead a few years later. A number had given up or returned to their homelands away from the central communities. Others had died in their jobs. Many of these had not been replaced by other Yolŋu but by outside staff. In a very short space of time, the work that had been done successfully by Yolŋu in the 1970s and early 1980s was being done by others.

It was evident when I visited east Arnhem Land communities in 1992/93 that Yolŋu were now very different from the people I had left in 1983. Many who had been living healthy lives on their traditional homelands were now dwellers in one of the central communities, usually unemployed and in very poor health. Many of their children were suffering from malnutrition.

Returning to Arnhem Land raised endless questions for me. In a nutshell, I discovered that *Yolŋu had lost control of their own lives*. This process started at the turn of the twentieth century and is now reaching its devastating climax. It is this situation that this book has been written to explore.

The Way It Is

In 1948 an American-Australian Scientific Expedition carried out medical research in three major communities in Arnhem Land. Concerning the people's health they stated: 'The general build is athletic. Shoulders, thighs, and muscles of the vertebral column are well developed and strong. Carriage, posture and gait are excellent. . . . In no instance was an obese adult encountered'.[2] When I first arrived at Milingimbi twenty-five years later, this was still a good picture of the condition of the Yolŋu. I lived, worked, laughed and cried with a proud, strong and healthy group of people, people who found death usually in old age.

Another twenty-five years on things have changed for the worse. The 1948 Expedition also found that 'Scabies were rare, only two cases being encountered'.[3] Today scabies are endemic. Other diseases like diabetes, high blood pressure, heart attacks, stroke, cancer, renal failure and obesity are decimating the people. Yolŋu are now dying in their early to mid forties or even younger, and at such a rate that life seems to lurch from one funeral to another. 'I am tired of standing at the edge of an open grave, week in and week out!' Djiniyini told me in 1996. 'Why are so many of our people dying so young?'

Other things have also changed for the Yolŋu—employment patterns, for example. When I left Arnhem Land in 1983, ninety-five per cent of the work on Yolŋu communities was carried out effectively by the people themselves. On my return in 1992, I found only a few Yolŋu remained involved in meaningful work. As one male community member said to me in 1997, 'Brother I have not had a job since you left here in 1984. There is no work around this place for Yolŋu; there is only work for outsiders.'

These days, receiving welfare is the central Yolŋu economic activity. Welfare leads to a level of dependence that is crippling and creates loss of roles, loss of mastery and, above all, hopelessness. And hopelessness in turn translates into destructive social behaviour—neglect of responsibility, drug abuse, violence, self-abuse, homicide, incest and suicide.

How is it that Yolŋu, who once enjoyed excellent health, resilient social stability and an economic system that stimulated international trade into what today is Indonesia, now find themselves in this demoralised state?

Everyone, from the Australian government down, wants answers to this question, but they are not apparent. At the time of writing two inquiries are underway, one initiated by the Northern Territory government looking into why Aboriginal education is failing, the other initiated by the Northern Territory Coroner's Office looking into the high suicide rate on some traditional communities. Policies keep changing in the hope of finding a solution, but the problems remain.

It is my conviction that the crisis *can* be understood and programs *can* be developed to deal with it. But finding its real cause will require us to look at the subject from the *other* side of the cross-cultural/cross-language divide—the side where Yolŋu live.

Evidence from around the world shows that this kind of crisis is not peculiar to Yolŋu or Aboriginal people. As far back as 1972, Charles Hughes, a professor of anthropology and psychiatry, and John Hunter, a professor of geography, wrote a paper on the consequences of developmental change in Africa. They suggested, 'Perhaps it would be useful for public health specialists to start talking about a new category of diseases . . . Such diseases could be called the "diseases of development".'[4]   The diseases and social conditions plaguing Yolŋu could be called 'diseases of development'.

What has caused them? Many people blame lack of adequate housing, poor nutrition, absence of proper sanitation, and high-risk behaviours. Others see a disinterest in learning or education and low levels of English literacy as the main problem.

But to understand what has really caused these 'diseases of development' we need to walk in the footprints of the Yolŋu for a while and taste life from the springs they now drink from. Of course, this is hard for any human being from another culture to do. However, by using stories from Yolŋu people themselves and case studies drawn from their encounters with Balanda culture, I believe it is possible to know some of the pain and frustration which is now a life-long reality for most Yolŋu.

The dominant culture of mainstream Australia—a culture with a foreign language (English) and legal, economic and social systems alien to Yolŋu—has now collapsed in on this ancient people. Balanda culture is as confusing to the Yolŋu as Yolŋu culture is to Balanda. As Djiniyini once put it: 'Balanda and Yolŋu do not understand each other. The Balanda are confused about how Yolŋu society works and Yolŋu are confused about Balanda society. We are missing each other all the time.'

English is a fifth or sixth language for most Yolŋu, and this leaves them severely intellectually marginalised in the dominant culture's world. Communication fails miserably between them and almost all dominant culture personnel, including doctors, teachers and bureaucrats. This communication failure creates immense suffering for Yolŋu. In the area of health, for example, some Yolŋu wait years to understand what is making them sick. Many never find out.

The root cause of these 'diseases of development' can be summed up in the words *loss of control*. Loss of control is caused by many factors, all of which are discussed in this book.

The crisis for Yolŋu is grave, but there is a way forward. When we understand the factors that create this loss of control then strategies can be developed to counter them. This will require a multi-disciplinary approach that is able to take in the total life needs of the people. Yet it is my strong belief that Yolŋu can learn the knowledge and skills needed to equip themselves for life in a modern world—if those of us from the dominant Australian culture will learn to construct knowledge in the way Yolŋu construct knowledge and deliver it in a language that Yolŋu think in.

As I write this Introduction, Australian troops are going into East Timor. Australia has responded to the physical violence there since the United Nations-sponsored election for independence. But Australia and other western nations were very slow to respond to the subtle institutional violence that has been evident in Timor for the last twenty years. In fact, it could be said that Australia, by its silence and its economic participation, has been as much a part of that institutional violence as anyone else.

In the same way, the Yolŋu warriors of Arnhem Land have sustained over 100 years of direct and indirect conflict with the dominant culture of Australia and they suffer greatly because of it. If the status quo remains then the great warriors of Arnhem Land will continue to lie down and die, because just like the East Timorese, they are left with no other choice.

Richard Trudgen

December 1999

PART ONE

THE YOLŊU OF ARNHEM LAND

Part One takes the reader from ancient times up to the painful recent history of the Yolŋu of Arnhem Land.

Chapter 1 tells the history of four wars spanning a period of about fifty years. Through these wars many Yolŋu clans were decimated, with some wiped out or on the edge of extinction and their traditional trade economy in ruins. Then came a period of mixed blessings during the mission and welfare eras. The physical wars stopped, but this 'peace' was tainted with the taste of a new, subtler battle, a battle in which Yolŋu fought against all odds to remain independent. In this fight many tried to remain on their homeland estates while others turned to mission life and learnt new trades, hoping to be accepted in the white man's world. Yolŋu thought they had finally made it in the 1970s when 'self-determination' and 'land rights' were talked about. These English words sounded like independence to them, but they meant something completely different to the Balanda who used them.

In the 1970s the missions handed over control of the communities to the people and the people dreamed of a new and brighter future. *Chapter 2* describes how the dreams of the '70s turned into the nightmare of the '80s. During this time more Balanda than ever came to Arnhem Land, outnumbering the missionaries who were there before them, many times taking over the jobs and positions that once were the domain of Yolŋu.

By the 1990s the people were suffering a crisis in health and living. *Chapter 3* lists some of the official reasons thought to be the cause of this crisis. It then discusses the unofficial but real reason behind many of the programs aimed at helping the people.

1
CHAPTER

Waŋarr's Gift is Broken

The Fifty Year War

From 1606 on several Dutch expeditions explored and mapped parts of Australia's north coast. They made things difficult for future white settlers. It was policy to capture natives both as specimens and guides. Since they used their guns too freely, and carried captives aboard bound and wounded, they left nasty memories of white faces.

Eric Rolls[5]

'Yolŋu', the Aboriginal people of central to north-east Arnhem Land, make up some thirty or forty different clan groups. This does not make them citizens of a single larger Yolŋu nation, as their primary allegiance is to their separate paternal clans, with different political alliances connecting them to other clan groups throughout Arnhem Land and beyond.

Each of these clans and larger nation alliances have deep and complex histories going back thousands of years—much too long to record here. The following stories represent a condensed overview of a general Yolŋu history, with some information recorded in Balanda history.

Many of the stories in this chapter were told to me by Yolŋu elders at the actual places where the events occurred. In the years I have spent with these people, they have shared much of themselves and their history with me and I have tried to reflect their teaching here. Where there might be differences between the Yolŋu and Balanda views of a particular event, I have stayed true to the commission given to me by the Yolŋu and have told it from their point of view.

The Maḏayin

All clans would agree that life started in Arnhem Land at the dawn of creation, when the Great Creator Spirit, *Waŋarr*, sent women as creators from the spirit land of *burralku*, an island to the east of Arnhem Land. They moved across the land creating fresh waterholes, the features of the land and the Yolŋu themselves. As they created, they gave the people the gifts of language and the way to live.

This way is called the *Maḏayin*. There is no equivalent for *Maḏayin* in English as it encompasses a whole system of law and living. It includes:

- all the property, resource, criminal, economic, political, moral and religious laws of the people;
- their *Ŋärra'* (restricted chamber of law) and other lesser councils;
- the objects that encode the law;
- song cycles that tell of legal agreements;
- the trading highways that criss-cross Arnhem Land;
- the embassy sites on close and distant clan estates that give travellers and traders protection at law;
- the protected production sites (hatcheries and nurseries) for different animals, fish and birds;
- the correct conservation and production of plants and food such as yams;
- the husbandry of fish, turtles, animals, birds and so on;
- the restricted places for dangerous country, e.g. cliff faces or tidal whirlpools;
- protection of the clan's assets;
- controls to regulate trade and production;
- set diplomatic rules and regulations throughout all the clans and nations.

The *Maḏayin* established the boundaries for each clan estate and empowered the clan and nation *Ŋärra'*, for the teaching and maintenance of a rule of law for all Yolŋu citizens. The *Maḏayin* taught Yolŋu warriors the *raypirri' dhukarr*—the discipline of mind, body and soul, along with respect for all life and the greater good of the community and cosmos over individual need or greed.

Since the beginning of time, the clans have assented to this law through a ceremonial process called *Waṉa-Lupthun*. In this process the *djuŋgaya,* the person responsible for looking after the law objects for that particular clan, stands on the water's edge holding these law objects, which encode the law, above his head. While he is doing this all members of the clan go into the water and immerse themselves. *Waṉa-Lupthun* signifies that all Yolŋu are under the rule of the *Maḏayin*—no-one is above it.

This complex *Maḏayin* system is seen as holy, demanding great respect. It was given at creation to establish and maintain a state of *mägaya*. One of the images the people use to describe *mägaya* is a flat smooth sea, or the surface of a lake without a ripple, wave or swell—a glass-smooth surface. It is this tranquil state, where every clan member can live in freedom from hostility or threat of oppression, that the *Maḏayin* produces.

Within their clans, Yolŋu young people go through citizenship ceremonies and learn the *Maḏayin* way. Clans select their political leaders, not as a law unto themselves, but as appointed keepers of the *Maḏayin* way, protecting the individual and collective political rights of the clan citizens—especially the rights to their own clan estates and resources against trespassers or thieves.

The Wind Traders

For at least a number of centuries the Yolŋu had been meeting visitors from across the sea.[6] When the *bärra'* (winds from the north-west) blew, the Yolŋu knew to expect traders from Macassar (Ujung Pandang or Makasar) in Southern Sulawesi. Yolŋu coastal clans waited with great expectation for their arrival. Many *praus* (Macassan boats) came each year; Matthew Flinders recorded sixty in his log in 1803.[7] They came to work and trade with Yolŋu clans, and Alfred Searcy, who for fourteen years from 1882 was Sub-Collector of Customs out of Port Darwin, noted over 33 semi-permanent 'principal camping-places to the eastward of Port Darwin'.[8]

Once the Macassans had left on the south-easterly winds at the beginning of the Dry season, the Yolŋu became very busy preparing for the next season's visit. They had many things to do. During the course of everyday work needed for survival, they also collected large quantities of *ralapiny* (pearls) from oysters and clams, ready for the next year's trade. The Yolŋu have no record of the quantities of pearls traded, but Searcy writes:

> Before our departure, four more proas arrived. . . . All had numbers of pearls, which I had produced, or at any rate what they thought fit, for the serang [a Malay crewman on Searcy's boat] of the cutter informed me that those forthcoming were only the inferior ones, the pearls being divided into firsts, seconds, and thirds. One of the bottles shown, for there were three pint pickle bottles, the master informed me would realise fifteen hundred rupees in Macassar. I received reliable information that a proa the previous season had taken away thirty-five catties-weight [21.2 kg] of pearls, no doubt the majority being inferior, but amongst such a quantity there were bound to be some of great value. The natives collected the pearls during the absence of the Malays [Macassans], for whom they saved them.[9]

But the Yolŋu not only collected the pearls; they also seeded oysters and large clams with sand to make the pearls grow. This was done by working over their oyster and clamshell beds in a methodical way, returning to the beds to harvest from a particular section after a number of years. Knowledge of how to do this seeding still exists today among descendants of the Yolŋu clans that participated in this trade.

Later on in the Dry season, when the wattle trees were in full bloom, the Yolŋu knew it was time to harvest the hawks-bill and greenback turtles, which were prolific.[10] The people would eat the turtles and clean the shell ready for trade with the Macassans.

This Macassan trade was based on trepang fishing.[11] The Yolŋu coastal estates contained shallow water where these big sea slugs thrived in large numbers. The

Macassans would come and work with Yolŋu to harvest the trepang. Then they would process and dry it for shipping back to Macassar where it was sold to Chinese traders. The Chinese used the trepang in soups and other dishes.

This trade between the Yolŋu and the Macassans was extensive, and Yolŋu recorded all these coming and goings in their *manikay* (historical and instructional 'song cycles'). These *manikay* also recorded the types of items traded and how they should be used. There are, for example, *manikay* for alcohol, tobacco, rice and muskets.

Balanda history has also recorded the extent of this trade, though it has since tended to ignore its existence. The South Australian government administered the Northern Territory from 1863 to 1910, and South Australian Parliamentary papers show the value of import duties that were collected from the Macassans from 1882 until Federation. These records show that duties for Macassan goods were levied only on 'Manufactured Tobacco' and 'Rice', although from Yolŋu oral, song and linguistic history we know that many other items were also traded in large quantities—knives, axes, nails (for fish hooks etc.), fish hooks, fishing lines, bottle glass (for scrapers), bolts of calico, blankets, string,[12] scraps of steel, alcohol, swords and muskets, to name a few.

These tariffs were levied at one penny per pound for rice and 2s 6d per pound for tobacco. The table below shows quantities of imports from Macassar during the 1890s and the value of duties charged on them. By comparison, duties for goods imported to the Northern Territory from America amounted to just £40 in 1894 (when duties on Macassan goods totalled £375) and £52 in 1898 (when the Macassan total was £299).

Table 1. Quantities and Tariff value of recorded imports into the Northern Territory from Macassar, 1894-1903[13]

YEAR	RICE WEIGHT (lbs.)	RICE TARIFF (£)	TOBACCO WEIGHT (lbs.)	TOBACCO TARIFF (£)
1894	69,060	287	698	88
1895	30,240	126	264	33
1896	25,020	104	206	26
1897	46,440	193	372	47
1898	54,990	229	559	70
1899	54,132	225	480	60
1900	46,432	194	535	67
1901	49,332	205	518	65
1902	52,024	217	692	87
1903	66,438	277	903	113

Note: South Australian Parliamentary Papers have no figures for Import Duties for goods originating in Macassar after 1903 as the collection of duties was handled by the Commonwealth after Federation (1/1/1901).

These ancient international connections affected the Yolŋu coastal clans in many ways. Some Yolŋu even made trips across to the port of Macassar in Southern Sulawesi. These diplomatic journeys strengthened the bonds between their particular Yolŋu clan and the Macassan families who operated the praus. It also meant that many Macassan and some Asian terms found their way into the languages of Arnhem Land. For example, the Yolŋu Matha term for bread, *rrothi*, seems to have been borrowed directly from the Indian word *roti*. Over 200 such terms have been recorded.

This extensive international trade became part of the everyday commerce carried on between Yolŋu and other Aboriginal people across Australia.[14] Boomerangs produced in Central Australia were traded from clan to clan until they reached Arnhem Land, where articles like boomerangs were not made. Items traded from the Macassans, along with others produced in Arnhem Land itself, were used in the reverse trade. This national trade with clans inland kept the Yolŋu busy all year round. Many items, such as steel products, were traded across the nation, even down as far as the Great Australian Bight.

Contact with White Humans

While the Macassans came and went for many centuries they respected Yolŋu sovereignty, coming only as far as the beach after they landed. Here they would wait for the Yolŋu owners to negotiate a trade agreement with them. There were only a few disagreements that turned into a battle or two over the centuries.

Throughout this time there were other visitors to Arnhem Land. These visitors were whiter than the Macassans and came in bigger ships. A few of the Yolŋu coastal clans met these visitors. (For the inland clans contact only came centuries later). Some who went to Macassar told their countrymen on their return about the 'strange white humans who sailed in big ships, had much wealth and strange customs and ceremonial ways. White humans who pushed everybody around as though they owned everything . . . white humans who came from a mystical land across the sea where things were made by magic . . . white humans that came to visit, stayed, and built their strange houses'.[15] But not many of the Yolŋu people believed these stories about the mythical 'Hollanders' (Balanda).

Different clans have different stories about their first meeting with Europeans. Djoma Gaykamaŋu told me the following story in 1983:

> Some people were out hunting one day when they heard a strange noise in the bush. They couldn't understand what it might be so they thought it must be a *malagatj* (a powerful being from the spiritual world, like a messenger or angel). Then they saw a strange thing that filled them with fear. The 'thing' had four legs and a odd-shaped body. It had two heads and it was larger than any animal they had ever seen or heard of. The people kept watching and following this thing. They were even more surprised when the body moved apart, and there stood an animal—a big animal with four legs, a large body and one head. Holding the animal was something that looked a bit like them, but its hands and face were the colour of a *mokuy* (dead person, evil spirit)[16]—that is, its face and hands were white like a corpse when the skin is peeling. The rest of its body was covered with a strange scale-like sheath (clothes).

When the *mokuy* pulled out its penis to urinate, the people knew it was male and that it was not a spirit at all but maybe part human or something. Then the people saw the *mokuy* join the animal part again and go back the way it had come. The people were afraid to follow because they felt they had seen a spiritual being of some sort and were frightened that it might kill them. So they returned to camp to talk and think it over.

White visits to the Yolŋu estates began several hundred years ago. An early map of the known world, made in 1603 by Father Matteo Ricci, a Portuguese Jesuit priest who had spent a long time in China, noted in the blank space where Australia lies: "No-one has ever been to this land of the south, hence we know nothing about it". In smaller characters he brushed [the Chinese characters] "Fire Land" and "Land of Parrots".'[17] Maybe someone from China had already visited Australia.

Some Portuguese and Dutch sailors also came and went, leaving only their names on maps to show they had passed this way. Probably the first European to come near the land of the Yolŋu was Dutch explorer William Jansz, who explored the north of Australia in the ship 'Duyfken' in 1605. In 1623 Williem Joosten van Colster, making his way back to the Netherlands East Indies from Cape York Peninsula in the Dutch vessel 'Arnhem', 'discovered' the north-east coast of 'Arnhem Land'. Van Colster left his gift—the name of his ship—and the name stuck.[18]

But although these and other Europeans came to Arnhem Land 150 years before Captain Cook sighted the east coast of Australia in 1770, they had almost no contact with Yolŋu. But Yolŋu saw them, recording the visits in their *Maḏayin* records, their art galleries located in rock shelters, and their song cycles.

Some of these early white humans were thought to have come from *burralku* (the heaven-island to the east) because they sailed across the ocean from the east. Their massive boats 'floated like clouds on the sea'. The Yolŋu saw these great ships had anchors and other metal objects that displayed incredible wealth. Until then the Yolŋu had only seen the small quantities of metal they had traded from the Macassans and fashioned into spearheads. Yolŋu 'blacksmiths' used a cold welding method to join scraps of metal to make a smooth, one-piece, 30 cm blade. These blades were highly valued and always in short supply. When Yolŋu saw so much precious metal on the ships, they wondered about the origin of these white humans. Many thought of them as spiritual beings returning from *burralku* as strange white *maḻagatj*, and they recorded them in their *Maḏayin*, giving them a powerful status.

It was not until 1803 that Matthew Flinders surveyed the east coast of Arnhem Land in a ship called the 'Investigator'. While he was doing this, Yolŋu from the Gälpu clan met and talked with him. During a second landing at Blue Mud Bay, one Yolŋu was killed in a clash with Flinders' crew.

Other stories of strange happenings in the south-east of Makarr-Yindi (the mainland of Australia) started spreading along the trading tracks. There were tales of strange beings and of wars between other southern Yolŋu and *watharr*

Yolŋu (white humans). The Yolŋu started to use the term Balanda for these white humans as they were not sure what they really were except to say they were like the white Balanda some had seen in Macassar. Other stories told of the strange animals, the *yarraman'* (horses), that these Balanda had under their control.[19]

Trade from the south of Arnhem Land started to come under pressure because the Balanda started fighting with the Aboriginal landowners. As Aboriginal clans to the south collapsed so did their trade, and items like boomerangs that originated in the Hermannsberg area of Central Australia no longer came, or came in very small quantities.

The First Pastoral War

Yolŋu continued living on their estates within Arnhem Land even though the trade from the south and the west was blocked by the Balanda. But by 1861, many Yolŋu, especially those living just north of the Roper River, were having to get permission from the Balanda police at Roper Bar to move down onto the 'cattle stations' south of the river. The Yolŋu had to 'wear a tin plate slung around their neck. Anyone not wearing a plate was simply shot.'[20]

The destruction of clans outside Arnhem Land was now occurring very fast. There were wars, skirmishes and massacres as the pastoral companies developed their leases. By 1885, unknown to the Yolŋu, the Balanda had also divided Arnhem Land into eleven pastoral leases,[21] an arrangement allowed under the 'Australian Colonies, Waste Lands Act 1842'.[22]

Yolŋu began experiencing the main challenge to the authority of their *Maḏayin* in 1885 when the pastoralist, J. A. Macartney, set up the Florida station, at a place the Yolŋu call Murwangi, in north-central Arnhem Land.[23]

Macartney was the first to try to take up the east Arnhem Land leases. The Yolŋu saw him and wondered who he was. This white man and his workers were different from other strangers like the Macassans. Where the Macassans had come only as far as the beach and waited there for the Yolŋu to come down and trade with them, these white men walked straight onto the land and then right through some clan estates without even stopping to think they were on someone else's land. This rudeness made many Yolŋu very angry. Traditionally, Yolŋu were supposed to travel up and down the *dhumbarpar dhukarr* (official trading tracks and highways), and if they wanted to enter someone else's estate they would light a smoke fire and let the owners know they were there. But these white men did none of the proper things and walked about anywhere as though no-one owned the land.

Yolŋu watched from a distance for a while but it soon became clear that the Balanda were going to stay. Yolŋu started to worry. This white man was very aggressive, firing guns at Yolŋu whenever he saw them.

The main area where Macartney roamed included all the area between the Glyde and Blyth Rivers where over thirteen clans lived. Macartney made the people furious when he tried to force them out of 'his' country so that he could run his cattle in peace. The Yolŋu were flabbergasted. 'How can this white man come onto our land and start pushing us around?' they asked. The only reason the Yolŋu didn't attack him outright was because he carried guns and the people had already learnt about guns from the Macassans. Some guns had even been traded to them, and the Yolŋu already had a *manikay* (instructional song) that taught them about firearms. So they hoped that if they humoured Macartney he might just go away.

The clans Macartney forced off the land could not, of course, go and live on other clans' lands across the rivers. Yes, they could visit for a while as some did, but when their 'holiday' was over they had to go home. However, when they went home, they found their country had been cleared from the ground up to the grazing height of the cattle. The Yolŋu could now see right through their country, making it hard to hunt large game.

But the Yolŋu could also see the white man's animals on their land eating their grass. According to the *Maḏayin*, any animals on their estate were rightfully theirs. The ancient law stated that as animals moved across the land on their seasonal migrations they became the possession of the clan whose particular estate they were on at the time. When the animals moved on to another estate, they became *dhulŋuŋu walalaŋ*, the private possession of the clan whose estate the animal was now on.

For thousands of years the clans had respected each other's estates. So when these Yolŋu saw the white man's animals eating their grass, they saw the animals as theirs. They started killing some of the cattle to feed their clan. They didn't know that this white man thought he had the legal right to the land.

When the white pastoralists found remains of cattle in some Yolŋu villages, they were very angry. At first they yelled at the people and made threatening actions with their guns. Then some months later the pastoralists came with one of their wagons, offering horsemeat to many of the clans. The clan leaders were overjoyed, assuming that at last the Balanda had recognised the lawful relationship that should exist between them as strangers and the estate owners. The leaders implored the pastoralists to stay and share the gifts of meat with everyone. But the pastoralists made signs that they must hurry on and share the meat with other clans before it spoiled.

As they left, the people started preparing the ground ovens with the right leaves to flavour the meat, looking forward to the feast. That evening they ate, thanking the pastoralists for their good gifts. It was only when some of the people became violently ill that the Yolŋu realised the Balanda had tricked them with some strange sorcery. Was it the white man's strange animal, the *yarraman'*, whose flesh was poison? Or did he have another strange poison? How was it that these white men were also cowards? They would not fight hand-to-hand but used the way of sorcerers and evil men to kill.

The leaders grasped the treachery of the white men and instructed everyone to vomit up the meat gift. As children and women writhed in agony, the leaders screamed in disbelief. How could any human being kill women and children in such a cowardly way? Have these white men no sense of law? To this day, many Yolŋu in north-central Arnhem Land will not eat horsemeat.

Members of many clans died that day and the first war between the Yolŋu and the white, lawless *warrakan'* (animals, because surely they were not human) was declared. Yolŋu struck back, fighting with spears against muskets and carbines. Soon the skirmishes became running battles.

The Balanda had the advantage of speed because of the *yarraman'*, and their guns outdistanced spears. But Yolŋu had the advantage of knowledge of the country, excellent marksmanship and courage, because they fought for their homeland estates. After a while the Yolŋu developed hit-and-run ambush tactics. They also discovered that if they could get the Balanda to fire a shot from a distance, it gave them three to five seconds to run in within spear range, throw and hit their quarry before the Balanda could reload. Many Yolŋu and some Balanda died in these battles. Yolŋu not only killed cattle for food, they killed them to get the Balanda to go back to the country they had come from.

Finally, in 1893, eight years after they arrived, the Balanda packed up and left the way they came. The Yolŋu warriors had won.

As *Wolma*, the thunder man, made noise that year and the clouds of the coming Wet season grew tall in the sky, the clan and nation leaders met in council and discussed the events of the eight year war. Some said they had heard stories of these Balanda from all over *Makarr-Yindi* (Australia). Some had seen the Balanda in Macassar and knew they didn't go away easily and would probably come again. Many wondered about the future of their estates.

But life returned to normal, and Yolŋu hoped it might be many years before they saw Balanda again.

The Second Pastoral War

Nine Wet seasons came and went, and then, as the season wind turned to the south-east and the tenth Wet season finished, new Balanda arrived. The first Balanda pastoralists had come in ships and luggers from the north up the Glyde River, but the second lot came overland, from the south, with large herds of cattle along the western side of the Goyder River.

At first Yolŋu leaders just watched. These Balanda came in larger numbers, and Yolŋu clan and nation warriors were still small in number because of the previous war. Initially the Yolŋu thought these Balanda might be different because they had made good friends with some of the southern Yolŋu clans, actually allowing these clans to come and live with them. Balanda even gave these southern Yolŋu guns and showed them how to use them. They learnt to ride horses and shoot from the saddle. Yolŋu leaders thought these Balanda would be different. They seemed friendly.

But within two years, the Yolŋu who had gone to live with the Balanda started to change. They were now talking like Balanda, saying such things as 'If any Yolŋu are caught killing cattle or stealing from the Balanda they will be arrested and put in jail at the cattle station'. They also started to call themselves 'native police' and said they had to arrest anyone who broke the white man's law. 'What law?' the other Yolŋu thought. "These white people know nothing of law when they march into someone else's estate and treat it as though they own it."

Now the Yolŋu were worried about the action and talk of the southern Yolŋu who were living at the cattle station. 'Will they turn against their own people?' they wondered. Some clans were not sure; they had never trusted them. Others said, 'No, they are our relatives. They will never turn against us.'

One day, members of a clan from south-west of the station who had been visiting their relatives to the east began the journey home. On their way they came across a pile of rolled barbed wire that had been left by Balanda ready to make a fence. The Yolŋu said to each other, 'These pastoralists have so much wire, maybe we can take two or three rolls. It will make good fish spears.' As they carried the wire off toward their home country, some stockmen and some of the friendly Yolŋu came up behind them on horses. The Yolŋu who were with the Balanda thought the white men would just bawl the Yolŋu out and take the wire back. But they didn't. They pulled their Winchester repeater rifles from their saddle pouches and shot all the Yolŋu carrying the wire. The Yolŋu who were with the Balanda tried to stop them, but it was too late.

Travelling with these Balanda stockmen was a 'part-coloured' Aboriginal man whom the Yolŋu understood to be a Murri (a Queensland Aboriginal). He was the one used by the Balanda to befriend the southern Arnhem Land clans. He learnt some of their language and lived with them at the cattle station. This Murri was the Yolŋu 'ganger' or leader. He was at the first shooting and actually took part in it. He immediately turned to the Yolŋu who were with the stockmen and said, 'That's the way it is. You have to follow us now or you will get killed by your own people.' The Yolŋu with the stockmen were too afraid to turn on the Balanda and the Murri, as they would now be blamed by their own people for this killing. The next day the stockmen rode on towards villages north of the station.

In one of the larger villages, the Balmbi clan had come together with other clans at their Dry season home, beside a beautiful big billabong full of waterfowl, water lilies and *räkay* (corm rush beds). Freshwater turtles would hibernate in the mud as the billabong receded during the Dry. It was still a cool Dry season morning, with some early mist that had rolled in from the coast. As usual, the people were up and getting ready for the day while the morning star was still high in the sky and the first birds were heralding the dawn. The previous night the men had agreed they would hunt *weṯi* (wallabies) and, if unsuccessful, get waterfowl from another billabong to the north. They had plenty of waterfowl in the billabong where they were, but they wanted to save them for later on in the season when food would get short. Much energy would be spent then getting food for the day. If they left the water in the home billabong alone and quiet, these birds would get used to the people's presence and it would be easy to harvest them when needed. Today's trip would be about two hours hard walking and would take them almost to the edge of their estate. They didn't like leaving the women and children, but there had been no trouble in the area for many years now, so all seemed well.

The men readied their weapons and checked through the small *bathi* (dillybags) they would carry with them containing the items needed for the day. These included string and beeswax to re-fix a spearhead if it came loose or broke off, a flint spearhead, a cutting flint for a knife, some fire sticks to light a fire and some possum fur that was being hand-spun into yarn. The men would use the fur as their in-between work, spinning every time they stopped for a rest or while they waited for the food they had caught to cook before carrying it back to the village.

The women concentrated on getting the men-folk off by warming some food from the previous day and cooking more yams. Some of the cooled yams were wrapped in paperbark to give the men energy on the walk north. Some men were given a meal of *ŋathu*, a heavy bread made from the cycad palm. Having eaten, the men straightened their spear shafts over the fire, letting the heat steam the timber so it would bend without breaking. When all the men had three straight spears, they set off. The sun had just broken over the horizon, its golden rays greeting the Yolŋu as it streamed through the leaves of the trees and played with the mist. The birds filled the trees with song.

Having got the men moving the women turned their attention to the needs of the children and readied themselves for the work they would do that day, collecting *räkay* (corm rush nuts) and harvesting *bäwaŋ* (yams) from the *gärul* (yam garden). They already knew which yams they would harvest that day because they had planted them the previous year and had been weeding them during the Wet season.

The women also gathered the material they needed to make and repair the mosquito nets for the babies, or the dilly bags they were working on. Some women, who had planned not to go with the others, would spend the day harvesting and producing woven material from the *gunga* (pandanus palm). This material was used in the production of a great variety of articles, including dilly bags, mats, mosquito nets, carrying bags for babies and objects used in legal and political ceremonies.

The women were in no great hurry. They had only a short distance to travel for their day's work. They spent some time cleaning the whole village, sweeping the ground with a brush broom made from bushes that grew at the edge of the village area. While this clean up was on, the children were sent off to play. The women finished and admired their hard work. The sweeping had made parallel marks across the ground. Some of the children had already been told not to walk across the swept area but to leave it tidy for everyone when they returned in the afternoon.

Suddenly a shout of alarm went up from some of the children who were away from the camp further in the bush. The alarm frightened the women to the bone because the children were shouting, '*Yarraman*'! Horses!' To the women that meant Balanda stockmen. Then the children called out 'Yolŋu!' and that made them relax, because if they were Yolŋu stockmen then it was okay.

Some of the men rode right into the village across the swept ground and all the children and women came together. The Yolŋu stockmen asked where the men were and were told they had gone north for the day. The Yolŋu stockmen then asked the women and children to line up so that they could see them all. This was not a Yolŋu thing to do and it worried the women. Their concerns were confirmed when three more horses broke from the cover of the bush, carrying two Balanda and the Murri stockman. The women wanted to run, but the Yolŋu stockmen demanded they stay and said everything would be all right. The two Balanda and the Murri stockman came up and stood beside the Yolŋu stockmen on their horses, facing the Yolŋu women and children. The women watched their every move. The Yolŋu stockmen were very nervous and that worried the women even more. One of the women yelled the command to run. As they broke the line and ran, all the stockmen drew their Winchesters and fired until no life could be detected. The women, children and even the babies were all slaughtered, their blood running down the sweep marks the women had made just a few moments before. Then the stockmen rode north after the men.

The men first noticed the horses when birds in the distance rose high in the air calling loudly that the *mägaya* (peace and tranquillity) was broken. Then the galloping horses came into view across the dry, hard plain. The men were still in the open a short distance from the billabong they were heading for. They were immediately alarmed because stockmen did not usually push their horses so hard, so they ran hard and fast toward the billabong. Those at the back were overtaken by the stockmen and shot as they ran. Some, knowing they would not reach the billabong, stopped and stood with spears at the ready. The lead runner also stopped but others urged him to go on and to think of the women and children. So he turned and again ran towards the billabong. The men who had stopped fitted the hunting spears to their woomeras, wishing they had carried some light, fast bamboo spears this morning. They knew that with the heavy hunting spears they had no hope against these stockmen. They had fought other stockmen before and won, but they knew this time the stockmen were armed with different rifles—Winchesters.

The men spread out as the horses charged. The stockmen stopped just short of spear range and drew their guns. At that distance Yolŋu knew they had no hope with spears, so they charged at the stockmen, weaving and dodging as the stockmen fired. Many shots missed and some spears were released, but it is hard to aim when you are running and dodging. In a minute or two it was all over.

The lead man reached the billabong and watched his brothers fall. His thoughts turned to the women and children. He knew the Balanda would come after him because Yolŋu stockmen were with them. They knew all the Yolŋu tricks. He thought quickly. He remembered how he harvested waterfowl—submerged in the water, he would move in on the birds from one end of the billabong and hide under a lily pad while breathing through a bundle of reeds. That way he could reach the ducks, pick the fattest, grab both legs with one hand and quickly pull it under the water before it made a noise to disturb the others. Now he would use this skill to protect his life.

He jettisoned his spears and dilly bag and dived into the water. He swam to a reed and water lily bed where he grabbed a handful of reeds, trying not to disturb any mud. He then swam to another part of the bed, chewing the ends off the reeds and swallowing them so they would not float on the water and be detected. Submerged, he found a place where he could hold himself on the bottom of the billabong and yet still breathe through the bundle of reeds. He knew he would have to hold himself down as long as possible because he would have no idea if the stockmen were still waiting for him to surface. He stayed there until he could hold himself down no longer. To him, the time seemed like forever.

Earlier he had heard the noise of people jumping into the water and he knew the Balanda had been looking for him. Now he slowly surfaced under a water lily leaf, still breathing through the reeds. He lifted his head carefully from the water, knowing that if a Yolŋu was watching from the bank he would probably spot him. But as he brought one eye out of the water and scanned the bank, he knew he was alone. He turned and looked behind. All was clear. He sat in this position for a while, maybe half an hour, then slowly made his way out of the back of the billabong.

The stockmen were gone. They knew that if the Yolŋu organised themselves and moved to the swamp country they would never be able to kill them all, which was clearly their intention. Their company was called the Eastern and African Cold Storage Company, and they had much experience in dealing with the native people in Africa.[24] There, white men had armed one tribe and used them to kill other tribes in order to clear the country for cattle. The manager in charge of the present operation, Billy Farrer, thought the same tactics would work in Arnhem Land.[25] And so far the plan was working. They had armed and trained one clan from southern Arnhem Land and now these Yolŋu were accessories to the murder of other Yolŋu the previous day.

The Murri was urging them on. He wanted to hit most of the main Djinaŋ clans that day and kill as many as possible before they had time to get organised. In a village at Bundhatharri, some Yolŋu fled before the horsemen into a small patch of tropical jungle. The stockmen tracked them down and shot them out of their hiding places in the trees. Then they turned toward the Murruŋun Wolkpuy clan at Naŋgalala. On the way to Naŋgalala they hit small Yolŋu families, killing them all before the Yolŋu knew what had happened.

The people at Naŋgalala heard the shooting coming closer and closer. Many of these people made for the Glyde River to get to safety, but the river was wide and strong and only a few could get across. The others made their way back to the jungle patches where they hid in the trees. The Yolŋu assumed that Balanda were doing the shooting—they didn't know that Yolŋu at the cattle station had turned against their own people. It was easy for these Yolŋu stockmen to track down the other Yolŋu. They even knew the names of the people from their footprints. So the stockmen found the hidden Yolŋu and shot them out of the trees, killing them all. Yolŋu tracks also told them that many had crossed the river. The stockmen headed south, back towards the homestead, running into more Yolŋu groups on the way. The Yolŋu stockmen and the Murri knew where to find the people.

The next day the stockmen left the homestead in force and crossed the Glyde River about ten kilometres to the north, where the Glyde was very narrow. They made their way back towards Naŋgalala on the east side of the river, to a place called Banambarraŋur. Here many clans had gathered overnight, ready to march on the cattle station. The women and children had already been sent further east to safety. The clash was vicious. The Yolŋu warriors and the stockmen fought in a cypress pine forest. Many spirits left their physical bodies that day, both Yolŋu and Balanda. Yolŋu used the cover of the forest to their advantage, moving around the Balanda, confusing them. Within half an hour the Balanda were running short of bullets. They turned and ran, carrying their wounded but leaving their dead. Many horses were wounded too. The Balanda headed straight for the homestead.

The war that would be fought over the next three years brought a number of the thirteen Djinaŋ clans of north-central Arnhem Land to the point of extinction. The war was not just confined to Yolŋu between the Blyth and Glyde Rivers, although this is where many of the main conflicts occurred. The stockmen even rode south and south-east, down the flood plains of the Rose River all the way to the Gulf of Carpentaria, killing any Yolŋu they could find. Their favourite method was to catch a family group in the open and ride straight at them to make them run. As they ran for safety, the stockmen and native police would ride up behind them and shoot them in the back of the head, then ride on to the next person and shoot until all of them, even the children, were dead.

These murderous traitors and their vicious leaders left the clans of south-east Arnhem Land confused and bewildered. They did not know how they would survive. It was now impossible for them to hunt on the open plains in the daytime, so they spent the daylight hours in hill country, coming down to the billabongs at night. This was the only way the survivors could get food. Many of them were broken. They grieved for their loved ones and for the time when the ancient *Maḏayin* created peace and serenity in their land. The men had thoughts of revenge against the killers, but they could see no way of succeeding against their treachery. Their numbers now were small and all they could think of was ways to survive.

For Yolŋu between the Blyth and Glyde/Goyder Rivers, the next few years were also hard. These people lived in comparatively open country where stockmen on horses could outrun them easily. The people west of the Blyth River remained untouched by this conflict. Those east of the Glyde/Goyder were also fairly safe, with no clashes taking place except for the large battle at Banambarraŋur. After the stockmen's humiliating defeat that day, they were too frightened to cross the Glyde again.

The remainder of the Djinaŋ clans now moved west or east. A large number of the men came together at a camp east of the Arafura swamp area. Many clans and the wider nation alliances wanted to rid Arnhem Land of the white scourge. According to Yolŋu thinking, anyone who would kill women and children in cold blood had no right to exist. They called these Balanda and the Murri the *gula'-mala*—faeces people. Their reasoning was that no human being who had a spirit and any sense of law, order and justice could do such a thing.

The Yolŋu also believed these *gula'-mala* had no respect for the law of the land, it's owners or for their resources. For thousands of years, the Yolŋu had treated visitors to their estates with respect. If visitors asked for a portion of the estate's resources, the owner would usually share willingly. But if visitors failed to announce their presence and took a lot of the estate's resources, the owners would be very offended. If a Yolŋu person stole from someone else's estate, he was seen as a thief and classed as a debtor who had to repay. If the offender did not repay, his whole clan would be responsible for the debt. Now the Balanda were acting like such people—lawbreakers, thieves, criminals and murderers. They were worse than the most disgusting, lawless, savage enemy the Yolŋu could imagine.

From the camp in the east the Yolŋu planned many campaigns. All were aimed at harassing the stockmen and getting back at the native police. Knowing that frontal attacks were doomed to fail against Winchester rifles, they devised other possibilities. Once they provoked the stockmen to chase a group of Yolŋu into an area of rock country where many warriors waited. They attacked the stockmen from above with a shower of stone spears, driving the weapons down through the backs of the stockmen into their stomachs. When the spears were gone, the Yolŋu pounced with stone axes, killing the remainder of the group.[26] The Yolŋu knew that the Balanda pastoralists would only fall for each trick once. They knew this was a life and death battle.

As the clans organised themselves, they called on their *riŋgitj* alliances to hassle the Balanda in any way they could. The Balanda in turn called in others to support the cattle station. The Yolŋu watched their every move. When stockmen were camping out, Yolŋu decided to take out any Balanda they could. If a stockman went to the toilet, Yolŋu waited for him to be 'busy' then attacked, at all times staying out of range of the rifles. One night a group of warriors crept into one of the stockmen's camps, stole all their rifles and threw them into the billabong. Another night, Yolŋu lit a grass fire up-wind of the stockmen's camp. Other warriors were waiting in the grass, covered by darkness. The retreating stockmen were silhouetted against the fire and easily attacked as they fled.

These skirmishes occurred over the whole area. The Yolŋu also harassed the main cattle station, moving across the swamp at night time, upsetting the horses, stealing stores and attacking the sleeping quarters. Then they retreated back into the night and across the swamp to safety. As they did this, the warriors killed any cattle and horses they could.

In the Dry season of 1908,[27] the Yolŋu saw the Balanda loading up flat-top wagons, rounding up what livestock remained and driving south. A small band of guards remained. Five or six days later the flat top wagons returned with a big team of stockmen, who loaded more supplies and rounded up more stock and headed south again. This time no-one was left behind. The Yolŋu moved straight in on the buildings of mud and timber and razed them to the ground. The victory was theirs.

But as they sat there, the victory seemed very hollow. So many of their countrymen were dead. Some clans were extinct, others on the edge of it. The Eastern and African Cold Storage Company lease covered 50,000 square kilometres, almost the whole of east Arnhem Land,[28] including the estates of fifty or more Yolŋu clans. By the end of this second Great War lasting five years, the Yolŋu of north-central Arnhem Land were tired. But at least they were not defeated.

The Yolŋu who had joined the pastoralists in the war left Arnhem Land with the Balanda. These Yolŋu lived out their lives in Borroloola, 300 kilometres south, too frightened to return and face the justice established by the Creator *Waŋarr* and maintained in the law councils of their people. The descendants of these Yolŋu only started returning to Arnhem Land and their estates in the early 1990s, the crimes of their fathers not being held against the children, in accordance with the ancient law.

The people had a time of rest from Balanda pastoralists and native police. However, Yolŋu further to the east, and people to the south-east of Arnhem Land, were to re-live the nightmare experience of these and other wars a few more times yet.

The Loss of International Trade

All the Yolŋu who had come together for battle now returned home to their clan estates. As the monsoonal winds started to blow, the coastal clans were excited to get home, wanting to prepare for the seasonal visits of the Macassans.

But the Wet season came and went and the Macassans did not come. The people wondered why. As they talked with each other along the coast, suggestions were made that it had something to do with the Balanda, but no-one was sure what. There were stories that some Macassan captains had said in previous years they might not be able to come in future because the Balanda out of Port Darwin would not let them land (some Yolŋu elders today remember their fathers in tears of disbelief when the Macassan captains told them this news). But many Yolŋu dismissed these stories. They said, 'Who are these Balanda? They have no say in the legal agreements between our clans and the Macassans.' No-one knew that in 1906 the South Australian government had revoked the licences for the Macassans to fish for trepang.[29]

The coastal Yolŋu were shattered, partly by the uncertainty. 'Maybe the Macassans did not come because so many of us were away fighting the Balanda, not here working with them,' they reasoned. 'Or have we done something else wrong that has insulted them?' Whichever way they thought about it, the clan leaders could not understand the situation because they knew there were legal trading agreements between themselves and the Macassans who were always good, honourable people. Some clans grieved even more, because they were expecting the return of clansmen who had travelled to Sulawesi with the Macassans. It is common knowledge that these Yolŋu clansmen lived out their days in the port of Macassar, never to return to Arnhem Land, and their descendants still live there today.

The coastal clans also worried about how they could continue trading with inland clans when they had nothing to trade. They knew some inland clans would still trade with them because of debts that were owed due to the Balanda wars. But sooner or later they would run out of credit. The biggest concern the coastal clans had was getting flint spear and axe heads. They had some left, but they knew they would run out in a few years.

Life became difficult for everyone in Arnhem Land when the Macassan trade stopped. The people had become used to using imported items like fishhooks and fishing line. Now they had to start making bone and wooden hooks. No-one was used to it and it took many hours of hard work to produce them.

Other things were also changing. Strange boats started appearing along the coast—Balanda-type boats with Asian crews. But they came looking to steal rather than to trade. These people were very different from the Macassans. The Macassans respected the rule of the *Maḏayin* and believed the Yolŋu estates and resources to be theirs, so they always asked permission. But the masters of the new boats just started stealing trepang and pearls and killing large numbers of turtles for their carapaces. They were always threatening the Yolŋu owners with guns. The Yolŋu started to fight back against this lawlessness, but it was a hard battle against well-organised and armed invaders.

The Third War

This was the beginning of the third major war that Yolŋu warriors had to fight in less than twenty years. This time the people approached the conflict differently. The boats were after goods that the Yolŋu had, but they also had tradable goods that the Yolŋu needed, such as fishhooks, tobacco and steel. It was hard for the people not to become dependent on these new visitors even though they were stealing from Yolŋu estates.

But some boat crews molested Yolŋu women, and this became their downfall. For thousands of years Yolŋu had sent their women away from any threat of conflict. Now some clans sent their women into the front line. These mothers and wives knew these were desperate times for their families and clans, and desperate times demand desperate actions.

If a boat crew was being troublesome, the women would be sent to the boat in a canoe just before sundown. Of course the women would be taken on board. Then an hour or so after sunset the men would paddle out in canoes, knowing the women would have worked at getting everyone drunk. Hearing the men's coded signals, the women would know their men were nearby and would try to keep the crewmen occupied. The men in the canoes would have a good view of the lantern-lit boat. When the right moment came, they would creep on board and kill the crew. The boat would then be pulled into a creek, stripped of anything useful and burnt at low tide while the creek was dry. The bodies of the crewmen would be buried in the sand where the crabs would eat them. The Yolŋu knew they had to make these boats just disappear. Many boats were taken this way, all around the coast of Arnhem Land.

Crocodile shooters also started coming to Arnhem Land. Many of them were treacherous people shooting anyone or anything they saw. Many of the north-central and north-east Arnhem Land clans attacked the crocodile shooters for their lawlessness.

In west Arnhem Land the shooters came for the Asian water buffalo, which the British had released when they abandoned Victoria Settlement on the Coburg peninsula in 1849. The buffalo were now present in large numbers, spreading south down the Coburg Peninsular and into west and central Arnhem Land.[30] The buffalo shooters were also rough men who knew no other law than the rule of the gun.

Yolŋu began suffering from new diseases such as smallpox, measles, scarlet fever and consumption (tuberculosis). In 1917 malaria swept from west to east through Arnhem Land.[31] These diseases at times wiped out whole family units. With the large number of boats operating along the coast and the coastal clans trading with them, there was plenty of opportunity for these introduced diseases to cross over to the people.

Yolŋu leaders felt the world had gone mad. Their lands and estates were constantly under threat. It was as though there was no rule of law left in the world.

The Lesser of Two Evils

In 1916 a new influence entered the scene in western Arnhem Land. This influence changed the direction of events for the Bininj (the Aboriginal people of west Arnhem Land) and went on to dramatically change the course of history for the Yolŋu in central to north-east Arnhem Land. This influence was in the form of a missionary - the Reverend James Watson.[32]

For over twenty years there had been many Balanda in the area—trepangers, buffalo shooters, pearl divers and others. A handful were good, but many were men like Paddy Mack, Ronnie Spencer, Mac and Tom. All these men had killed Bininj, and Bininj had killed them in return. Ronnie Spencer had also caused many problems for Yolŋu down in Arnhem Bay where he was eventually killed by them.[33]

The Bininj man who dispensed with Mac and Tom was the same man who, after a number of years in a Darwin jail, acted as interpreter and guide for Reverend Watson on his 1915 trip into Arnhem Land.[34] Watson was not trusted at first because he started building the Methodist Overseas Missions station at South Goulburn Island right on top of a restricted law council place. This place was seen as holy and was only visited at special times.

Watson might not have lasted long except for the fact that he talked about a man who was like *Namumuiag* (the Great Creator Spirit in the Bininj language). He said this man had come and died for everyone and that he wanted to teach people about him. The Bininj thought this Balanda might be different—if he knew about the Great Creator Spirit, maybe he would also know the way of the Great Creator, the rule of the ancient holy law. So they decided to watch and help him. Watson paid the Bininj who worked for him in rations. Only one or two Balanda had treated the people fairly in this way before. Many had looked on them as slaves, shooting or flogging them, locking them up in irons without food for many days or killing them with poisoned flour, damper or meat.[35]

Watson's station soon became a place where Bininj and Yolŋu went to trade, sometimes travelling from hundreds of kilometres away. Some coastal clans had fallen so deeply into debt that, by the time the mission station was set up on South Goulburn Island in 1916, they sent canoes to the island filled with tradable goods such as pearls and turtle carapaces. One man travelled from Cape Arnhem to South Goulburn Island and back, taking three months to do the trip. They could see that *Bäpa* (father/Reverend) Watson was a fair trader.

This pattern was repeated throughout Arnhem Land. The Church Missionary Society (Anglican) established missions at Roper River in 1908 and Emerald River (Groote Eylandt) in 1921. This continued until the 1950s when the Nunggubuyu people from the southern Blue Mud Bay area, who were camped at the Roper River mission, asked the missionaries to establish a mission at Rose River. So Numbulwar mission was established in 1952.

But back in 1921, other Balanda from the Methodist Overseas Missions came to north-central Arnhem Land to set up another station. At first they settled on Elcho Island.[36] Then oil shale was discovered and a mining company moved in. The missionaries could not see how a Balanda town could work so close to a mission, so in 1923 they shifted to Milingimbi. Here they camped and started building a new station on the site of an old Macassan trading camp. The Yolŋu were very suspicious at first, but they quickly learned to trust these new missionaries because of *Bäpa* Watson's reputation, which had spread throughout north Arnhem Land. He had partnered Bininj in disputes with Balanda pearlers, trepangers and crocodile shooters. Bininj wondered how this unarmed Balanda could argue with other armed, angry Balanda and win. 'Why don't these Balanda just shoot him, like they have Bininj?' they thought. 'Does he have some special power and authority? It must be he has power and authority from the Creator, whom he is always talking and singing about.'

The Bininj and Yolŋu talked about Watson's power and authority for many, many hours around the camp fires, in meeting places and even in their councils of law. They asked themselves, 'If one Balanda knows the Great Creator *Waŋarr* and his *Maḏayin* rule of law, then how come these other Balanda are so lawless, vicious and destructive, especially of human life?' Many concluded that the missionary was sent by *Waŋarr*—even though he called the Creator by a different name—to save the Yolŋu from the other uncivilised, lawless Balanda. They also concluded that, even though these missionaries were ignorant of many of the ways and laws of the Yolŋu, they did recognise the Yolŋu had a *birrimbirr* (spirit) which made their life holy, and that they were not just a resource to be used like animals.[37]

A number of Yolŋu clans and nation parliaments decided to work with the missionaries and use them to try to defeat the other Balanda. Many coastal and island clans decided to get to know the missionaries so they could learn the secrets of Balanda power and authority. The missionaries acknowledged the Creator as superior, so they were clearly the preferred foreigners and the lesser of two evils.

The mission era brought a new experience to the Yolŋu. The people found they now had more access to Balanda medicines, which were definitely more effective than their own medicines against Balanda diseases. Some inland clans, however, tried to stay away from the missions because they were still not convinced of their motives. This was especially true for some of the eastern clans.

Baḻayni

In the Dry season of 1927 or 1928, the Yolŋu again experienced the treachery of the white foreigners that had wreaked destruction on the other clans some twenty Wet seasons before.

One cool Dry season morning, the sun had lifted above the trees and driven away the coolness of the night. A Yolŋu family group, of the Dhaḻwaŋu clan, were enjoying life in their main village beside a beautiful billabong, at a place called Gäṉgaṉ. They were the southern family group of their clan and they lived above the Koolatong River in south-east Arnhem Land.

The family had woken before dawn. Some of the women had already visited their yam garden and returned with yams for the day. The men had had a successful hunt the day before and the village had a good supply of cooked wallaby and emu. Because there was ample food at hand, the men and women had settled down to produce or repair baskets and mats. The men were particularly keen to fulfil a *buku-djugu'* (verbal contract) they had with a neighbouring clan for baskets that were used to pack flint spearheads. The contract was for twenty baskets and today would be a good day to get them finished.

Some of the children joined in the production, learning as they went from their parents and other elders. The group sat under a *warraw'* (bough shelter) that was the main production site. As they worked they talked about many things. Sometimes, some of the younger children lost interest in the work and played *matjka* (cat's cradle) with string made from bush fibre. They made different funny shapes and sometimes would tease each other with their creations. As the day wore on, some of the older boys went along the billabong spearing fish and some of the young men went off to try and kill a wallaby, so they would have some fresh *gonyil* (protein food). Three of the older girls had gone to the end of the billabong and were returning with *dhatam'* (water lily stems and bulbs). They planned to roast the bulbs so the workers and old people would have stems and roasted bulbs to chew on as they finished their work.

The three girls were just 200 metres from the village when one of their brothers, who had been spear fishing further down the billabong, ran up behind them puffing and yelling at them to run. Balanda were coming on horses! They all ran towards the village, yelling, '*Djärraŋ! Djärraŋ! Djärraŋ!*' (the Macassan word for horse or horses). These young people had never seen horses or even Balanda, but the stories they had heard of these murderous monsters had prepared them for this day.

Their elders had told them of the massacres that had killed whole Yolŋu families and clan groups south of the Koolatong River and up into central Arnhem Land. They also explained how Balanda were carried by strange, powerful animals that made the noise of thunder when they raced over the ground. They said even when these strange animals walked they struck the ground with a hard, thudding noise. This young man had only listened and watched for a moment before he was convinced these animals were the dreaded *djärraŋ*. When he had seen a white man on one of the horses, he knew he must run as hard as he could to give the families time to prepare. So he ran almost without touching the ground, with fear swelling through his body.

Upon hearing the dreaded word *djärraŋ*, the men in the village immediately went for their fighting spears to ensure everything was in order. They ascertained from the young man that the horses and men were still a little way off, giving them time to get organised. The headman instructed the women to gather the children and make for the thick jungle patch at the top end of the billabong, with the strict instructions not to come out until somebody came to get them. The women left carrying the babies, some food, sleeping mats and digging sticks. The men then set about covering the women's tracks and trying to make their village look as though only men were there.

Balanda and horses had not been in this area for over twenty Wet seasons. 'Who can these Balanda be?' the men wondered. The only Balanda in the area were missionaries at Roper River and Groote Eylandt and some Balanda trepangers along the coast—maybe it was some of them. If so, everything would be all right. As they questioned the boy more, they started to grow uneasy. He said he didn't get a good look at them because he was frightened and ran. They were still asking him questions when they saw the men and horses for themselves. They were coming from the south up the eastern side of the billabong, straight towards the village. In front was a Balanda, behind him was another Balanda. Two Murris and some Yolŋu from southern Arnhem Land (who now lived on one of the cattle stations further south) brought up the rear.

The horses slowed to a walk, stopping about forty or fifty paces from the village men. The Yolŋu on the horses moved up closer and asked where the other men were. 'Still out hunting,' they said. The southern Yolŋu asked if they could camp with them for the night. The village leader responded, 'Yes, you can sleep here with us.' 'Good,' the visitors said, 'then tomorrow we can travel on to another billabong.'

So the visitors camped with the men that night. The southern Yolŋu called themselves 'police trackers', and they said the head Balanda came from Pine Creek and his name was Baḻayni. They said Baḻayni, the other Balanda and the Murris were native police. When the village men heard this, they were very concerned, remembering stories from the pastoralist wars and how the native police at Murwangi had been involved in most of the massacres. The only thing that allowed them to sleep during the night was the fact that these other Yolŋu were with them, and they felt that they would not do anything wrong. But still the men watched the intruders' every move.

In the morning the men relaxed as the visitors went down to the billabong and washed themselves. Then they set about cooking breakfast. As a goodwill gesture the visitors made damper from white flour and shared it with the men of the village. The men appreciated this and relaxed as they told light-hearted stories together over a shared meal. But as the men ate and talked, the policeman Baḻayni moved over casually to where the Yolŋu had stood their spears against a tree. While no-one was watching, he smashed the butt of his rifle against a bundle of spears, shattering their shafts, then breaking the bottom half of the spears by putting his foot on them.

He had broken two bundles when the Yolŋu closest to him, an old man, ran at him saying in Yolŋu Matha, 'Hey, why are you breaking our spears?' Balayni turned and hit him in the face with the butt of his rifle. By this time all the Yolŋu were on their feet, shocked that Balayni had broken their weapons and had hit the old man with such force. Their first thoughts were for their old father, now lying motionless on the ground. They thought he was dead. They realised then that they were trapped, their weapons broken and out of reach. Before they had time to think, Balayni, the other Balanda policeman and the Murris opened fire, shooting the unarmed men where they stood.

As they tried to get away, every shot brought another Yolŋu life to an end. The guns continued. Only one young man was still standing. His mind raced. 'I must get away so I can come back for the survivors,' he thought. Taking large leaping strides, he reached the edge of the billabong. There were fewer shots now as some of the killers had run out of bullets and were reloading. He reached the water and dived.

Bullets zinged into the water beside him. He swam deep and long, coming up under a water lily. Taking a quick look, he saw chaos. The killers were running all over the place looking for survivors. One was already shooting any victim still moving on the ground. Some were looking for him. His mind raced again: they would find him! Then he remembered from his childhood a space under the bank that existed when the water was at this height. He dived and swam for the spot, found the bank and went under. The water was just low enough to let some air in, so he thanked *Waŋarr* the Creator for his provision so that he could live to tell the story and perhaps avenge his family's killing. His thoughts were filled with wild rage as he wept for his father, brothers and other relatives.

The young man did not know how long the Balanda would look for him, so he stayed in the tiny cave until after dark. When he left his refuge, he broke the surface of the water silently with just his head. All was quiet—deathly quiet. He did not dare move, knowing the men could still be above him. Then he heard night birds in the trees and knew the men were not nearby. But they could still be hiding somewhere.

Every muscle in his body was tense and twitching as he made his way up along the billabong. He still was not sure where the Balanda were, so he decided to head up to where the women and children had gone. He fought the emotions within him as he went, wanting to break down and scream in fury at the horrors he had witnessed that morning. When he reached the jungle, he found the women and children safe, except for one old woman who had gone to investigate the shooting and not returned.

Two days later a Yolŋu man of the same family arrived home after visiting relatives to the north-east of Gängan.[38] Before he entered the village he found the swollen body of one of his relatives and could see he had died from a hole in the back that did not look like a spear wound. He was very confused and moved forward with great caution. He soon came upon horse tracks and his greatest fears were realised: horses meant Balanda and Murris, and that meant death for Yolŋu. He was on the north side of his village and could see that the horses had gone further north, so he moved with greater speed towards the village. There he found the bodies of his dead father, brothers and other relatives but none of the women or children. After coming to grips with his grief he wondered where they might be, but soon constructed the picture from the tracks on the ground. He realised that the horses had come from the south, so he guessed that there had been time for the women and children to go to a hiding place. That would be the jungle to the north-west.

At first he followed the horses' tracks north. He saw them joined by the footprints of one of the women, whom he recognised from her prints. He could see how they had chased her and caught her because her footprints disappeared. This woman was never seen again. To his surprise the horses then turned away from the jungle patch. Maybe the captured woman had led them away from the other women and children. When the man reached the jungle, he found the women and children and the young man who had escaped.

Balayni's murderers rode north and then split up. One group went north-west and travelled overland right up to Milingimbi. Balayni called in on the missionaries at Milingimbi to make his trip an official patrol through Arnhem Land. On their way to Milingimbi, they attacked a group of Yolŋu at Raymaŋgirr, killing an old man and an old woman. Many Yolŋu groups discussed whether to attack and kill Balayni or not, but they decided it was probably unwise because it was difficult to catch the party by surprise. They knew they were being watched.

The other half of the group travelled north-east. They came upon another innocent Yolŋu family near Biranybirany. The group consisted mainly of women and children because the men were busy on another part of the estate. The horsemen taunted the women, using stock whips and saddle stirrups, herding them in different directions until the women and children were able to get away into some thick jungle. But in their folly they killed one of the women and left her screaming, traumatised child beside her.

The group left the women and travelled further north-east, coming upon a larger Yolŋu family group. They killed a number of the people, but this time the Yolŋu were able to fight back, killing one of the Yolŋu police trackers. This unnerved the remaining killers and they retreated, waiting at a meeting place for Balayni to come back from Milingimbi. On his return, the party attacked the family group again, this time killing others and capturing one Yolŋu man who was taken back to Katherine. This man was tried for the murder of the police tracker and sent to jail in Melbourne.

The Fourth War

Balayni's murderous campaign started yet another war between the clans of north-east Arnhem Land and the *mulkuru* (foreigners). Until now, these north-eastern clans had not had their sovereignty challenged to the same extent as clans in southern and central Arnhem Land. Now they also knew, like other Yolŋu, that these white men had no sense of law or justice. Perhaps, they thought, they didn't even have a conscience, stained as they were by the blood of women and children.

It became clear to Yolŋu that because of their greed the Balanda intended to wipe out all Yolŋu. Many warriors vowed to fight to the death to save their womenfolk and children. And any Yolŋu who joined these lawless murderers would be treated in the same way as these Balanda.

All along the coast, Yolŋu families, clans and clan estates continued to come under pressure. In north-east Arnhem Land the extent of this pressure can be seen from the large number of boats, usually with Japanese crews, that became involved in the trepang and pearling trade. By 1936 it was reported by T. T. Webb, Superintendent of Milingimbi mission, that there were 'fifty boats operating in the Crocodile Islands area alone, with Japanese crew totalling nearly 800'.[39] If there were fifty boats in the Crocodile Islands around Milingimbi alone, there must have been hundreds along the whole coast of Arnhem Land.

For coastal and island Yolŋu this pressure was just too much. Many of the coastal clans were pushed to the point of extinction. Everywhere Yolŋu were being verbally and physically assaulted, their women molested and raped, their traditional estates pillaged. Yolŋu men became increasingly angry and resolved to correct things. Their hatred for the Japanese trepangers was now as great as it had been for the white pastoralists.

The north-east clans kept a vigil. There were too many foreigners to attack all of them, so it was decided that any foreigner who acted in a lawless way, such as threatening Yolŋu with guns, demanding or stealing their women or setting up residence without permission of the estate owners, would be dispensed with.

Only a few foreigners were allowed on Yolŋu estates. Besides the missionaries, trepanger/trader Fred Grey was the only long-term foreign resident in east Arnhem Land, living at Umbakumba on Groote Eylandt. He had good relations with Yolŋu estate owners there and treated them fairly, as the Macassans had. The mission at Groote Eylandt was also used as a trading centre.

In September 1932,[40] Japanese trepangers set up their trepang smoking and working camp on a beach in Caledon Bay. They had Goulburn Island (Bininj) crew members to sail their two boats. Initially the Djapu clan members watched them to see if they were people of law, and at first the Japanese offered the estate owners tradable items. Some Yolŋu even decided they would work with them on the trepanging as they had for centuries with the Macassans.

But the Yolŋu became worried because these Japanese always carried guns wherever they went, even while working. Soon the Japanese started threatening the workers. Then at night they started coming to the workers' homes, demanding that the men let them have their young wives and daughters. One Yolŋu man was shot at for no reason as he approached the Japanese one morning to ask for work. Another time one of the Japanese had an argument with a Yolŋu worker, picked up some guts from the trepang they had been cleaning and hit the man across the face with them. This last action cast the die for the Japanese.

Violent acts like shooting at somebody would not be tolerated. 'They are talking to us as though we were just animals, pointing their guns at us and now shooting at us,' the people said. 'Then they come and insult us while they steal from us. These Japanese are like Baḻayni and the pastoralists, with no sense of law and justice. We must drive them from our estate. If they won't go, then they must die before they kill us or assault our women.'

The Yolŋu discussed how they would get the Japanese to leave. They knew the foreigners would shoot them if they tried to force them out. For the next few days, every move of the Japanese was watched as Yolŋu tried to understand their intentions. In the end it was decided that the Japanese must be killed. The men discussed how they could even the odds and get past the guns. The Japanese had already forbidden the Yolŋu to bring spears into the work camp, so any attack on them would be difficult. They talked until the plan was worked out in detail.

Next day everyone was up early. The people were camped about a kilometre up the beach from the trepangers' camp. As morning broke the children were told to play by the water so the Japanese would not notice anything wrong. When the men were near the camp, the children were to return to their mothers. The mothers and children were then to go to a predetermined place on the estate where they would be safe. Everyone was anxious. Ten Yolŋu men would go up against the six Japanese with guns. The Yolŋu had no argument with the Goulburn Island crewmembers and they would stay out of it. But the Yolŋu were aware that each spear had to count before any of the Japanese got to a gun.

As the early morning sun broke over the top of the headland, the men started off down the beach in as normal a manner as possible, even though everyone was very nervous. As they neared the camp they split up to go to their work areas. The Japanese had already come ashore. Anger at the rude, lawless, rapist thieves swept through each Yolŋu warrior as they justified what they were about to do. They thought: 'Haven't these men got wives and daughters of their own that they would want to protect from ruthless foreigners who came to use and abuse? Haven't they got a home of their own that they would fight and die for? Or are they just ruthless exploiters who travel to other people's homeland and plunder and steal, rape and kill?'

The Yolŋu warriors were now in place, well within spear range of their enemy. At a coded signal from their chosen commander each man dug his foot into the sand and flicked up three spears that had been hidden the night before. These spears quickly found their mark, with only one of the enemy reaching his gun before they were all dispatched. The men then set about dismantling the camp. Any stores and materials that would be of use were collected to take back.

In the confusion, however, the men had not realised that one Japanese crewman had been in the bush when they attacked. He escaped with the two Goulburn Island Bininj, travelling overland to Milingimbi. So the clan returned to normal life, not knowing that their actions were about to cause a series of events that would bring the whole of Arnhem Land under yet another wave of threats.

On hearing the news, the Balanda in Darwin decided that the Yolŋu of Arnhem Land had to be 'taught a lesson'. A police patrol would be sent out to arrest the 'murderers'. The patrol travelled to Groote Eylandt where they picked up guides, then crossed over to the mainland looking for the Yolŋu who had killed the Japanese. The policeman in charge captured the wife of one of the men and handcuffed her to himself overnight. For the Yolŋu this marked the policeman's death. They were tired of these lawless Balanda who treated their women with no respect. The next day they completely confused the patrol and the husband killed the adulterer/rapist with one spear to the chest. The Yolŋu stayed under cover. The patrol was in turmoil, retreating to Groote Eylandt and then back to Darwin with their dead leader.[41]

The news of the policeman's death hit Darwin. The Balanda were enraged at the people of Arnhem Land. 'How dare they kill a police officer while carrying out his duty?' they cried. Punitive raids were planned with Balanda volunteering to go and really 'teach a lesson' to these natives of Arnhem Land.[42] Meanwhile, also late in the dry season of 1933, two Balanda itinerants, W. Fagan and Frank Traynor, were killed on Woodah Island for sexually assaulting Yolŋu women.[43]

News of these killings broke in the newspapers in southern Australia, along with news of the pending punitive raids. The response from the south was different. Strong protest was expressed across the nation by humanitarian and church groups saying 'enough is enough'. This pressure forced the Commonwealth government to send a peace expedition of missionaries from Groote Eylandt mission. They travelled to the mainland talking to Yolŋu. In the end, the Yolŋu involved in defending their home and country decided to go to Darwin with the missionaries. On arriving at Darwin wharf, however, they were arrested and taken away screaming, and spent the next four months in jail, kept in irons until their trials commenced in August 1934. The missionaries felt terribly betrayed as they had been led to believe that they would be responsible for the men until proper police interviews had been conducted.

In all there were three separate trials. In the first trial, three Yolŋu were convicted of murder of the Japanese and sentenced to twenty years' jail with hard labour. The second trial resulted in the acquittal of the two Yolŋu charged with the murder of the itinerants on Woodah Island. The third trial found 'Dagiar' (correct spelling 'Dhäkiyarr') guilty of murdering the policeman and sentenced him to death. In each of the trials, only a small part of the story from the Yolŋu defendants was heard and the trials have been described as 'a mockery of British justice'.[44]

The verdict from the third trial was subsequently challenged and the conviction quashed. Dhäkiyarr was released from Darwin prison but disappeared shortly afterwards, never to be seen again. Many Yolŋu still believe he was murdered by the police. The others returned to their homeland with Donald Thomson, a patrol officer/anthropologist, after a few years in jail.

In response to these killings, Yirrkala mission was established in late 1935.[45] Some of the clans from north-east Arnhem Land started to use Yirrkala as a trading post. Yirrkala was set up mainly out of Milingimbi mission. With the establishment of all the missions, the massacres stopped and the tit-for-tat killing between the foreigners and Yolŋu ceased.

Yolŋu had sustained almost fifty years of war and uncertainty and were now emotionally distraught. Many of the survivors had seen their families slaughtered and their homeland sovereignty shattered and they carried deep emotional wounds. The whole of Arnhem Land was in chaos. Clans felt vulnerable and a number of the coastal clans came to the missions to survive. Other southern clans went further south, offering themselves for work on Balanda cattle stations in return for protection from other whites and native police.

Some inland clans tried to stay on their estates even though it was extremely hard going. As an old man, a clan leader, said to me in 1975, 'We were almost starving because it was hard to get the things needed to survive'. The traditional trading network had broken down and essential items were not coming along the trading tracks any more. Other clans in north-central and western Arnhem Land were forced further west to Pine Creek and Darwin. This move from their estates created a new and profound experience for the people.

The Battle for Survival Continues

The early missionaries saw their job as being to save Yolŋu from the ruthless Balanda, to 'civilise' them and of course to teach them about God. Many of the missionaries never knew that Yolŋu already understood the ways of *Waŋarr*, the Great Creator, and that their laws and ceremonial way of life came from *Waŋarr*.

These were hard days for everybody. Some of the missionaries tried to learn the way of the people and their languages; others didn't. Most missionaries were good in nature although ignorant of much within Yolŋu reality. Others saw their job as saving Yolŋu from their 'pagan', 'primitive' and 'hunter-gatherer' ways.

James Robertson, based at Milingimbi, was one of these. He did much of his communicating with a stockwhip. One Sunday afternoon, as Yolŋu were finishing a 'cleansing ceremony' after the funeral of a loved one, Robertson came down to the people and told them to 'finish it right away because it was the "Lord's Day". You should not be doing your pagan ceremonies on the "Lord's Day".'[46] When the people refused, Robertson started smashing up the ceremonial structures.

The Yolŋu wondered what to do. They knew they could not attack the missionaries because then their clan would lose favour with the Balanda. So the offended clan looked to another clan that was in debt to them and offered a *djugu'* (contract) for them to kill Robertson. After all, he was now acting like the pastoralists and Balayni, so he must be dealt with!

A few Sundays after the offence, a clan from the mainland attacked Robertson and wounded him seriously in the forearm and side. The Yolŋu involved in the spearing were arrested by patrol officers, taken to Darwin and jailed. The givers of the contract went untouched and acted as translators in the court case for the mainland clan.

Things were still in turmoil in Arnhem Land when the Balanda went to war with each other in Europe in 1939. The first that Yolŋu heard about it was when they were told in February 1940 to build airstrips and dig holes in the ground, under contract from the missionaries, first at Milingimbi and then at Yirrkala.[47] During the construction the English word 'contract'—or *gundurak*, as the Yolŋu pronounced it—came to mean airstrip. Yolŋu found a lot of paid work at this time, so it seemed good that the Balanda were fighting each other instead of fighting them.

Then in 1942 about 350 Balanda men came ashore at Milingimbi.[48] Yolŋu were shocked to see so many Balanda. They unloaded tons of wire mesh to line the airstrips, plus tractors, trucks, guns and supplies. Milingimbi and the Gove area near Yirrkala were set up as RAAF bases to fight the Japanese. When Yolŋu discovered it was the Japanese that the Balanda were fighting, they were happy because they had never liked them. The Balanda also asked the Yolŋu to help kill the Japanese if they came. At first the Yolŋu were not sure about this, thinking it was a trick—it was only a few years since Yolŋu had been jailed for defending their homeland against the Japanese. 'Why have things changed now?' they wondered.

In 1944, many people from the inland clans decided to join the Balanda to fight the Japanese. The patrol officer Donald Thomson used his contacts with the Yolŋu people of north-central and north-east Arnhem Land to form a surveillance unit. Yolŋu men in this unit left their estates to fight another war, this time with Balanda at their side. Many of them were not interested in the Balanda war, but they wanted to stop the Japanese coming onto their lands and threatening their families. The men stayed away from home for three years, operating all along the coast. Others went to work for the army and airforce in Darwin and Katherine, only returning after the war. Some did not return until the 1970s. These men were not officially recognised for their service until the mid-1980s.

When Japanese bombers did hit places like Milingimbi, it was again Yolŋu who felt the heaviest blow. When the bombers flew over, all the Balanda were in the holes in the ground (trenches)—a silly place to be to fight an enemy, the Yolŋu thought. They stood with their spears at the ready and watched the planes come in low. They had fought the Japanese before and beaten them, and they intended to do it again. As they watched the canisters fall from the planes, they did not know this was another new, strange Balanda weapon. As the bombs exploded the only people killed or wounded that day were Yolŋu. The firepower unleashed during the attack really shocked the people. 'Where do Balanda get such power from? And where do all the equipment and the goods come from?' the people wondered.

After the war, mission life in Arnhem Land was hard. It was difficult for the missions to get staff and supplies were short. The missions in most cases were forced to become self-sufficient. This made them very dependent on the Yolŋu who were now living there. Many of the new mission staff knew little of the history that the Yolŋu had lived through, and they told the people to give up their old ways and live for the future. The Yolŋu became confused about this: 'What do they mean "give up our old ways"? Do they mean to forget production and trade, and the rule of law as the *Maḏayin* teaches us? What does this mean?'

Only a few mission staff learnt some of the language of the people, even though it had been mission policy since 1927 for all staff to learn language.[49] So intercultural communication was still very poor. It was not until the 1950s that language was taken seriously, when a teacher/linguist at Milingimbi, Beulah Lowe, started in earnest to understand and decode the language. This was a major job and is still unfinished today.

In the early 1950s, the government paid a subsidy to mission stations to provide a daily hot meal for each child. This, together with the instruction from Balanda to 'give up the old ways and learn a new way to live,' convinced Yolŋu that the Balanda were going to feed them into the future. When the Yolŋu looked at the missionaries, they saw they had seemingly incredible wealth. Their food came ready to eat in bags and tins, not like Yolŋu food that had to be harvested and prepared with lots of sweat. The people did not know the source of this great wealth. On many things they saw the words 'Made in England'. Maybe this land across the sea was like *burralku* (heaven), the old people thought. The missionaries even brought all types of fruit trees and root vegetables that grew abundantly. Some Yolŋu thought, 'Where does all this come from? Is there a land where these things just grow or appear? But if so, how is it that they grow in this ordinary land, where we must sweat?'

Despite these pressures, some Yolŋu did not like the way of dependency that missions created. So they stayed on their own clan estates trading crocodile skins, bark paintings and other traditional crafts with the missionaries, in order to buy the extra supplies they needed to survive.

Missions caused another problem: the people living there were on someone else's clan estate. Most of these estate owners became tired of all the strangers, both Balanda and the mission Yolŋu, living on their land. A number moved away, insulted by the fact that they could not control what happened on their own land.

For many Yolŋu who moved into the missions, it became a tit-for-tat game of trying to get the mission authority on side with one's own clan. None of these clans had any real right in traditional law to live on these estates for extended periods of time. They also had no right to take resources from the estates. So everything was done in the name of the mission. When mission staff sent Yolŋu workers out to 'get' (that is, steal) timber from the estates of other Yolŋu, the workers told the estate owners, 'The mission sent us, please don't blame us'. When fishing industries were set up by the mission, Yolŋu felt guilty stealing fish from other clans' waters; but they reasoned it was the new way of the Balanda and so they must steal to survive. It seemed the Balanda, including the missionaries, respected no-one's private possessions. Maybe the old way, the way of honour, respect, production and trade and the rule of law, was a thing of the past.

So these Yolŋu followed orders and got on well with their new Balanda masters. Others decided they would rather starve than become like Balanda, and many did.

The 1960s were a period of comparative peace and prosperity and became a time of consolidation for Yolŋu. However, for those in east Arnhem Land around Yirrkala, this peace was short-lived. Bauxite was discovered in 1952,[50] and there was talk of a big mining company coming onto their lands and building a town where Balanda mineworkers would live.

The Yolŋu estate owners of much of the Gove Peninsula were the Lamami clan. The Lamami people, whose family name was Galipala, had suffered greatly when the Macassan trade was stopped in 1906. In addition, like many of the landowners, they were in dispute with the missionaries because the mission was partly on their land. Their last surviving male member had died just before the Second World War.

Now the few surviving Lamami women knew that their lands were going to be stolen from them. Other clans, from Port Bradshaw to Cape Shield further south, had moved into the Yirrkala mission and had become the intermediaries between the missionaries and the Lamami owners. Now they gathered around to do battle in a new war. This was Milirrpum and Others v. Nabalco P/L and The Commonwealth of Australia (1971), known as the Gove Land Case, where men from other Yolŋu clans took the battle to the Balanda on behalf of the Lamami clan.

The case was lost and the Yolŋu grieved. In the past they had fought long, hard battles to maintain rights to their homeland estates. With events like the declaration of the Arnhem Land Reserve in 1931[51] and the coming of the missionaries, the Yolŋu thought their rights might at last be recognised and they might survive as a people into the future. Now all this was in doubt. Some missionaries supported the mining idea; others stood with the Yolŋu in the battle, knowing that mining would bring destruction to the people's way of life.[52]

From the missionaries Yolŋu had learnt that the Balanda had councils of law, called courts and parliaments, and they hoped that if the Balanda did understand law after all, then they would be able to recognise *Madayin* law. During the court proceedings, the leaders revealed to the Balanda some of their ancient 'title deeds' that showed their estate ownership rights according to their councils of law. But the court did not or could not recognise their ancient system of encoded law. This last act shattered Yolŋu leaders.

When the Yolŋu lost this court case, many of the old men wondered if it were possible for Balanda to *ever* understand law in any form. They had thought that if the Balanda 'law men' could see their 'title deeds' then they would realise that Yolŋu were the owners of their estates from the beginning of time. But the Balanda were unable to read the ancient encoding or even see the significance of the very valuable, holy law objects. This left the clan leaders with a sense of great shame. Not only had they been unable to stop Balanda gaining control of their estates and resources, they had also revealed their precious encoded law to the ignorant and therefore were in great danger of insulting *Waŋarr*, the Creator Spirit, himself.

This was the last straw for these old warriors in a world that made no sense any more. They spent much time thinking and discussing among themselves what had gone wrong. It seemed that in this new Balanda world the lawless prospered, with great power and authority. So what had happened to the way of the Great Creator and the rule of law that he had given at the beginning of time? Why had these lawless Balanda won so many times? Was the *mägaya* (peace and tranquillity) of the *Madayin* law gone forever?

The deep sickness caused by this thinking made many of these old warriors lie down and die.

2
CHAPTER

A Crisis in Living

Into the Self-determination Era

*It seems, however, that the path of self-determination that I was once
expecting has all but collapsed . . . All this has caused me to feel inferior
and disillusioned. What started as a dream . . . has turned into a nightmare.*

John Waṉamilil Malibirr[53]

Yolŋu Life Pre-1970

The 'mission days' from the end of World War II until the early 1970s were in general a time of stability for the Yolŋu. A few clans rebuilt their numbers and tried to come to grips with living in two worlds. By the mid to late 1950s, the Methodist Overseas Mission stations boasted the highest population growth in Australia and none of the diseases that later became chronic were evident. All missionaries were told they must learn the language of the people so they could work with them effectively.

During the 1960s the level of government funding to missions increased.[54] This allowed mission stations to use their self-generated resources to create further work opportunities for Yolŋu. The many industries included sawmilling, cattle, farm crops and pastures, vegetable and fruit gardens, hatcheries, fisheries, bakeries, craft and the like. Yolŋu also learnt trades as carpenters, plumbers, electricians, painters, fitters and turners, and mechanics. A trade school was set up at Yirrkala mission where potential tradesmen from along the coast came to learn technical skills. Also under mission sponsorship, many young potential leaders were sent away for a Western-style education in Brisbane.

For others who remained on the missions there were other jobs to be trained for—nursing, teaching, domestic aides, administration, bookkeeping, post office and bank agency operations, retailing, butchery and more. Yolŋu learnt as much as they could about the Balanda systems so they could survive in a changed world. The mission staff too wanted Yolŋu to learn the skills necessary to control their own lives and lands in the future, believing that things would continue to improve. In 1969, when the Commonwealth government started to pay a training allowance for every Yolŋu trainee, things were definitely looking up.[55]

Apart from the significant battle over mining in the Yirrkala area discussed in the last chapter, Yolŋu in general looked to a brighter future. Young and middle-aged Yolŋu had learnt much from the missionaries and were confident they knew the Balanda way. Many hoped and dreamed that the days of Balanda domination were over and that the future would bring independence, growth and stability.

But older people with memories of the 'bad' old days weren't so sure. They saw the way ahead as potentially full of trouble. They knew that if the way of the *Maḏayin* was not followed it would lead to death and destruction. The promises of Balanda money and housing had not convinced them. Many predicted, 'Our people will lose both their culture and their lives'.

As the clock ticked into the 1970s, to most observers it would have seemed unimaginable that in a couple of decades the warriors of Arnhem Land would have lost control to the point where they would be suffering a *crisis in living*.

From Dreams to Nightmares

The 1970s and '80s promised much, with well-intentioned policies like 'self-determination' and 'land rights' coming into their own. But in the end these delivered little to Yolŋu other than confusion and disillusionment. Prepared for it or not, the 1970s were a decade of great change for Yolŋu. It would take another decade for the full ramifications of all that happened to become evident.

The town of Nhulunbuy was built for the Nabalco bauxite mine. This was very unsettling for the Yolŋu landowners and other clans associated with the area, especially when they saw strip mining and other large developments.

For the Yolŋu clans who had stayed on their lands away from the missions this period had mixed blessings. They received a major blow in 1972 when the killing of crocodiles was banned.[56] The crocodile skin trade was the major cash income for these people, allowing them to buy much needed goods from Sheppy (Reverend Harold Shepherdson), a missionary who flew out to their homelands each fortnight and traded with them. Without these skins it was very difficult to continue the trade. At the same time, the northern missions and then the Commonwealth government developed a policy of helping Yolŋu return to their homeland estates. So just as the homeland movement was being assured into the future, its economic independence was almost destroyed.

Meanwhile, missionaries along the north coast were talking with Yolŋu about the prospects for placing the management of these communities in their hands. In 1972 the Federal Labor government came to power, with a platform that included 'land rights', 'self-determination' and a new department for 'Aboriginal Affairs'. It seemed a new day was dawning for Yolŋu and other Aboriginal people.

In 1974 the Methodist Overseas Missions, now under the United Church in North Australia, conducted their own 'Commission of Inquiry' in an attempt to find out from Yolŋu their true feelings about the proposed changes to self-governing communities. Many of the younger men, who had been educated through the Balanda school and college system, were optimistic. Those who listened to influences from outside Arnhem Land thought it would be good if the mission left. 'If we start moving and start something for ourselves,' they said, 'our children will take over from us and they will be able to build it up to a good place.'[57]

Some of the old men, however, wept and said directly to the missionaries, 'Don't leave us. We will not survive without you against these other Balanda.' Another said, 'Are we going to live by ourselves or is the mission going to be here with us? If we push you, the missionaries, away the other Balanda will come . . . We ourselves are just frightened of the other Balanda. I still myself know we want the missionaries to stay with us.'[58]

A Yolŋu elder put it bluntly: 'We would like to know if European people are going to leave us alone to run the place all Aboriginals, or what? Because we really feel we don't like Aboriginal people to be left alone to run the place by themselves. It is too early to do this. We don't think that way. We can't stand properly because we fall back. We see to look in front of us [to the future]. We don't like to be left alone.'[59]

There seemed to be two main reasons for this hesitation. First, the people were not sure of the government's intentions. One elder stated: 'In many ways the Government has been good, helping to build roads, providing vehicles, helping in financial ways. But the trouble with the Government is that they have the power to take lands—for a long time ever since they landed here they have done it because they say the Government has all the powers.'[60]

Secondly, Yolŋu elders knew they were not ready. 'We are pretty sure we still need someone to work with us, to teach us and train us for many things we do not know. We want this until we are ready to take over and have a company run just by Aboriginal people.'[61] They realised they still did not know how the Balanda world really worked.

The elders were also not sure who was driving the process of change. The Yolŋu were being told that it was up to them to make the decision, but they were doubtful. 'There is jealousy about who is giving the decisions and it is presently the Balanda who is doing that, even though they have spoken about it as if they are not making the decisions.'[62]

In essence there was nothing wrong with policies like 'self-determination'; their failure had more to do with their implementation. If the policy of 'self-determination' had been true to its meaning, the transfer of assets and authority to run the communities would have happened in full consultation with Yolŋu, if and when they were ready. In reality, other political forces drove the process.

By the end of the 1970s, despite the reservations of Yolŋu elders, the former Methodist Overseas Missions had bowed to political and social pressure from outside Arnhem Land and transferred almost all their assets and authority to Yolŋu-run councils, housing associations and companies. Once again, Yolŋu had to live with the results of someone else's decisions.

Confusing Balanda Structures

As someone who lived in Arnhem Land throughout this period of transition, it seems to me that two major factors affected all those involved in the decision-making at this point. One was the inability of Balanda and Yolŋu to *truly hear each other*. This poor communication and its devastating effects are dealt with in Part 2 of this book. The other factor was that Yolŋu had to deal with confusing Balanda structures set up by the missions so they could transfer assets to the 'Yolŋu community'.

These structures were confusing for several reasons. First, the community councils and housing associations were all legal bodies that came out of Balanda law. Yolŋu had no more idea how these structures worked than Balanda knew how *Madayin* legal systems worked. The incorporation of councils left Yolŋu very confused. An old man said in 1974: 'I think I want to ask the question which I do not understand. I have heard the word many times, the word called "incorporation". What does it really mean?'[63] Even today, twenty-five years later, many Yolŋu remain confused about Balanda legal systems and what words like incorporation really mean.

Secondly, Balanda did not see Yolŋu as themselves having any real legal system which defined the rights of separate clans, each with its own estates and resources. So from a Balanda point of view, public ownership of assets and industries was a good way to go for Yolŋu. But to Yolŋu this concept was and still is totally foreign. The *Madayin* law given by *Waŋarr* the Creator defined which clan owned which estates and resources, and to think in terms of publicly owned assets and industries went against this ancient law.

The third problem followed the second. The new Balanda structures also did not recognise the owners of the traditional estates on which the missions/communities were located. According to the *Madayin*, everything is privately owned by only one clan, or through one of the *riŋgitj* nation alliances. This is how it had been for thousands of years, and Yolŋu were not going to change to some form of quasi-socialist system just because this was the Balanda way of organising.

Many Yolŋu saw themselves as just visitors to these communities. 'Aboriginal people do not really understand how to control other people, or how to run the town,' said one. 'It is easy in Caledon Bay [a clan homeland centre] because people are from the same tribe. They are the same *mala* [group]. The problem at Yirrkala is there are people not from his own tribe, and it is hard to give orders. Even though people understand and have brains and an idea of running the town, it is hard because of so many people from different tribes. The people in the administration and in the store are the right people to run the whole show because it is their country. We are only filling in the gaps.'[64]

'Community ownership' of assets was a totally foreign concept to the Yolŋu, nevertheless, many of the people came to believe that this was the 'new way' that earlier missionaries and government had spoken about. They concluded that the church or government owned everything and provided work for everyone. Talk about 'community' councils, 'community' gardens and other 'community' industries made little sense to Yolŋu, but if it worked for Balanda then it must be a more sophisticated way than the old clan enterprises. 'Maybe there is no more private enterprise with private clan ownership anymore,' many Yolŋu thought.

The confusion surrounding community versus private (clan) enterprises was to become a major problem in future development.

The Collapse of Industries and Services

During the 1970s, industries and services were transferred to Yolŋu, but because many of the previous mission staff eventually left, a number of industries and services collapsed. This left Yolŋu blaming themselves for not being able to make things work. 'Did these projects fail because we are Yolŋu?' many asked me in 1994/5 when I was researching why transferred projects failed. But public ownership of industry did not work in Russia, so how was it supposed to work for Yolŋu?

Many industries and projects failed because clear lines of ownership and authority were not understood by the people and did not make any sense according to Yolŋu law. The following are two examples.

Galiwin'ku Fishing Industry

The Galiwin'ku industry consisted of several small fishing boats made from local timbers at Galiwin'ku by the Yolŋu and mission staff. The Yolŋu named these boats with holy names from their clan or *riŋgitj* nation alliance. The boats were owned by the mission but were skippered and crewed by different clans. Some small clans would come together in a *riŋgitj* alliance to make up a crew. As Clem Gullick, a former missionary who helped build the fishing industry, recalls, 'The skippers were paid a certain amount per pound for fish and for any crocodile skins. From this they would have to supply their own food and fishing gear like hooks, sinkers etc. The mission supplied nets and maintained the motors on the boats. This industry employed up to 45 Yolŋu men and women and exported between 1,000 and 2,000 pounds (450 – 900kg) of filleted fish per week, plus mud crabs, to Darwin. '[65]

These clan groups would use the boats and sell their catch to the mission for processing and re-sale to other places. The people clearly understood that what they caught was theirs until they sold it to the mission and they benefited directly from their catch. From the point of sale on, it belonged to the mission. This arrangement satisfied the legal requirements of both Yolŋu and Balanda systems of law.

When the mission at Galiwin'ku handed the fishing industry over to the Yolŋu council in 1974, everything proceeded well for a while because the mission staff also transferred to the council. For most Yolŋu nothing really changed. Then in 1975 it was decided to try and get a loan from the government to develop the industry. The Aboriginal Development Commission 'decided' to bring in a consultant to look at the viability of the loan and how it could increase the efficiency of the industry. Following the consultant's recommendation, one big, modern fishing trawler replaced the small boats. In the dead of night, the small boats were *burned* on the beach and one was cut adrift, to 'convince Yolŋu of the need to move up to the big boat'.[66] Within six months the whole fishing enterprise at Galiwin'ku had collapsed and Galiwin'ku became an importer rather than exporter of fish products.

There are many reasons suggested as to why the industry collapsed. But from a Yolŋu perspective the collapse happened because the separate clans and nation alliances found it impossible to work under one Balanda boss on the trawler, as the trawler captain now had to be licensed. Moreover, Yolŋu were insulted and grieving over the destroyed boats. With no clear lines of ownership the people could not see that any authority had passed to them.

In the traditional Yolŋu economic system, the clan is the corporate body that people trade under. At Galiwin'ku there were twenty-six clans. Traditionally, individuals from these clans would trade with individuals of other clans, but all this trading was done under the name of their clan. If an individual failed to fulfil his responsibilities under a trade contract, the whole clan would become liable.

To expect all the clans at Galiwin'ku to believe they collectively owned the fishing company was like telling twenty-six Balanda companies that they collectively owned an industry incorporated as an association at Balanda law. Yes, Balanda groups can join together in an association and have co-operatives for a particular purpose, and Yolŋu have *riŋgitj* alliances that do some of these same things. But this is not how the community structures were set up. Because Balanda believed that Yolŋu did not have a complicated legal structure, they set up the simplest form of community association and assumed some form of ownership and commitment to the new association would develop. According to the *Maḏayin* law, however, no such agreement existed. The Yolŋu fishermen did not see themselves working for their own gain anymore; in fact, many now thought the captain of the new trawler would reap the dividends. They had become just wage earners, and the incentive to work and build the industry for their own benefit was gone.

On top of this, people had become confused about where these wages came from. In the past they saw a clear trade with the mission—so much fish for so much money. This trade was what the Yolŋu were used to. Now they got wages no matter how many fish they caught. The steps in the development of a cash economy, with its system of wages-for-labour, are many. The Yolŋu were catapulted into the cash economy with little preparation.

With all this confusion, only conflict could occur, and economic development through industries like fishing was lost.

Galiwin'ku Garden

Another example of failure was the Galiwin'ku garden project. The Galiwin'ku garden was the equal of any mission garden along the northern coast, if not the best. Galiwin'ku was also an exporter of garden products and grew bananas, paw paws, pineapples, mangoes, melons, sugar cane and sweet potatoes. At one stage, sugar cane was crushed and the juice sold as a drink to the community.

The garden ran well under mission authority and continued to run well after the mission transferred the project to the council. The transfer to the council included the transfer of the mission staff member. It was soon after this person left that the project folded.

As with the fishing industry, Yolŋu working in the garden saw themselves as working for the mission in a foreign work context on a work-for-pay basis. Before it was transferred, the garden was seen by Yolŋu as being clearly owned by the mission. The person in charge was a missionary, and the garden grew on ground that, having been taken from the traditional Yolŋu owners, was now referred to as 'the mission'. The missionaries were seen as foreigners with a powerful foreign authority. When the foreign authority was not there anymore, and the people thought the government was now sending the money for wages, the garden workers started slacking on the job and the garden stopped producing.

When 'award wages' replaced the training allowance, many Yolŋu believed they had truly discovered the 'new way' that earlier Balanda had told them they would learn at the mission. They had been told that incorporating as community associations meant you could get government money, so they concluded that the government must print or somehow get money and send it for wages through these special associations. In 1999 a relative of a Yolŋu man approached me and said, 'You must come and help (so and so).' 'Why?' I asked. The person continued, 'My (relative) got our group incorporated a few years ago, but no money is coming from the government. If it doesn't happen soon my (relative) will go mad trying to work it out.' From our discussion it was clear the whole group believed that becoming incorporated meant money would flow from the government because of the incorporation and for no other reason.

Bank Agencies

Along with the collapse of many industries that provided employment and income for Yolŋu, some services collapsed as well. Bank agencies were an example of this.

Each mission ran a Commonwealth Bank agency during the 1960s and early 1970s so that the people could save the money they earned. Almost all Yolŋu adults had a bankbook and saved up to fifty per cent of what they earned. As the agencies went over to the community councils in the mid to late 1970s, many problems started occurring.

When the missions ran the agencies, it was done through the mission head office in Darwin, with smaller agencies on each mission station. In other words, there was one central agreement and the mission head office made sure things were done correctly. With the transfer to councils, the Commonwealth Bank found itself having to deal directly with many separate Yolŋu councils. Some of these councils had Balanda support staff, some did not. The Balanda staff from the Commonwealth Bank, who were based in Darwin and regularly changed positions, had no understanding of how to work with Yolŋu councils or Yolŋu bank staff.

Troubles began shortly after the agencies were transferred, mainly because the Yolŋu running the agencies were young people. The older people—the ones with authority in a Yolŋu community—did not know anything about bank agencies or the laws governing them, so they were unable to support the young people as they would have done in a traditional clan setting. In the end money went missing, most of it stolen by the bank agency operators over a period of time.

At Ramingining, for example, a large amount of money went missing. In the days when the mission was running the agencies, if $100 had been unaccounted for the bank would have contacted mission authorities and jumped up and down until it was found. Now thousands of dollars went missing over a period of a few months, but the bank said nothing until the total reached $42,000.

The Yolŋu staff knew how to run the agencies back to front. Many who were trained in this period could do the work in a fraction of the time it took Balanda to do the same tasks. The actual skill in running the agencies was not difficult for the people to learn. The problem was that they did not know where money came from or the law behind it!

In the 1970s, many Yolŋu thought money came from the Queen. They worked this out because it was the Queen's head on the money, and because the Balanda had a strange ceremony where they would stand very straight and stiff and ask the Great Creator Spirit to save her, every morning. The missionaries, soldiers and airforce men would all do this important ceremony. If anyone did the ceremony incorrectly they would get into big trouble. Yolŋu concluded from this that it must be the Queen who creates all the money in the world. From her it came either to the mission, the government or the bank – to which one, they were not totally sure.

When the bank agency workers started trying out the system by stealing small amounts and nothing happened, they reasoned that it must be all right for them to use some of the money. When the bank finally contacted the councils to complain, asking that the money be paid back, the workers were shocked. In the end, the Commonwealth Bank closed down the agencies.

Some have speculated that the bank purposely allowed these small, unprofitable agencies to get into trouble because it wanted to get out of running them. I believe it had more to do with *bad communication*. Many Balanda who had had no previous contact with Yolŋu were almost frightened to communicate with them. When a problem occurred, the Balanda just hoped it would go away. But it didn't; it got worse.

When the agencies closed all over Arnhem Land in the mid 1980s, the good saving habits of Yolŋu were destroyed. Now people had to cash their whole cheque or have all their cash wages in their hands. This led to another mammoth crisis because the people found it very hard to spread their income over a two-week period. The disappearance of banking services was devastating to Yolŋu. Imagine trying to live without a banking service in modern society! This crisis remained unresolved until the mid-1990s, when the Traditional Credit Union was opened in north-east Arnhem Land.

Yolŋu Workers Displaced

The people were now suffering enormous, rapid change. Many industries and services that created stability and employment were now gone. But the change did not stop there. Even employment that some Yolŋu had in the servicing of their communities was under threat. This included the work in running the communities' administration offices or the essential services, like power, water, rubbish collection and sewage services. Balanda were coming in to take up many of these jobs. Now there were more Balanda on Yolŋu communities than in the mission days.

Some work for Yolŋu still existed in housing construction at the beginning of the 1980s, but over the next decade even that was taken over by outsiders. The case of Waṉamilil Malibirr is a clear example of this and shows how Yolŋu dreams of a prosperous future turned to nightmares.

Waṉamilil was born in 1949. He is a member of the Ganalbiŋu clan of north-central Arnhem Land, a *bäpurru* with a very proud and honourable history. When the pastoralists were massacring Yolŋu in the area between Milingimbi and Numbulwar during the Second Pastoral War, the Ganalbiŋu, along with other clans and nations, fought a gallant war pitting their spears against Winchester rifles—and won. While many other clans subsequently moved onto missions, the Ganalbiŋu remained in their traditional homelands and had little contact with Balanda or the dominant Australian culture until the early 1970s. Waṉamilil was one of the first of his clan to 'move over' into the Balanda-dominated world, living at the mission and then training as a builder.

Waṉamilil's story comes in the form of an open letter that he gave to me to share in this book. He had it typed for him by a friend. He writes:

> I attended and completed schooling at Milingimbi, during which time the mission was responsible for the welfare of the Aboriginal people. Schools in those days consisted of literacy and numeracy acquisition, as well as basic subjects that we were expected to know about Western culture. In the afternoon, schooling consisted of skills training, including farming, carpentry, plumbing, commercial fishing, store work and vehicle repair.
>
> After several years of schooling at Milingimbi, I was selected to attend Yirrkala Technical School (YTS). I successfully completed my certificate at YTS in woodwork and metalwork after one year of study, in 1965. I was awarded second prize for my achievements behind Gatjil Djerrkura, a prominent Aboriginal leader (Chairman of ATSIC) and businessman today.
>
> Having successfully obtained my certificate from YTS I was then selected to study interstate. My first taste of Western ways was my stopover in Darwin, where I spent one night. Subsequent stopovers were in Adelaide and Melbourne, until I reached my destination, Tasmania.
>
> Despite loneliness, isolation from friends and family, and occasional racism or ignorance by European Australians, I persisted with my studies in Tasmania and completed my course in woodwork after one year. During my time in Tasmania without any family members from Arnhem Land, I was

billeted with a host family, who taught me about the Western way. In due time, I had acquired sufficient knowledge of the English language, culture and society at large to function adequately in a previously hostile environment. I had learnt the Balanda way.

In 1968 I started work at Milingimbi as a carpenter, but also attended to plumbing and painting jobs. For one year, I worked at Milingimbi until I decided to seek employment elsewhere.

Having adequate skills and knowledge of Western society, I chose to go to Darwin to seek work. Upon showing my certificate from Tasmania to the unemployment office, I was immediately employed by the John Holland Company. The first job I was given was the construction of the Lynx [Lim's] Hotel in Rapid Creek. After completion of the hotel, a team of us worked on building houses at Rapid Creek. This went on for a while, until I decided to return to Milingimbi.

Back on the island, the mission employed me, again as a carpenter. In time, I proved my abilities and was consequently given more and more responsibilities, until the superintendent was satisfied that we could cope without mission intervention or assistance. This was the beginning of self-determination.

A contract saw me and my team of young men leave for Yirrkala, where we worked for the mission for a period of time.

Since 1968 to this day I have been employed, working competently and studiously, and trying to live in both the Balanda and Yolŋu worlds without compromising either. As such, I attend ceremonies when my presence is required and return to my work commitments when practical.

It seems, however, that the path of self-determination that I was once expecting has all but collapsed. *Where Yolŋu were once building their own houses in communities, contractors have now taken over the jobs.* Where once I was supervising and guiding a team of builders and carpenters, I am now without any team or assistance. *All this has caused me to feel inferior and disillusioned. What started as a dream at Milingimbi has turned into a nightmare at Ramingining.*

The change in events caused me to stay home on occasions—for the first time in my working life, starting from 1966 and continuing to 1997. *I sometimes get headaches thinking about how the situation has turned around for me and for the community, and inevitably get bedridden for several days from the pain this causes.*

I no longer feel useful or challenged at work and wish for the good old days when I felt satisfaction from doing a good job. When I seek assistance from government bodies, I am told I need to re-train or update my skills or enrol in further courses. I feel all this is unnecessary and a waste of time, since I learnt everything I need to know about carpentry during my schooling years and two decades of work experience.

I do not know what other avenues are open to me, but I hope you will take the time to consider my dilemma and to offer me a possible solution.

John Waṉamilil Malibirr, Ramingining, May 8, 1997 (emphasis added)

Up until 1985, Waṉamilil headed a team of Yolŋu builders who constructed all the cyclone-coded housing at Ramingining. They had one Balanda 'resource person' who assisted with the legal requirements related to building the houses, ordered building materials and helped Waṉamilil break up the house-building project into separate contracts so that the Yolŋu building team could construct the houses under traditional *buku-djugu'* contracts.[67] The bookwork for the housing project was done by a Yolŋu person.

Throughout the late 1980s and 1990s, Waṉamilil's story was repeated hundreds of times. Prior to this, Yolŋu held down jobs as plumbers, electricians, carpenters, painters, bricklayers, brickmakers, farmers, mechanics, bookkeepers, agency operators, plant operators of all types, boat captains, boat operators, fishermen, bakers, foresters, timber millers—name any job in the community and Yolŋu were doing it. Now the only jobs that Yolŋu are involved in that they were doing pre-1980 are teaching in schools, health worker roles, craftwork and (for a few) administration. Even menial jobs like rubbish collection are being done in some communities by outsiders.

New Decision-Makers

As we have suggested, there are many reasons why Yolŋu have lost control of their lives. For Waṉamilil, the straw that broke the camel's back was the shift in authority and the new approach to decision-making that this brought into play.

All the people with whom Yolŋu have battled since 1900 have had one thing in common: the desire to exercise control over Yolŋu and their resources and exert authority over them. However, if we look at the profile of those who had authority over Yolŋu in past days, such as missionaries, and those who exercise authority over them today, we see some interesting differences.

For example, in 1983 a representative of the Aboriginal Development Commission (ADC) came to a meeting at Ramingining (which I attended as an interpreter/facilitator) and told the local council that they were not building houses quickly enough. The ADC was the funding body at the time for Aboriginal housing. At that stage the community was building three houses a year. The ADC officer said that the Commission in Canberra wanted to see more houses built and built faster. The council argued that they wanted to build all their own housing, and also to slowly build up a bigger building team so they could build more houses. The officer agreed to let the community continue to build three houses a year, but also said that the ADC would get contractors to build the additional houses that were approved in each subsequent year's program.

The council argued against this, saying they did not want contractors in the community because they caused too much trouble, bringing in alcohol and assaulting the women. In the end the ADC officer said, 'If you don't accept the fact that contractors are to come and build the extra houses, you will not get any money at all for housing next year.' In the end the council agreed to the proposal because they could see they were in a 'no-win' situation.

(Incidentally, the local ADC officer who had to put this 'proposal' to the council was not happy with it himself. He had been instructed by ADC officials in Canberra to increase the number of houses being built in east Arnhem Land to the ADC-Canberra's prescribed level. His instructions included, 'If the councils don't agree to contractors then they get no funding'.)

Yolŋu continued to build their own houses using *buku-djugu'* contracts given to each individual worker on the building team. This arrangement allowed the building team to come and go, attend to traditional legal requirements and so on, but with some limitations which they organised among themselves in order to meet the building team's requirements. These Yolŋu builders used the old method of house construction where every stud and joist was measured and cut individually. Yet the whole process was cost-effective, with the housing coming in under the budget estimate and with three houses being built each year. The outside contractors, on the other hand, arrived with pre-fabricated housing, worked day in, day out for three months and put up five houses.

It was not long before community members started criticising the Yolŋu building team. 'Gee, you guys are slow. Look at those Balanda over there. They can put up three or four houses while you put up one. Just goes to show that Balanda are smarter and more sophisticated than Yolŋu.' These comments usually came from other clan groups who were not in the building team, but sometimes they came from within the builders' own family or clan. Most of the comments were from people who were sitting down on unemployment benefits.

Other people said, 'Why are you trying to be like Balanda, working all the time? Give up. You will never be like them. Look how fast they are.' Within about a year, the Yolŋu building team were so demoralised that they disbanded.

So it was that many Yolŋu who did battle to learn Balanda ways under the mission system now found themselves completely lost as the authorities in Darwin and Canberra set new criteria for communities. It is strange and tragic that the very structures that were supposed to bring 'self-determination' and later 'self-management' to the people were, in part, very destructive.

New-style Resource Staff

A second problem came for Waṉamilil with the change of resource staff in the Ramingining community. The new staff came with no orientation and no idea of the history of Arnhem Land before they arrived. They were not required to learn language, and even if they wanted to learn it there were almost no resources to help them. So as the long-term staff, with their different degrees of skill in speaking Yolŋu Matha, left the community and were replaced by staff with no language skills, no long-term commitment and no sense of local history, Yolŋu like Waṉamilil found they were not being understood. This led to them losing even the little control they still had over developments in their communities.

Some may wonder, 'How is it that paternalistic missionaries were able, at least in some cases, to get it right?' I believe this was because the missionaries, although just as paternalistic as their contemporaries, had to rely on Yolŋu for the daily survival and operation of the missions. For example, the mission lugger that supplied all the northern mission stations for many years was not only crewed by Yolŋu but also skippered by one, Wili Walalipa. This reliance naturally developed many close and friendly relationships.

The nature of the missions also meant that the missionaries lived with the people in their communities on a long-term basis, developing a degree of familiarity with them and their way of life. This meant that decision-making in the mission days was, on the whole, done with a degree of consultation with the people. Today, many of the people making decisions for the people do so at arm's length. Generally they do not even know the people for whom they are making decisions, so how can they appreciate the complexities that exist at the cross-cultural/cross-language interface? Wrong decisions continue to be made and the people continue to be disempowered.

Life has changed for John Waṉamilil Malibirr. Now he and his colleagues fight and suffer in a new war, one that is neither honourable nor makes any sense—a war that defeats them with unknown weapons as they suffer a crisis in living.

Yolŋu Elders Lose Control

The period of the 1970s and 1980s was also disastrous for Yolŋu elders. In the mission days, most of the missions had a village council which the elders of each clan had a right to attend. These councils, from the Yolŋu viewpoint, were primarily to take instructions from the mission superintendent, but they were also a place where the elders could keep up to date with the latest happenings and give advice to the superintendent if he were receptive. With the advent of the community councils, the village councils ceased (except on one community where the elders kept it going, sometimes in opposition to the community council).

Many assumed that the elders would take control of the new community councils, but in most cases this did not happen. The main reason for this was that the community councils were set up under Balanda-type constitutions, and these constitutions demanded Balanda-type elections. Elections were and still are a very foreign concept to Yolŋu. Their political leaders were selected inside *Ŋärra'* law councils. The old people understood these traditional processes very well, but the new Balanda processes were only understood by some of the younger, Western-educated Yolŋu. Many of the Balanda now visiting and living on the communities found it easier to work with these younger Yolŋu, and they gave lots of advice to the effect that it would be better if the younger people ran everything for the older people. As early as 1974, one elder commented, 'Before this came [the Government's policy of self-determination] there were supervisors [older Yolŋu] in every department, but since then it really ruined a lot of young people, being placed in a position of big responsibility and having to hold it.'[68]

Many of these young people had really been 'pumped up' at college. They were told, 'When you return to your people, you will be able to do a lot of good for them because you will have the education to run the community.' Through the new council structures, some of these younger Yolŋu took the opportunity to assert their self-appointed authority. Having been there through this period, and as a Returning Officer on many occasions at the request of one of the new community councils, I know the confusion that was sown and the manipulation that was attempted. Many times the new community councils were seen to be in direct opposition to the traditional Yolŋu leadership. As one leader put it, 'Even though there is a Council, there are still Aboriginal leaders which we will keep.'[69]

On some communities attempts were made to reflect the *Maḏayin* law in the new constitutions so that the clans or *riŋgitj* alliances could use their traditionally-selected political leaders in the new structures. At Galiwin'ku and Ramingining they established 'Riŋgitj Councils'. But in both cases the constitutions of these councils were challenged by government officers. These officers, one from the Department of Aboriginal Affairs and one from the Northern Territory Department of Local Government, considered the Riŋgitj Councils to be unconstitutional. At Ramingining the constitution was altered under the threat that if the people did not change they would not receive any more Local Government funds. The new constitution stated that the council was to be elected from the work departments within the council. This alienated not only the Yolŋu elders but the whole community. Now the workers in the council could vote for themselves to be the councillors, and they did.

The Galiwin'ku constitution did not change, but through some strange process the Electoral Commission came in and held elections for the community council, even though the constitution spoke of *riŋgitj* selection, not secret ballot elections. It could be that the Balanda involved had no idea of what a *riŋgitj* was.

This in a nutshell is why Yolŋu lost control. The period of 'self-determination' became a time when outsiders and many self-appointed leaders determined the future of the people, instead of the traditional leadership through the traditional democratic processes.

Changed Community Attitudes

When community elders lose control, lifelong dreams turn to nought, meaningful employment is lost, and people experience a crisis in living. When a community experiences such a crisis, many seemingly abnormal things occur. One of these is that basic community attitudes themselves will change.

The story of Tommy Mulumbuk Gurralpa illustrates this. Mulumbuk grew up at a time when Yolŋu went to great lengths to get their children a Western-style education. But by the time Mulumbuk was an adult himself, the community he lived in displayed a very different attitude to Western education—a direct result of the loss of control Yolŋu were experiencing.

Mulumbuk's parents sent him for education to Dhupuma College, near Yirrkala, when it was available in the 1970s (the college was closed by the Education

Department in 1980). He was one of the young people who came back and took up responsible positions in the Ramingining community in the late 1970s as the mission handed over control.

In June 1997 I was visiting Ramingining when Mulumbuk, whom I had not seen for a number of years, came up and greeted me.

'It's good to see you, friend,' I responded. 'I've been worried about you.'

'Why have you been worried about me?' he asked.

'I've been worried because I heard you were in Darwin on the grog, and I was worried that something would happen to you and you might get yourself killed. That's all.'

'Yes,' he replied, 'I have spent a couple of years wandering around in Darwin on the grog.'

'Why?' I asked. 'With your education and skill you could get a job anywhere.'

Mulumbuk replied with a question. '*Wämut*, what's that school over there for?' He pointed to the school at the end of the road.

I was puzzled. 'You know what the school is for,' I said.

'No, I don't,' he insisted, 'I don't know what it's there for.'

This threw me because I didn't know what he was driving at. 'Come on, Tommy,' I repeated, a bit frustrated, 'you know what the school is for.'

There was a long pause as I waited for Mulumbuk to show his hand, but he didn't. He just stood there looking at me as if *begging* me for an answer. So I said, 'You know the school is there to teach the kids how to read and write so they can get a job when . . . '

Mulumbuk stopped me mid-sentence. 'I know that stupid story,' he said. 'There's no work around this place if you are Yolŋu. There's only work for Balanda or Aboriginal people from outside.' After a pause he added, 'I haven't had a proper job since you left here in 1983.'

I had known Mulumbuk as a person with the ability and skill to run the accounts section of virtually any office. In Ramingining he had also run the essential services for eighteen months. This included controlling the powerhouse, the sewerage system and the water supply. He himself did all the paperwork related to the contract. His work was of a very high standard.

The reason he left this job was because officers of the Department of Housing and Construction in Darwin, and perhaps others, didn't trust Aboriginal people to run the essential services contract. So they sub-let a similar maintenance contract to an outside Balanda company. The result was ridiculous. Tommy would perform his maintenance duties according to the contract—change all the oil, filters etc., clean down the motors, clean out the power house, then do all the related paperwork—a task that took him and his Yolŋu offsider a day or so. Then he would go to pick up a Balanda contractor from the airport, take him to the powerhouse and watch while he did everything again that Mulumbuk and his mate had done the day before. The Balanda, of course, was able to do it in a couple of hours because the entire job had been done already. After he had changed the oil and filters again, he would simply walk around with his piece of paper and tick off the things he should have been doing but which were already finished.

When we asked the department why this was happening, they said it was just to make sure that everything was right. But if that were the case, why did they throw out brand new filters and oil worth hundreds of dollars that had only done one day's work?

After this occurred numerous times, Mulumbuk knew it was happening because the department did not trust an Aboriginal person to do the work. In the end, he got tired of being insulted and left the job.

Mulumbuk ran his own contracting business after leaving the essential services work. The Ramingining store manager at the time contracted Mulumbuk to carry all the stores from the barge to the store. The contract included doing the paperwork with the barge captain to make sure all the stores were received in good order, then delivering the stores to the correct place in the community store. No Balanda was involved in the process. On barge days the store manager would leave everything to Mulumbuk.

The store manager told me a story that showed the quality of Mulumbuk's work. One day there was a roll of 'Log Cabin' tobacco tins missing. Mulumbuk said, 'It was there when I checked it off at the barge landing. It must have fallen through a break in the wrapping on the way up from the landing.' The store manager accepted Mulumbuk's word, as the damage rate to the stores under his supervision was extremely low. Six months later, when the annual burn-off of long grass occurred beside the road, some Yolŋu found a roll of 'Log Cabin' tobacco tins and knew it was the one Mulumbuk and his crew had lost. The store manager nearly fell over in surprise when Mulumbuk presented the lost roll to him!

Such was the level of integrity and ability that Mulumbuk displayed. But today he cannot get a job, while outsiders are imported into the community to do the work. Many Yolŋu like Mulumbuk will stand back from the aggressive Balanda way, as though it is the last great insult to lose your very soul in the dog-eat-dog Balanda world.

Mulumbuk concluded our discussion. 'That's why I asked you about the school. The government is wasting its time and money trying to educate Yolŋu kids because there will be no work for them. When they leave school, they will go straight to kava,[70] because since the mission days there has been no work for Yolŋu.'

The Resulting Nightmare

When any group of people lose control of the basic things in life, the result is disaster. Normal things become abnormal and the people concerned start to suffer in all sorts of strange ways. This is the case in present-day Arnhem Land.

The 1970s' dream of self-determination turned into a nightmare in the 1980s and 1990s, and the nightmare is continuing and intensifying.

Many Yolŋu are just giving up. Self-mutilation, attempted suicide and suicides are all on the rise. Domestic violence, alcoholism, drug abuse and homicides are also increasing. Apathy and general social disintegration abound. Where Yolŋu once enjoyed full employment and were highly interested in contemporary education, chronic unemployment and disillusionment with education are now typical, as high truancy rates in schools indicate. There is no longer a rush to send young people away for training and Balanda education because it has amounted to nothing.

All this impacts on the people's physical well-being. People who were comparatively healthy twenty years ago now have high levels of sickness and death. For example, there has been a ten-fold increase in End Stage Renal Disease for Yolŋu in the past six years.[71] Death rates for Yolŋu due to heart disease, as for Aboriginal people elsewhere in the Northern Territory, are rising.[72] Where once elderly people with walking sticks were a common sight, now almost no old people exist. Many are dying in their late 30s or early 40s.

Other Australians know little of this reality and of the long and destructive history that the Yolŋu have suffered, a history that leaves the once great warriors of Arnhem Land not dreaming of a brighter future, but thinking only of a nightmarish past. It is a history that leaves them in a *crisis of living*.

3
Chapter

'The Trouble with Yolŋu is . . . !'

Official and Unofficial Views
on the Current State of Yolŋu Health

The answers [to health problems] must include imbuing people with a sense of personal self-worth, a sense of being needed or loved, an ability to influence and control their own environment, and an ability to manage their own problems.

Trevor Hancock[73]

As the history recorded in chapters 1 and 2 shows, the destructive relationship between Yolŋu and most of those who have come to their lands is clearly a factor in the present day crisis. Little can be done about it, but the people *do* live in its wake and it needs to be understood. There are, however, many others factors that can and do continue to impact on Yolŋu today. These factors can be analysed and addressed.

One of the most pervasive of these is also one of the most hidden: the unofficial, unspoken attitudes held by members of Australia's dominant culture towards Yolŋu. These attitudes are rarely examined, yet they play a powerful role in shaping most dominant culture responses to the Yolŋu health crisis.

There is an official perspective and this is what demands most of the government resources that go into attempts to intervene in the crisis. But behind the official perspective are these unofficial and commonly-held views that have enormous impact on Yolŋu, their problems and the programs that are designed to solve the crisis.

Perspectives on the Health Crisis

Various groups of people from the dominant culture who have the interests of Yolŋu at heart, or who have statutory responsibilities, have made comments and issued statements about why the health crisis exists. Some, for example, like to express the view that poor living conditions are the main cause of the people's poor state of health.

Others say the people need better access to medical services, better housing and improved water and sewerage facilities. Still others blame low levels of English literacy, or point to the excessive participation by Yolŋu in high-risk behaviours.

The position of the Northern Territory Health Services is stated in its 'Aboriginal Public Health Action Strategy and Implementation Guide, 1997-2002'. This says in part:

> Aboriginal people make up one quarter of the NT population and suffer excessively from premature death and preventable illnesses and injury. Aboriginal mortality rates are three to four times higher than non-Aboriginal rates in the Territory. The direct causative factors include poor nutrition, poor environmental conditions, smoking, and alcohol misuse . . . These factors, in turn, result from a complex interaction of people with their physical, social and cultural environments. People make choices to behave in certain ways but those choices result from what people know, what they believe, what they are able to do, and the conditions around them.[74]

These and similar points have come to represent the 'official' responses to the problem of Aboriginal health. It is this thinking that drives most of the programs set up to address the crisis.

But there is another view behind these responses that is usually not talked about in official communiqués. This view is submerged in the dominant culture's mind-set and only surfaces in private meetings and committee rooms—even in the meetings where health and other types of programs are conceived and given form—or when individuals speak 'off-the-cuff'. It is unofficial and in some cases even illegal, yet like many clandestine forces, it continues to exert great influence—to the detriment of all involved.

This unofficial view can be summed up in the phrase: 'The trouble with Yolŋu is . . . ' Different people complete the sentence in different ways, but the result is always the same: Yolŋu are in some way blamed for their own predicament.

The impact of this perspective is massive. It subtly controls the thinking behind many of the programs devised to resolve the crisis, rendering them useless before they leave the drawing board. And when these programs are implemented they actually make things worse by adding to the burden and responsibility that Yolŋu are already carrying.

Naming, Blaming, Lecturing

'The trouble with Yolŋu is . . .' view is expressed whenever the dominant Australian culture tries to find answers to the problem by *naming* Yolŋu or their ways of life with derogatory terms, expressions or names; *blaming* them or their culture as though they possess some genetic or degenerative defect, thereby creating the crisis by the fact of who and what they are; and *lecturing* them on how they should 'just change' and then everything will be all right.

This 'unofficial' naming, blaming and lecturing view (or more simply, 'naming') permeates dominant culture thinking. It is very subtle and seemingly harmless, but I suggest it has far-reaching consequences.

Some of the 'naming' I have heard includes:

- 'The trouble with Yolŋu is they are *not futuristic*—they only live for today.'

- 'The trouble with Yolŋu is they are *too simple* to understand complicated health issues.'

- 'The trouble with Yolŋu is they are *hunter-gatherers,* and therefore their culture is *not intellectual enough* for them to understand the reasons for disease and sickness.'

- 'The trouble with Yolŋu is they are *too childlike* in their understanding of the world.'

- 'The trouble with Yolŋu is they are a *primitive* culture.'

'Blaming' includes:

- 'The trouble with Yolŋu is they have *no culture of learning*—that's why they are too hard to educate.'

- 'The trouble with Yolŋu is they *can't speak or read English* so it's too hard to teach them.'

- 'The trouble with Yolŋu is they *don't worry* about their children's health.'

- 'The trouble with Yolŋu is they *blame all sickness on spirits,* therefore they *will not listen* to any other reasons for bad health.'

'Lecturing' includes:

- 'Yolŋu *should forget the past* and *live for the future.'*

- 'Yolŋu *should trust* their health workers.'

- 'Yolŋu *have to change* their old cultural ways and *join the real world.'*

- 'Yolŋu elders *should get out there* and *show their communities* what to do'.

- 'Yolŋu communities *have to become responsible* for their own health.'

I have personally witnessed this naming, blaming and lecturing many, many times over the past twenty years. The above is only a fraction of it. Whenever it occurs it blocks the thinking of those involved, stopping any creativity by simply laying the cause of the problem at the feet of Yolŋu.

But Yolŋu are the ones in crisis! This naming, blaming and lecturing is equivalent to telling a drowning person while they are still drowning: 'You're drowning because you're not buoyant enough (or can't swim). You should wake up and get out of the water before you get hurt!'

Naming is a general dominant culture response rather than a dominant culture professional response. However, because it comes from the dominant culture, it also affects these professionals within the private and public sectors who are there to help Yolŋu improve their health.

What Yolŋu say

Yolŋu also have views on why they are suffering from this health crisis. The many responses I have heard over the years include the following:

- 'We are sick because we now live in one place, in communities, not moving around like we used to before Balanda came.'

- 'It's because the Balanda are not telling us everything: they are keeping secrets.'

- 'We are confused about why there is so much sickness, especially now, because we have money and we live in Balanda houses.'

- 'There is no more law so everyone is taking law into their own hands and using sorcery to kill people.'

- 'It's because we are black, black people are always sick.'

- 'It's because of sorcery business, everyone is killing everyone these days.'

Some of these comments start to reflect the dominant culture naming. Some other Yolŋu (and other Aboriginal people) use the full dominant culture naming, blaming and lecturing in response to why Yolŋu health is so bad. This is because of the strong influence the dominant culture's naming is having on them.

Yolŋu who reason this way usually do so only when they are talking with people from the dominant culture about their own people. Others do so when they have left their roots and are trying to live in the dominant culture world. To be accepted in this world, they find themselves speaking about their own people as the dominant culture does. Many Yolŋu in this situation now believe the naming to be correct. When they use it, it makes them feel a cut above their own people, more like those of the supposedly sophisticated dominant culture because they have accepted the 'truth'.

Yolŋu suffer from every angle whenever their way of life is misunderstood by the dominant culture. Misunderstanding leads to conflict. Both cultures see the other as strange, and both 'name' the other with derogatory terms which take on a life of their own. But the derogatory terms Yolŋu have for the dominant culture do not affect that culture; in fact, the dominant culture does not even know these terms exist. In contrast, the dominant culture's derogatory names for Yolŋu affect them in a very negative way.

The Effects of Naming

If this naming were correct in any way, I would leave it unchallenged, say (along with others) 'It's all too hard' and walk away. But it is not correct and it must be challenged. In fact, it is incredibly wrong—a form of cultural imperialism that makes the problem worse, destroying the people along with many of the programs designed to combat the crisis.

Naming, blaming and lecturing creates a destructive intercultural environment between the dominant Australian culture and Yoḻŋu. The full implications of this naming will become clear as you read through this book, but we will briefly survey the effects here.

Direct Effects on the People

Naming has two direct effects on the people. First, it *destroys their belief in themselves and their cultural heritage.*

An example is the way Yoḻŋu traditional doctors and midwives have been named as evil and primitive by the dominant culture. This has disempowered these Yoḻŋu intellectuals, and along with their demise has gone much of the rich traditional knowledge that for thousands of years taught Yoḻŋu the practical skills for living.

With their self-esteem in tatters, Yoḻŋu find all motivation to act is dead. Over time the negative naming takes on its own reality and for many people becomes the 'truth'. 'It's hopeless because we are only useless blacks,' an old Yoḻŋu man said to me in 1995.

Paulo Freire, the Brazilian adult educator, had seen the effects of this kind of naming when he wrote in the 1960s:

> Self-depreciation is another characteristic of the oppressed, which derives from their internalization of the opinion the oppressors hold of them. So often do they hear that they are good for nothing, know nothing and are incapable of learning anything – that they are sick, lazy and unproductive – that in the end they become convinced of their own unfitness.[75]

Naming in this context is one of the factors that actually create the crisis by disempowering the people to the point where they do nothing. Why? Because they now see themselves as hopeless and must wait for the 'sophisticated' ones to come and solve their problems for them.

The second direct effect is just as harmful. Naming *shifts the responsibility of the crisis onto the Yoḻŋu* as though they were the only players in the drama. This "victim-blaming" leads to stagnation in thinking and an inability to be innovative on both the Yoḻŋu and the dominant culture sides. The dominant culture must understand that it is an integral part of the crisis, otherwise nothing can change.

Trevor Hancock, Associate Medical Officer of the Department of Public Health in Toronto, Canada, comments on this kind of 'victim-blaming':

Such 'victim-blaming' approaches have not worked in the past and will not work in the future. Furthermore, 'blaming' the victim ignores the determinants of (healthy or unhealthy) behaviour and thus excuses the community, society, and environment within which the individual lives.[76]

Policies and Programs That Fit the Naming

Naming also affects the health policies and programs devised by the dominant culture. It turns them into further assaults on the people, compounding rather than alleviating the crisis.

This occurs in two ways. First, policies and programs are affected by the naming because it creates the paralysed thinking environment within which the dominant culture's policies and programs are developed. An example of this is the education programs often devised for Yolŋu. Most of these have one common characteristic: they are 'simple', for supposedly 'simple people'. At times their simplicity even makes them very inaccurate. Yet these subjects are at times complex, and the people need accurate and comprehensive information to truly understand them—information that Yolŋu have no problem learning if it is thought through and delivered in the right way. But the naming mentality stops programmers and policy-makers looking at what is needed to deliver competent education programs.

Secondly, the new policies and programs escape intellectual assessment and evaluation because 'The trouble with Yolŋu is . . . ' inevitably becomes the validating excuse for any failure of these programs or policies.

Policies and programs created within the naming view generally find good acceptance in the dominant culture precisely because they fit the dominant culture's naming of 'the Yolŋu situation'. But they do not work effectively because they do not address the real situation on the ground.

The Factor of Naming

The dominant culture's naming, blaming and lecturing is hidden but very powerful. Policies and programs are constantly being created on the basis of this naming rather than on the basis of good science or knowledge. Many dollars are committed by government to help Yolŋu deal with their health problems, but the naming, blaming and lecturing endemic in dominant culture not only renders these funds ineffective, but in many cases makes the crisis worse.

It might be that this naming, blaming and lecturing comes from the sense of frustration and failure felt by many in the dominant culture system. They seem to believe that all has been tried and all has failed. They feel helpless and frustrated. To keep their sanity, they start naming, blaming and lecturing Yolŋu for 'their' troubles.

But there are reasons why the present health crisis exists. These factors are complex yet, at the root, surprisingly simple in nature. When they are understood, it will allow something to be done so that great warriors do not continue to lie down and die.

PART TWO

A WAR OF 'WORDS'

As we saw in Part 1, the process of colonisation for Yolŋu has been nothing short of disastrous. This sad history is an important factor in the current Yolŋu health crisis, and the fact that it is largely unacknowledged in the contemporary Australian context is another.

But even with this knowledge it is hard to see why things have not changed for the better in a so-called 'enlightened age'. Why does the problem get worse? To find the answer we need to look at life through Yolŋu eyes. We need to catch a glimpse of the daily reality that Yolŋu face in a modern world.

When we do so, it soon becomes clear that *poor communication* is a central factor in the crisis. This communication problem is not easily understood by the dominant Australian culture. In fact, many times it is dismissed as 'humbug' with statements like 'The people should just learn English' or 'I can make them understand using English'. In reality it is yet another war that Yolŋu are being forced to fight—a war of words.

This war of words is as destructive as any of the wars Yolŋu have fought in the past, and like them it goes on almost unnoticed by the wider Australian community. Yet the wider Australian community is an active participant in the war without realising it. Ignorance about the communication crisis leads many to become unwitting agents in the battle. Government funds also unknowingly become weapons of destruction rather than tools of empowerment for the people.

At times Yolŋu have named one of the main weapons of this war 'secret' or 'hidden' English. This sums up their sense of alienation and exclusion from the dominant Australian culture. Yet their calls go unheard. Some, not being able to communicate their high level of frustration, have called for help through their actions—by non-compliance with Balanda demands or by simply walking away and not participating in the Balanda world.

Other Yolŋu blame themselves, their people or their own language and culture as the problem, believing their traditional ways are incompetent in some way. These same people now believe the weapon of English is more sophisticated, even magical, so that when spoken—even if not fully comprehended by the speaker—it can have powerful results.

Many Yolŋu have come to believe that the war they are now fighting is normality. So many things remain confusing. Maybe, they think, that's just how it is in the crazy Balanda world.

4
CHAPTER

The Essence of Human Interaction — Communication

The Crisis in being Understood

The choice of language and the use to which it is put is central to a people's definition of themselves in relation to their natural and social environment, indeed in relation to the entire universe.

Ngugi Wa Thiong'O[77]

ood communication is fundamental in all human activity. Without it life becomes meaningless. For Yolŋu, a marginalised minority cultural group, lack of effective communication with the dominant Australian culture has become a nightmare. Apart from casual and superficial conversations, very few Yolŋu understand and speak English with any degree of confidence or competence. From a Yolŋu Matha point of view, English is still predominately a foreign language. Even those Yolŋu who seem to be very competent in English can get into great difficulties when more complex English is used.

In 1997 a community council chairman commented to me in Yolŋu Matha: 'We Yolŋu sit in meetings all the time, listening to English, but we don't understand it. Sometimes we can hear most of the words but the whole sentence just doesn't make sense. We are too ashamed to say we don't understand what the Balanda are talking about, so we sit there saying nothing and asking no questions. Sometimes we just say, 'Yo, yo (yes, yes)' to anything. When we can't understand what the Balanda are talking about we think *maybe they're talking about nothing*, so it doesn't matter if we don't understand it anyway.

'I see many Yolŋu acting this way', he continued. 'I used to act this way too before I started to ask for things to be explained or interpreted. Sometimes I don't need the whole lot interpreted, just the concept that is being talked about. As soon as I know what area is being talked about I can follow the rest of the discussion. I only need to refer back to the interpreter when the discussion comes to another foreign concept.'

Poor communication stops people receiving almost all news or knowledge from outside their language and cultural domain. This includes day-to-day news and general information. It also includes what may well be life-saving information from health professionals. It stops them knowing what they are giving consent for, how to comply with medical instructions and how to intervene in their own health problems. In this way, poor communication directly impacts on high mortality rates.

Similarly, poor communication ensures that advice from legal professionals is misunderstood or just not heard, negating Yolŋu hopes of a 'fair go'. It destroys Yolŋu attempts to acquire meaningful education and training, thereby preventing them from gaining control of their future. Even worse, it gives them a distorted view of themselves and the world. The comparative absence of much meaningful information from the outside world leaves the Yolŋu marginalised to a point where they lose control of their communities, homeland estates and resources.

Clans became extinct during the pastoral wars 100 years ago. Now many other clans are on the verge of extinction because of a persistent war of words.

The Role of Communication

In any great civilisation, from the ancient Chinese and Inca civilisations to those of Alexander the Great and the British Empire, communication with the people has been a high priority. The leaders of these nations understood that their prosperity and community harmony depended on good communication. To this end, leaders and scholars have always developed specialised oral languages, forms of writing and other communication networks (such as radio in the modern era) to make effective communication possible.

Yet as we launch into the twenty-first century, a vast communication gap exists between Yolŋu and the dominant Australian culture.

For most Yolŋu, local, national and international news is inaccessible because of the communication factor. Let me give two examples.

Example 1: In November 1999 Australian citizens were asked to vote on the Republic issue. This was complex enough for most dominant culture Australians, who listened to the news in English and were used to dealing with Balanda political systems. But for Yolŋu it was a nightmare. As they listened to the Yes and No cases in English (because that was the only service available), they became more and more confused. They knew the referendum was important, but as citizens they did not have an equal opportunity to really hear the two cases or *any* of the background information so they could make their own informed decision about what was best for Australia's future.

Right up to the referendum, my colleagues and I were asked: What is a republic? What is a preamble? What is a constitution? Will Pauline Hanson be the President? How can we get rid of the Queen because she is the landowner? If we cut the Queen off, who can help us? What will happen to the Governor-General? The people wanted to hear answers to these and many other questions about the confusing Balanda political system, but they did not get the chance.

Example 2: Throughout the Asian economic crisis, only a handful of Yolŋu knew the crisis existed. Even fewer would have had any idea of its cause. As well, almost no Yolŋu knows of the economic crisis in Papua New Guinea. Yet the people of Papua New Guinea are close neighbours, and Asia was once a trading destination for coastal Yolŋu.

These examples show that without good communication Yolŋu will find it almost impossible to secure a future through democratic participation, and will remain as confused about present day economic realities as they were in 1906 when the Macassan trade stopped and they did not know why.

Because communication skills between Yolŋu and Balanda are so poor, when people from the dominant culture are employed as trainers or resource people, Yolŋu learn very little good information from them. In fact, poor communication can and usually does lead to a breakdown in relationships. It quickly follows that dominant culture individuals get control of the available jobs and in many cases the communities themselves. Paradoxically, the lack of communication stops Yolŋu being in control of the very organisations and programs that have been initiated to give them more control. In the end, even policies like self-determination fail because of it.

I believe this communication gap is the main reason underlying the people's continual loss of control over their lives. And it is this loss of control, this powerlessness, that manifests itself in the current crisis in health.[78]

Someone might ask, 'If it's just a communication problem, why hasn't it been understood before?' The reason is simple. It hasn't been understood *because* it is a communication problem. This communication gap is cemented into the system so deeply that it is not even noticed by the dominant culture.[79] However, it continually stops Yolŋu from communicating effectively with the dominant culture, learning new information about the world around them, and influencing the dominant culture in any positive way.

Effects of Poor Communication

This ineffective communication affects all aspects of Yolŋu life. Because this book concerns the health crisis, the examples I use will generally be drawn from that area.

I share the following story as one example of how poor communication affects the people.

Tumour—A Boil or a Cancer?

The phone call came about 7.30 p.m. one Tuesday night early in 1997. It was from the Royal Adelaide Hospital. A Yolŋu friend of mine from north-central Arnhem Land was on the line. He was in Adelaide with his older brother who was to undergo an operation the following morning. My friend had recently attended a course in interpreting and was in Adelaide as an escort/interpreter for his sick brother—his English would be classed as extremely good.

My friend said he had rung because he was not sure that he had obtained the right story from the doctor. I asked him what he knew.

'My brother has a problem, something up the back of his nose,' he said in English. 'It's like a *mäpan* (boil) up in the back of his nose. The doctors operated once before and drained it, but now it's bad again. They want to operate and try to drain it again.'

'How are they going to operate?' I asked.

'Up his nose.'

I asked what effects the boil was having on the brother. 'He's been falling over (fainting),' he said, 'and can't see properly.'

This response rang alarm bells in my head. I asked my friend what words the doctor had used to explain this boil. He thought for a moment. 'He called it'—he paused—'a tum-mar.'

I took a deep breath. 'Do you know what a tumour is?' I asked.

'No,' he replied, 'but when I asked the doctor before what it was, he said it was like a big boil.'

When I told my friend in English that a tumour is a cancer, he nearly dropped the phone. 'True? True?' he kept saying.

'You'd better ask the doctor to talk to me and give me the whole story,' I said. 'Then I will tell you.'

The doctor wasn't available at that time, but the anaesthetist was there questioning my friend and the patient. It was this that had prompted them to ring me. The anaesthetist told me as much about the patient's condition as he could. He had a tumour on the brain stem which was blocking the cerebrospinal fluid from draining from the brain cavity. This was causing a build-up of pressure around the brain, which was in turn causing fits, blindness and periods of unconsciousness.

The anaesthetist said the doctors had operated on the patient and fitted some 'plumbing' in his head to bypass the tumour and relieve the pressure. But the tumour had continued to grow and the plumbing was no longer working. The pressure was building up again. The medical team planned to operate again in the morning. They would open the whole top and side of the patient's head so they could remove the tumour from the brain stem. The anaesthetist pointed out that while this was a dangerous and complicated operation, they did have the top specialists in Australia on the team. To do nothing would mean certain death, but the chances of a successful operation were fairly good.

I asked to speak to my friend. I knew he was the patient's younger brother and it was hard for him, traditionally, to hear about his older brother's sickness. In fact, a younger brother is in an *avoidance relationship* concerning knowledge about an older brother's sickness.

'Do you want to hear this story?' I asked.

'Just a little bit of it,' he said.

Now I spoke in Yolŋu Matha. 'This is a dangerous operation your brother is to have. The cancer is growing against the brain stem, but the best doctors in Australia will be doing the operation.'

He listened to my explanation then said, 'Will you talk to my brother directly?' This I did, taking the patient through the whole story in Yolŋu Matha, stressing also that after the operation he would wake up in intensive care where he would have to stay for one or two weeks.

At one stage my friend came back on the phone and said in Yolŋu Matha, 'We've already signed the forms for this operation. How can we stop it?'

'If you want to, you can tear up those forms,' I responded. 'That's why the anaesthetist is talking to you now. He wants to make sure you understand everything. After I've finished talking to your brother, you need some time to think about all this information and then decide.'

I finished telling the patient what was happening and asked if he had any questions or anything he wanted to say. 'I thought it was just a boil,' he said, 'and that they were going to operate up the back of my nose. What you are saying, *Wämut*, is that this is a big and dangerous operation.'

'Yes,' I replied, then reminded him that he had the best doctors in Australia.

After a bit more clarification the patient said he would like to think about it. I suggested that I phone back in two hours to see what they wanted to do.

When I rang back the hospital staff wanted to talk to me before putting me through to the patient. They were upset because my friend, the younger brother, had gone. 'How could he leave when his brother is so ill?' they asked (beginning to slip into naming and blaming mode to explain my friend's actions). 'The consent situation hasn't even been sorted out!'

'Because culturally it's not right for a younger brother to be involved in a matter like this with an older brother,' I explained.

'Then why did he come as an escort?' they asked.

'Because he thought his brother just had a boil at the back of his nose which was not really life-threatening. The family didn't know he had a cancer on his brain stem.'

I explained that the patient had already been treated in Darwin and sent back home before being sent to Adelaide. He had seen many doctors, but no-one had given him or the family a clear story that he had a tumour. 'The younger brother and his family would have thought it was okay for the younger brother to be involved in such a minor matter as a boil up the back of his nose,' I said. 'Now they know the depth of the problem, I'm not sure if you will see much more of the younger brother.'

At this stage the staff put me through to the patient. 'I've been thinking about this, *Wämut*, and I want to get this thing out of my head. Can you talk to the doctor?' he said.

'Are you clear how they are going to operate?' I asked.

'Yes,' he said. 'I know they will have to cut across the top of my head and down the side and I will have to be very careful after the operation.'

'Can you see that something might go wrong in the operation?' I asked again.

'Yes,' he replied. 'I know operating on the brain is a dangerous thing. But I don't want to be blind or falling over all the time.'

I asked one final question. 'Do you know that the doctor there with you now (the anaesthetist) will be your companion throughout the operation to make sure you are looked after properly?'

'Yes,' he said. 'I saw that before, when you were talking to me.'

I finished by saying I would talk to the doctor, which I did.

This story, and many others like it, indicates the immense communication problem that exists between the medical professionals and their clients. In my experience alone, a large number of Yolŋu have found that they have been involved in operations they knew nothing about, or in which what they thought would happen was completely different from what did happen. There are many legal and moral ramifications here.

This whole process would have been much easier if the hospital had had a proper conference phone so that the doctor, patient and patient's relatives could have had a discussion together, with me as facilitator. I could have played more of a straight interpreter/educator role instead of having to relay messages on the same phone to two or three different people. But this language problem is not taken seriously, so no such facilities exist.

If good communication does not occur when it is *legally* necessary, such as when consent for life-threatening operations must be obtained, how can it occur in the many everyday, non-legal contexts of life?

Communication Problems and Health Delivery

From the perspective of health, this communication crisis stops the dominant culture being able to:

- *diagnose* a Yolŋu patient's complaints in the normal question-and-answer way;
- *inform* Yolŋu patients of their condition (sometimes life-threatening) and obtain proper consent before carrying out medical procedures;
- deliver *health education and prevention* information to patients in a time and cost effective way;
- accurately diagnose the overall problem and *develop programs* that are culturally sensitive and appropriate;
- *evaluate* these programs and modify them so they become more effective.

Let's look at some examples of these realities.

Difficulties with Diagnosis

Some time ago I visited an old friend in hospital and asked her in Yolŋu Matha why she was there. She said she had been getting splitting headaches down the back of her head and into the upper spinal area.

'How long have these headaches been occurring?' I asked.

'About four years,' she said, then added, 'I've been in hospital four times for the headaches, but they haven't been able to find out the reason for them.'

I asked my friend what treatment she was getting. 'None,' she said. 'I've been here three days and they haven't told me anything.'

I volunteered to find out what the doctor was thinking. When I inquired about the patient's condition the doctor said, 'We're waiting for results because we think she has hookworm.'

This threw me a bit. 'How would hook worm cause splitting headaches?' I asked.

'What headaches?' the doctor responded.

I told him she had splitting headaches down the back of her head. He knew nothing of this. I suggested we both go back and see the patient again.

It turned out that the diagnostic problem was not just one of communication between doctor and patient—the nursing sister back in the woman's community had sent confused notes with the patient, indicating she had a severe pain 'that could not be located'. The doctor told me he had not picked up from the patient even once that she had a headache. In fact, he had been treating her for pains in the stomach region.

Every day, doctors, sisters and other dominant culture professionals are having extensive problems like this communicating with Yolŋu clients. Throughout my twenty-year association with the people of Arnhem Land, I have spent many hundreds of hours working to bridge the gap between health professionals and their Yolŋu clients. At times health professionals have come to me in frustration over communication, especially during my eleven years at Ramingining. Yolŋu patients and their families have also asked—at times pleaded with me—to help them get information from the health system.

Sunday Afternoon with an English Doctor

One Sunday afternoon a couple of years ago, I had a telephone discussion that gives some insight into this situation. An English doctor had been brought out to Australia from London to look at the training needs of new doctors going to rural areas, and someone had told him he should talk to me.

'How many doctors now working with Yolŋu in East Arnhem Land have the language ability to be able to make a correct diagnosis of their patients' conditions?' he asked.

'No-one that I know of,' I replied. 'In fact, in my twenty years' experience in Arnhem Land I've worked with a large number of doctors, but I've never met one who had the language skill to consistently make a correct diagnosis.'

'Then what training is provided to doctors so they can communicate more effectively with their Yolŋu patients?' the visiting doctor asked.

'None that I know of,' I had to say. 'Some doctors have told me that the only informal training that occurs is the teaching of the 3 F's.'

'What are the 3 F's?'

'Well,' I said, 'some doctors who have come through the Royal Darwin Hospital have told me that when they've had trouble getting Aboriginal patients to respond to questions about their condition, their doctor peers have advised them, "Remember the three F's. Only talk about family and football and forget medicine". Many dozens of doctors have told me, both in cultural awareness workshops and in private communications (sometimes when they're at the stage of pulling their hair out), that they've found it almost impossible to get Yolŋu to respond to a question.'

Curious about the possibility of effective communication in such a situation, the doctor asked, 'So how can doctors make a diagnosis?'

'Like a vet treating an animal,' I replied.

'Well, yes,' the visitor responded. 'But vets have special training to be able to make a diagnosis without spoken communication with their patients. In England, some doctors and nurses do specialised training, especially if they are going into an area where there are a large number of migrants who speak English as a second language. What procedures exist in Arnhem Land to overcome these communication difficulties?'

I explained that many people would see the Aboriginal health worker program filling this role, with cross-cultural communication as part of the job of the health worker.

'And does that work?' he asked.

I tried to describe the many problems I see with using health workers. 'The main one is the huge expectation put on them. They're expected to understand complicated medical terminology in a foreign language with almost no training, as well as managing clinics and be clinicians, health promoters and education experts. All these responsibilities are rolled up into the one job. Health workers keep leaving the service because those in the system can't see that what they expect of them is impossible for any human being to cope with.'

I also pointed out that Yolŋu Health Workers come from the same cultural group as the rest of their people, and many of them have some of the same problems understanding Balanda diseases and the related issues of Western-style living conditions as other Yolŋu do.

Using Health Workers as Interpreters

In July 1997 I found myself in an argument with another doctor, this time on a community. He overheard me make some comments to the local nursing sister similar to those above. The doctor was fairly new to the area. 'How can you say we can't communicate properly with the people when we have the health workers to interpret for us?' he said abruptly.

Hearing the words 'health worker' mentioned, one of the Yolŋu health workers came out to see what was going on. I didn't answer the doctor directly, but turned to the health worker, whom I knew, and asked her in Yolŋu *Matha*, 'How much of the doctors' language do you understand when they ask you to help them with a patient?'

The health worker replied, '*Gaŋga märr* (only a little bit).'

I then asked her in English, 'Is some of the language the doctors use hard for you to understand?'

This time she answered in English, 'Very hard.'

I asked again in English, 'How much of the doctors' English do you understand?'

'A little bit,' she answered.

The doctor was shocked. In fact, he didn't feel like returning to work knowing there was no mechanism for him to ensure good communication with the patients he would see that very day.

I believe that between seventy-five and ninety-five per cent of a doctor's communication with Yolŋu patients fails whether a health worker is involved or not. Some doctors, depending on their skill in working with English-as-a-second-language speakers, do an incredibly good job in this area despite all that is against them. But the ability of even the best doctors to diagnose is severely limited. As Dr Margaret Clark, an expert in cross-cultural medical practice, puts it,

> Without language, the work of a physician and that of a veterinarian would be nearly identical.[80]

I am not blaming health workers or doctors for this. The problem is that the dominant culture does not understand this communication gap and so makes no allowances and provides no special training. This means that doctors in many cases have to rely on observation and medical tests alone, making quick, accurate or complete diagnosis very difficult and sometimes almost impossible. In many cases it also means that patients do not hear in any clear way what their condition really is. This stops any discussion of treatment options, outcomes, the impact of the disease on their lifestyle or the need for behavioural change.

Clark summarises the problems of diagnosing a patient's complaint without properly trained interpreters:

> In cases where there is little or no common understanding between patient and practitioner, the necessary use of interpreters is sometimes satisfactory, but in other instances is fraught with difficulties. Lay interpreters may know little

medical terminology, and may require careful explanations about the kind of information that is required from the patient. In some instances, interpreters may come from a different educational or social stratum from that of the patient, and social distance and rules of decorum may render communication difficult. In my personal experience, a well-educated or highly acculturated member of an ethnic category is often reluctant to report patients' statements accurately if those statements seem to reflect what the interpreter regards as 'ignorance' or 'superstition'. Much useful medical information can thus be lost.[81]

The Two-way Crisis

This communication crisis operates two ways. While dominant culture professionals are unable to communicate meaningfully to Yolŋu even the most basic concepts affecting their life and well-being, Yolŋu in turn can neither explain what is happening in their lives nor share with the dominant culture the wisdom which has been part of their culture for thousands of years.

This problem is not unique to Yolŋu but is common to Aboriginal people throughout Australia. A renal specialist in Alice Springs commented, 'Some of the patients I've looked after for five years and they will have talked to me one dozen sentences, in spite of the fact that I see them fairly regularly—at least once a week.'[82] Such communication failure is not only frustrating but also dangerous:

> There are many situations where Aboriginal or Torres Strait Islander people can be disadvantaged or harmed through being misunderstood. For example ATSI health workers, often untrained in interpreting, constantly provide the link in communities between ATSI patients with little or no English, and English-speaking medical and nursing staff. In these cases poor communication can result in poor patient treatment or in the extreme cases, serious harm. At the very least, it results in ineffective health service delivery.[83]

Policy-makers too are severely disadvantaged by this communication breakdown because they cannot hear in dialogue what the people are saying—or even that they are asking intelligent questions. Government committee after government committee and consultant after consultant goes out to consult with Yolŋu, but each one returns with very little because they cannot really hear the people. Some English is spoken during these meetings, but it is usually a simplified form. The visitors accept these simple English words as being the people's deep, complete thoughts because the dominant culture tends to see the people as simple. But what the people say in English is just a faint echo of the powerful knowledge and information they want to share. So the world loses the chance to hear wisdom that is thousands of years old while the people are passed off as an almost muted race.

Communication Mores

Of course, this communication crisis is more than just a 'war of words'. Different communication mores make communication very difficult across cultures.

Communication mores—or behaviours associated with communicating—are learned from birth and are fundamental to how we communicate throughout life. These mores cannot simply be forgotten or changed quickly; they can only be shaped or changed by learning new ways over a period of time. Therefore, when two parties operate according to vastly different communication mores, serious breakdown in the communication process occurs, inevitably resulting in unsatisfactory outcomes.

There are many differences in communication mores between the dominant Australian culture and Yolŋu. Here are some of the main ones:

Eye contact. Yolŋu are taught to speak indirectly to a person, with almost no eye contact. Dominant culture people, on the other hand, speak directly to a person with very strong eye contact.

Traditional Yolŋu find strong eye contact threatening and it makes them feel very uncomfortable and vulnerable. Many Yolŋu will look away or down to avoid the strong privacy-invading glare of dominant culture people. As someone said, 'Dominant culture society communicates eyeball to eyeball. In Aboriginal society, communication should be heart to heart and mind to mind.' This communication is like hearing the inner soul of a person.

Actually, the best position for communicating with a Yolŋu person is side-by-side, looking at something as though there were a third party in front of the two people talking.

Speaking. Most of the time Yolŋu use indirect communication modes, and their style of speech fits into this indirect approach. If a hard subject is to be broached, people will use *mayali'mirr dhäwu* (speaking with deep meaning in a polite but indirect way) rather than a direct or embarrassing question. A quiet tone is almost always used, even a whisper—a loud voice is understood to convey rudeness or aggression. Dominant culture people, on the other hand, use a more direct approach to conversation and assertiveness is accepted.

In Yolŋu society, to look away from or over the shoulder of the person being spoken to is an accepted stance and is not understood as 'rude'. Dominant culture people find this very hard to deal with and tend to look around to see what the Yolŋu person is looking at.

Listening. Yolŋu practise active listening. They give full attention to what a person is saying to them. This means they are not preoccupied with their response until they have truly heard what the person is saying. Sometimes they will ask a clarifying question or make a check-back statement as part of the listening/hearing process.

This means that Yolŋu people, in general, will not start to think about a response until the speaker has finished and they have heard what is being said. Dominant culture people, on the other hand, will be thinking about their response even before they have fully heard the question. They assume or try to guess the direction of the person's thought, rather than actively hearing what is said.

Thinking through the response. Yolŋu are taught from birth to think carefully about what they are going to say before they say it. In contrast, dominant culture people are taught to respond immediately when asked a question.

Sometimes this means Balanda do their thinking with their mouths open, with lots of 'Ah . . . ah . . . um . . . (pause) . . . *some*times . . . ' and so on. Asian cultures see this as barbarian, undisciplined, selfish, even a fearful form of communication, and Yolŋu would agree. When this is going on Yolŋu find it very difficult to participate. A disciplined warrior 'statesman' thinks before he responds.

Response times. All these accepted conversation forms or mores affect the response times that Yolŋu use in a conversation. The dominant culture response time between question and answer is about half a second or less, but in many Asian cultures the 'response-processing time' can be as long as ten seconds. Add to this the fact that Yolŋu must translate from English into the language they think in and their first response might take up to twenty-five seconds or even longer. Once the conversation is under way, and the Yolŋu person has put the subject matter into context in his/her head and 'tuned in' to the particular English tone, these response times can be greatly reduced.

Body language. Body language speaks almost as loudly as words for Yolŋu, who in fact have developed a comprehensive sign/body language. Many messages are transmitted this way. Standing where a person can just see you, for example, is like telling them you want to speak to them.

Body language is also part of listening. Yolŋu listen by watching the whole body language of the person speaking. This is partly why it is offensive to stare or look directly at a person when talking to them, because it is like invading their thinking. So the body language of the speaker will be assessed by quick glances or out of the corner of the eye.

Dominant culture people usually use strong eye contact as the key body-language indicator. This indicates if the person is telling the truth or not. Yolŋu assess truthfulness, fear, friendliness and much of the actual content of what is being said from the whole body language.

Not interrupting the person speaking. In Asian cultures it is uncivil to interrupt anyone while they are talking, and so it is with Yolŋu. The Yolŋu style is to allow the speaker to have their full say. The listener will listen to what is said and then think of the appropriate response. Their attention is directed towards hearing the person correctly in the first place, not working out how to respond before the person is heard properly. Most dominant culture people, on the other hand, want to jump in and correct a speaker before they have finished.

This difference causes many of the arguments that occur in Aboriginal communities. In the first week of November 1997 I was asked to intervene twice between a Balanda and different Yolŋu staff in one community because of this problem. These situations had the potential to lead to violence and were causing great distress to the Yolŋu and Balanda concerned. In fact, one Yolŋu person suffered heart attacks during this time and was hospitalised. In both these cases, the dominant culture person had not given the Yolŋu speakers their full say, coming in half way through the Yolŋu person's discourse. Balanda see this as normal, but from their vantage point, Yolŋu interpret this kind of interruption as aggression, rudeness, anger and an unwillingness to let them have their say.

A Problem with Silence

Very often Yolŋu people do not speak simply because they don't get a chance. For example, a doctor or sister may ask a question, wait two seconds (which to them seems like forever) then ask the question again. This will immediately interrupt the Yolŋu person's 'response-processing time' so they will start it all over again. After the doctor or sister has asked the question three or four times, getting louder and louder and expressing the words more definitely each time, they will go into a 'telling mode'—telling the patient what they think is wrong with them and what they should do.

Dominant culture people do this to cope with the *silence*. They find this uncomfortable and even threatening because it does not fit their culture's communication mores. Some dominant culture people will run a hundred miles to get away from such a strange experience. Most will not understand why the problem has occurred, and many will return to negative naming of the people to cope emotionally. Yolŋu have similar feelings, also withdrawing into their own group and using negative naming against Balanda. Many will find it difficult to force themselves back into the same experience with the English-only speaker again.

The Victims of this War

This communication crisis affects Yolŋu far more extensively than it will ever affect the dominant culture. People from the dominant culture can get on with their lives, using their own language and communication mores to operate in a society and worldview that is theirs. But Yolŋu are affected deeply by the communication crisis in every area of their lives. This is not a choice they make—it is the natural outcome of colonisation. As a cultural group of people with their genesis in Asia, they must now live under another dominant group of people whose cultural, language and historical genesis was in Europe.

As in all wars, the victims of the 'war of words' are left confused, anxious and even angry. They withdraw from the battle—in this case, from communication and interaction with the dominant culture.

Yolŋu know the painful cost of this war but they alone cannot stop it. The dominant culture must acknowledge the large part they play in it. Only then can things change so Yolŋu do not have to continue to be casualties of this 'war of words'.

5

CHAPTER

'What Language Do You Dream In?'

Uncharted English

Language is called the garment of thought; however, it should rather be, language is the flesh-garment, the body of thought.

Thomas Carlyle[84]

When *Waŋarr* the Great Creator Spirit sent women as creator beings from *burralku,* the heaven island, they gave different gifts to the people. One of these gifts was life itself; another was the law the people were to live by. The third great gift was the gift of languages. These helped define who the people were and where they fitted into the world in relation to other clans. Some languages were completely distinct from each other; others were grouped around a central language as dialects of that language.

All of these languages were beautiful in their poetic form and rhythm, and each clan spoke its language with great pride. It was through these languages that *Waŋarr* brought meaning to the world, for it was with language that all the living creatures, the landscape features and even the people themselves were named. Through these languages the people gained knowledge of trade and commerce, political and legal systems, the seasons, natural farming techniques, philosophy and religion. It was these languages that carried messages up and down the trading tracks and across the seas to Macassar. This great gift from *Waŋarr* allowed the people to contemplate things of the past and to dream dreams of their future.

However, the people never dreamed that one day this gift of language would fail them when they tried to communicate with the white foreigners who would come to dominate their land. Some thought, 'Could it be that *Waŋarr* gave a more powerful language to Balanda? Surely not, as that would be against his character.'

Strange New Words

All languages are a complex mixture of sounds arranged in particular patterns that convey meaning to the people who can speak or 'hear' that language. A strange or unfamiliar language is not one that we 'can't hear' with our ears, but one that our mind cannot process because we have not filed the necessary 'decoders' in our brain. Each of us has a language in which we process information, and to know what it is, all you have to do is to ask the question: 'What language do I dream in?' The language you dream in is the language you think in. Most, if not all, Yolŋu dream and think in Yolŋu Matha.

Traditionally Yolŋu were masters of communication. It was not uncommon for them to learn as many as fifteen languages and dialects. During more than 400 years of contact with the Macassans, many Yolŋu also learnt their language.[85] Then as Balanda started entering their lands, Yolŋu had a new challenge. The language that the Balanda brought was very different from any that Yolŋu had ever tried to learn before. To add to the problem, Balanda were generally not masters of 'many tongues' as the Yolŋu and Macassans were. So only a few Balanda ever tried to learn Yolŋu Matha.

Although in the 100 years that Yolŋu have had continuous contact with Balanda some analysis has been done between their languages and English, much more needs to be done. Unfortunately for Yolŋu, the speakers of English are not traders from over the sea whose visits over many years allow this analysis to be done over a long period. No, the speakers of this new language are now the dominant culture of the Yolŋu world. Moreover, only a few of these newcomers have learnt much Yolŋu Matha, and almost none have learnt the people's deep intellectual language. So two-way analysis of the languages has been very slow, leaving Yolŋu to believe that Balanda have a 'secret' or 'hidden' language that Yolŋu are unable to find meaning for.

The learning of any language is very difficult, especially if it is the language of a foreign culture. The following story shows just how difficult this job has been for Yolŋu.

Back in the 1930s, some Yolŋu men were working with a team of Balanda men who were exploring for oil on Elcho Island. When the day's work was over, the Yolŋu men sat in their camp talking about the language that Balanda speak (English). One old man suggested it was not a language at all, but just the squeaking of the little bats that lived in caves throughout Arnhem Land. It made no sense at all, he said. Others argued with him, saying, 'No, it must be a full language just like ours.'

The man who believed it was just the squeaking of bats said, 'I will prove it to you.' He got up and went over to one of the tents of the Balanda and started squeaking just like a bat.

A Balanda heard the noise and came out of the tent to see what it was. When he saw the old man making the squeaking noise, the Balanda turned, went into the tent and came out with some food, which he gave to the 'bat man'. The Yolŋu man went back to his friends and said, 'See, I told you, they just squeak like bats.'

The response interested the other Yolŋu watching, so a second man got up, went over to the tent and squeaked like a bat. The Balanda gave him food too. Soon, all the Yolŋu men were squeaking like bats every time they wanted something from the Balanda exploration team. Truly, they concluded, the squeaking that Balanda used was unintelligible.

The Yolŋu men in this story could hear the sounds of English, but their minds were not able to process it. Their 'mental processor' used a different language as its encoder. Many English-only dominant culture people experience the same thing when they listen to Yolŋu Matha, leading them to assume that it is a simple language. In fact, Yolŋu Matha is as complex as any other language.

English versus Yolŋu Matha

Dominant culture people still seem to believe the linguistic myth that some languages are superior to others—even though it has been comprehensively proved by linguists like D. Crystal that 'this has no basis in linguistic fact. . . . The fact of the matter is that every culture which has been investigated, no matter how 'primitive' it may be in cultural terms, turns out to have a fully developed language with a complexity comparable to those of the more 'civilised' nations. . . . All languages have a complex grammar.'[86]

I remember, while working at Ramingining in 1981, trying to get permission to translate the Northern Territory Government's 1980 'Five Year Community Development Plan' into Yolŋu Matha. After waiting many months, I was finally refused permission on the grounds that Aboriginal languages were 'too simple to convey complicated concepts'. This still seems to be the general dominant culture response today.

When we look seriously at Yolŋu Matha, however, we find something quite different. R. M. W. Dixon pointed out in his 1980 book *The Languages of Australia* that Yolŋu languages have 'an intricate structure so that the description of the main points of grammar requires several hundred pages'.[87] Linguists like M. Wilkinson and M. McLellan support this.[88] It is true that many of the semantic concepts in English have no equivalent in Yolŋu Matha, but the same is true in reverse, so this proves nothing. In fact, this is true of all languages.

Language Is Not Taken Seriously

Spoken and written language is the basis of good communication, yet when it comes to cross-cultural communication in Australia, language *is not* taken seriously at all.

This may be because the dominant culture in Australia, and now even many other Aboriginal people are basically monolingual, speaking only English. Therefore the language needs of other indigenous groups like Yolŋu are not really understood.

However for some strange reason the need to understand European or Asian languages still seems to be clearly recognised in Australia. An example of this was given by a participant in a Cultural Awareness Workshop I ran in 1998.

A young doctor who had been in Arnhem Land for only a couple of months commented that when he came to the area to practise medicine, no special preparation or training in communication was required of him. However, he said, a colleague who went to Europe to practise was required to study the language of his host community for three months before he went. The doctor commented: 'Isn't it strange? It's considered *necessary* for a doctor going to Europe to undertake three months of language learning before he goes, but when a doctor like me comes to Arnhem Land there is no consideration given to the need to learn language or communication skills in any way.'

And this is where the problem lies.

Almost all Yolŋu think and operate in one of the traditional clan languages of the region. In other words, these people construct knowledge of the world around them using one of these languages to encode knowledge in their minds. Because this fact is not recognised by the dominant culture, both generally and by professionals within it, many current programs fail to help Yolŋu in their fight for survival.

I saw this at first hand when the Commonwealth Minister for Health visited an Arnhem Land community in 1997. The minister came to speak about health issues and to listen to the community about their concerns. He spoke to the council for about one-and-a-half hours, talking about how his government saw the health issues.

The next day I saw the chairman of the council. 'We should have had you here yesterday because we had the Minister for Health here,' he said.

'Why would you want me here?' I asked.

'To translate for us,' he said. 'The minister talked about many things, but we didn't understand what he said. We also tried to say things to him, but I know he didn't understand us. We should have had you here to help us hear each other.'

This case is typical of almost all government and professional contact with Yolŋu. True communication rarely occurs, leaving the people feeling frustrated and lost because their language is not taken seriously.

'English Makes Me Tired'

One of the key communication issues for Yolŋu is that English is a difficult language for them to grasp. An incident that occurred in September 1997 illustrates this clearly.

One Sunday afternoon I was with my sister-in-law, who was visiting us from Townsville. She wanted to see something of the Nhulunbuy area, so we drove to one of the local beaches. While we sat on this beautiful stretch of sand talking, we noticed a group of Yolŋu kids playing with a football down the beach near their family group.

After a while the football came close to us, and one of the Yolŋu kids ran to retrieve it. I said hello to him in Yolŋu Matha. As soon as he heard me, he called the other children to come and check out this white fella who spoke his language.

Three or four children joined us and we started talking about where we came from and that sort of thing. The children were from a homeland centre I had never visited, so they didn't know me.

I chatted with them in Yolŋu Matha for some time, trying them out on many subjects. I was interested to determine their level of general knowledge. We talked about a wide range of things, from economics to general niceties. I was surprised at their depth of intellectual language.

The children, in turn, were keen to test out some of the funny stories they had heard about Balanda. They asked to see inside my mouth. They wanted to know if I had any 'toy *lirra*' (toy teeth).

'No,' I said, 'I don't have toy *lirra*.'

'Open your mouth so we can see!' the kids insisted.

I opened my mouth, grabbed my teeth with my fingers and pretended to try to move them. I thought they were talking about false teeth. But while my mouth was open they looked inside, and with joy and glee they spotted what they were looking for. The 'toy *lirra*' were my fillings! I tried to explain what fillings are, but they were not convinced. To them they were 'toy teeth', not real.

We had been talking for about three-quarters of an hour, all the time in Yolŋu Matha, and the children showed no signs of tiring or becoming bored. Question after question came. We began talking about languages, and I asked the oldest in the group how many languages she spoke. She was twelve years old and said that she spoke five languages, counting them off on her fingers as she recalled them. I tried her on one of the languages that came from north-central Arnhem Land. She was a bit scratchy in that one, but in the other four she was well ahead of me.

I had been translating all this back to my sister-in-law and she now joined the conversation. She asked the girl in English, 'Do you speak English?'

The children were kneeling in front of us in a line. When the girl heard the question, her shoulders drooped and she sank down onto the sand. After a long pause she said in perfect English, 'English makes me tired.'

We talked on for a while but the spell was broken. Before long the children disappeared down the beach, having lost their interest when the switch to English occurred.

My sister-in-law sat there stunned. She is a teacher, and before the children discovered us we had been talking about education (both schooling and health education) and why it was not working for Yolŋu. I told her it was not the people's fault but the fault of the system itself: everyone still expected the people to work in English all the time. I pointed out how teachers, nursing sisters and doctors come to Arnhem Land with no understanding of the language problem.

'But the people just have to learn English,' she countered.

'Yeah, but English is a fifth or sixth language to most of them,' I argued in turn.

Now my sister-in-law had seen it for herself. These children had participated fully in conversation, unrestrained, handling many different subjects—until the switch to English. We had both seen the oldest child slump, noticed her long pause and then heard her say in perfect English, 'English makes me tired.' To her, the switch meant having to use a language she did not think or dream in.

'It's Like a Bomb Being Thrown Down in Front of You'

Another case drives the point home. In October 1998, the same week I was drafting this section of the book, I was working with the chairman of an organisation in east Arnhem Land. We were going through a number of vital issues in relation to the organisation, from level of debt liability to the actual structure of the organisation itself. We had spent one day on it already and he returned first thing next day to continue the discussions.

I greeted him with the Yolŋu Matha equivalent of 'you're up bright and early this morning' and he responded enthusiastically. 'Yes, I got really excited with what we were talking about yesterday. I went home and was thinking about it knowing that I can really understand the structure and problems of our organisation. Usually when I talk with other Balanda staff who work in our organisation, they just talk a lot of English words I can't understand, and that leave me confused.'

'How does it make you feel when that happens to you?' I asked.

'When I go into the office,' he replied, 'the Balanda staff start speaking to me in English. I hear about three sentences and then it's like they throw a bomb down in front of me and I want to run away. The next day I don't want to go back to the office again because of what happened the day before. I get sort of frightened that the same thing will happen again and I won't have a clue what is being talked about and how I should respond. I can see the staff members have a problem or concern they want to share with me, but my mind just doesn't pick up what they're trying to tell me. It's just like a big bomb being thrown down in front of you. It's the same sort of feeling.'

I remembered my young friend on the beach. 'Does it also make you tired?' I asked.

'Yes, very tired, because I can't work it out, even though I speak English fairly well. That's what makes it harder. I think I should be able to understand what the staff are saying, but I just can't. The first bit is okay—like the first or second or third sentence—and then comes the bomb and I want to run away.

'It's not just me, you know,' he continued, 'it's the whole committee. They come to the meetings and the first bit is okay and then comes the bomb. They keep sitting there, but they don't understand anything. Then they start asking, "When is the meeting going to finish?" and we've only just started. We get to lunchtime and the committee has lunch and most of them disappear. Why? Because they are wanting to get away from that experience, just like you would want to get away from a bomb if it was thrown down in front of you.

'But when I come here and we can talk these business things through in Yolŋu Matha, it is easy. I can understand and be a real person. I still get a little tired, but not like I do when it is only English coming at me.'

What's So Hard About English?

What is it about English that makes a Yolŋu child so tired, or a chairman and his committee want to flee? The answer is not simple. First we must look at language itself—what is it? Then we must look at some of the specific problems that Yolŋu have with English.

Coping with a Foreign Language

Language is sound waves in a code form used to transmit the thoughts of one person to another. These coded sounds are converted to electrical impulses that are carried to the brain where they create chemical deposits at the synapses on the neurons. These sounds are a language, and all the information that comes into the brain through the sound waves (and the other physical senses) is encoded in the brain around this particular language structure. The brain uses this language structure to organise thought, and to think in. It is through this thinking process that we construct knowledge. This makes the language we think in very important, as it is the medium that the brain uses to construct knowledge. It is the 'code' we think and dream in.

Now when people are thinking in a language different from the language that is being used in a particular communication session, there are always major difficulties. If, for example, the language used by a doctor is English and a Yolŋu person—a patient, health worker or whoever—is thinking in Yolŋu Matha while trying to listen in English, then a vast potential for miscommunication exists. In this situation, the Yolŋu person has to work much, much harder at communicating than the English-only speaker.

Of course, the severity of this problem varies according to the bilingual skills of the two individuals. This can be truly understood only by bilingual speakers who find themselves in this type of situation on a regular basis.

Specific Difficulties with English

But what is it about English specifically that makes Yolŋu tired when they have to use it? English in itself is no harder than other languages to speak and 'hear'. But English in particular makes Yolŋu mentally tired for a number of reasons:

1. Sounds. Some of the sounds used in English syllables are quite different from Yolŋu Matha. Several components of English syllables or phonemes cannot be 'heard' by Yolŋu Matha speakers. The same is true for English-only speakers: they cannot 'hear' many of the component sounds in Yolŋu Matha syllables, even though all Yolŋu Matha languages have a large number of similar sounds.[89]

2. Grammar. The grammar and sentence construction (syntax) of English and Yolŋu Matha are not at all alike, whereas Yolŋu Matha dialects all have a great deal of similarity. A Yolŋu Matha speaker can use up to fifteen Yolŋu Matha dialects and languages simply because the construction of the languages are so similar.

3. Concepts. The construct of English concepts is quite different from the construct of Yolŋu Matha concepts. This is because English constructs have their

genesis in Europe and Yolŋu Matha constructs have their genesis in Asia. There are many different languages in the Yolŋu Matha group, but they all have the same concept constructs because of their Asian origins. English concepts from the European context are extremely different.

4. Encoding. If a Yolŋu person has been able to get through the preceding three difficulties, they still face a major hurdle to communicating in English: only a handful of Yolŋu use even some English to construct knowledge in their minds. If you were to ask Yolŋu Matha speakers, 'What language do you dream in?' they would point to one of the Yolŋu Matha languages, not English. So when they are listening to English, their mind is processing the sounds into Yolŋu Matha. This is exhausting if conducted for any period of time.

Computers Are Understood—Humans Are Not

We understand this concept of encoding when it comes to computers, but it is seldom considered when it comes to the human mind. When we try, for example, to process data on an IBM computer that has come from a Macintosh, we end up with gobbledegook. The reason is simple: although both IBM and Macintosh computers use basically the same hardware—silicon chips and so on—they use different operating systems or *languages* to encode information. So the only way IBM and Macintosh computers can shift information back and forward, and make sense of it, is through a 'translator' built into one of the computers.

So it is for Yolŋu. When English is used, it requires the Yolŋu Matha speaker to:

- hear, or tune into, as much of the strange English sound waves as possible;

- hang on to and decode what they salvage from those sounds;

- translate or encode meaningful aspects of what they hear into the language their own brain is operating in, so that the incoming data can access the information and pre-existing knowledge filed in the brain;

- think through or process the incoming data in Yolŋu Matha and try to comprehend what is being said;

- think of a response in Yolŋu Matha;

- translate the response from Yolŋu Matha into English;

- speak the response in English.

This, of course, is the process any person hearing and speaking a relatively unfamiliar language must go through—a process that is extremely tiring.

If the English discourse becomes long and fast, or if the subject is beyond the English comprehension level of the hearer, Yolŋu become very confused and anxious. This blocks the communication flow to a point where the Yolŋu person *goes into overload* and almost all communication stops. The Yolŋu person just 'wants to get out of there' because they experience a total loss of control, an insult to their capacity as a human being to respond in a controlled, dignified manner.

Any person who has been in the situation where a foreign language is being spoken around them and at them will know what this feels like. But imagine this happening to you on an almost daily basis. Most of the dominant Australian culture has no appreciation of the fact that Yolŋu are trying to translate rapidly in their heads when English is being used as the medium of communication.

The degree of difficulty that Yolŋu experience with English obviously depends on how familiar they are with English. Many have no English; others have some familiarity. But very few possess any degree of mastery. In general, English needs to be seen as a foreign language for well over ninety per cent of Yolŋu.

Uncharted Languages

There is another reason why English is so difficult for Yolŋu Matha speakers: English is still for them in many ways an uncharted language. By 'uncharted language' I mean one that has not been fully analysed. For Yolŋu this is the case with English, and especially for what they refer to as 'secret' or 'hidden' English. This covers the English equivalent of what Yolŋu call *gurraŋay matha* (intellectual language). Many of the English terms that cover commerce, law, economic and medical areas of knowledge have not been linguistically analysed by Yolŋu.

And the same is true for Yolŋu Matha from the English point of view. There are many terms and concepts in Yolŋu Matha intellectual language, including abstract nouns, that have not yet been fully discovered and analysed so that English speakers can comprehend them.

The linguistic analysis between Yolŋu Matha and English has only been going on for about forty years. If we compare this with the many centuries of linguistic work between European languages, we can see the problem. The analytical work between European languages, and even between European and many Asian languages, has allowed comprehensive dictionary development. In fact, the analysis has been so complete that computer translation programs now exist between most European languages. But the work with Yolŋu Matha has been on a stop/start basis. A Yolŋu Matha speaker still cannot pick up a comprehensive dictionary and discover in their own language the meanings of English words or concepts. So these words and concepts remain 'secret' and 'hidden'.

> English words, which connote a wide range of intentional activity, are unlikely to be understood by Aborigines in the same way. Rather, the Aboriginal learners of English-as-a-foreign-language will impose their Aboriginal semantic structures upon the new word and construct an individual meaning for it.[90]

A person using an uncharted language is like a sailor who enters uncharted waters: the way ahead is unknown. There will be times of great excitement when new riches are found, and there will be times of great danger. It is the same with an uncharted language. And because language is used in daily life, any mistake can be very dangerous indeed.

Patient/Doctor Communication: A Yolŋu Perspective

How do these language problems impinge on the health clinic situation on a daily basis? Yolŋu have been used to bad communication with the dominant culture for so long that some bad habits have set in. One of these is to say 'yes' to almost anything that a doctor, sister, teacher or instructor asks them.

When I point this out to Balanda, they often say, 'Why do they say "yes" to things they don't understand? Isn't that lying?' There are a number of factors here.

First, when English is used, the Yolŋu Matha speaker cannot make much sense of what is being said. Therefore they tend to think nothing important is being said and just agree with it because it is irrelevant.

Secondly, all of us have been in conversations where we haven't really understood what a person was talking about *even though they were speaking to us in our own language*. When this happens, we continue to follow the conversation, hoping the next sentence or two will give us some clue as to what the person is talking about. At the same time, we are desperate with fear that the person will ask us a question or make a statement that they expect us to respond to. This desperation arises because we have been affirming the person with 'yes . . . yes' while they have been talking, even though we haven't got a clue what they have been talking about. We are afraid of being 'caught out' or shamed for not understanding what is being said.

When Yolŋu listen to English, they desperately want to understand, but there is so much working against them. They hear some English words, but the whole conversation just does not come together. In the meantime, they have committed themselves to the other person in conversation, affirming them as they try to catch up and understand. The level of shame people experience at this point is substantial—not just for themselves, but also for the other person, who may have been explaining something to them for a length of time and still they have not understood. Sometimes the English speaker may have been talking on the subject over many days or even weeks. The level of shame the Yolŋu person feels in this case is immense. At this point, if a Yolŋu person is asked if they understand, they will probably say 'yes' while still desperately trying to work it out—and hoping at the same time the subject matter was not too important.

There are other reasons why people might respond with a habitual 'yes'. If Yolŋu were to say, 'Sorry, I didn't understand that', they know from experience that they will probably get the same confusing thing said to them again. The responses of 'yes' or 'yes, I understand' become an unintentional coping mechanism.

And there are yet other reasons. Here is an example of a conversation between a Balanda doctor and a Yolŋu patient:

> Doctor: *Have you had your pain for a short or a long time?*
> Patient: *Yo* (yes).
> Doctor: *Can you tell me where your pain is?*

Patient:	*Yo.*
Doctor:	*Were you sick last night?*
Patient:	*Yo.*

Why do Yolŋu patients answer in this way? It is not because they do not know the answer to the questions. It is because they cannot hear the *whole* question. Some old people with little or no English will not hear anything. Others might only hear certain words: 'you', 'pain', 'short', 'or', 'long', 'time', 'tell me', 'you sick'. People just do not hear many of the joining words, so the sentences might sound something like this:

> '. . . *you . . . pain . . . short or . . . long . . .?*'
>
> '. . . *you tell me . . . pain . . . ?*'
>
> '. . . *you sick . . . ?*'

Often the people can understand all the words separately, but when they are put together—and especially if the speaker is speaking quickly or even just at moderate speed—the whole sentence becomes a blur. So the listener tries to salvage anything that is familiar, sometimes only ending up with one or two words that make any sense. These one or two words are the only communication that survives, and the listener tries to make sense of what is being said using these words only.

It also should be remembered that different cultures construct conversation in different ways. To the second question above, 'Can you tell me where your pain is?', 'yes' would be an appropriate answer in many cultures. The question is taken literally: 'Yes, I can tell you where the pain is.' English speakers do not answer this sort of question literally but see it as an opening to describe where the pain is. Yolŋu, like many other non-English-speaking people, would answer this question with a 'yes', then expect the doctor to ask further questions about the location of the pain. When this does not happen, the Yolŋu patient is left hanging. And so is the doctor, because 'yes' to him is not an appropriate response to the question.

A Grieving Mother

In 1997 a young, grieving mother from east Arnhem Land told me the following story. The story and the conversation that followed were both in English.

'Last year I lost my five-year-old son,' she began. 'He died of pneumonia. I took him to the doctor in our community, but that doctor did nothing, just gave him an injection. That doctor should have sent him to hospital in Gove, but he didn't. I just took my son home. When he got sicker, I took him to the clinic. The sister there did nothing either. She should have sent him to hospital, but she didn't.'

'Did the sister give you anything for your son?' I asked.

'She gave me Panadol and Amoxil and told me to take my son home,' she answered. 'At home my son just got sicker and sicker.'

I asked her if she had given her son any of the medicines, and she said she had given him the Panadol. 'Do you know what the Panadol is for?' I asked.

'Yes, it's to make his temperature go down and to make him feel better.'

'Did you give him the Amoxil?'

'No, because he was so sick. I didn't know what it would do to him.'

After a couple of days, she continued, she knew he was going to die. 'I was frightened for him and angry with the sister and the doctor for not sending him to hospital. I picked my son up and started carrying him to the clinic. He died at the corner, just before the clinic.'

After sympathising with the woman, I asked her if she knew what pneumonia was. 'Yes,' she said, 'It's a sickness that makes people very ill and weak, and sometimes they cough a lot.'

'Yes, that's right, but what causes the weakness, cough and so on?'

'Phlegm.'

'But what is phlegm?'

'Stuff you spit up.'

'Do you know what's in the phlegm?'

'I don't know.'

I asked her if she knew what Amoxil was. She said, 'Yes, it's an antibiotic.' I continued, 'Do you know how antibiotics work or how they can make you better?' 'No, it's Balanda medicine,' she said. 'I know its name and all that, but I don't know how it works.'

I left the discussion at that point because I could not bring myself to reveal to her that not giving the Amoxil was like a death warrant for her son.

The grieving mother in this story could use all the correct English terminology, but she did not know the meaning of the key words that would have allowed her to take control of the situation and save her son's life. This may be hard for monolingual English speakers to understand, because when they hear these key words, a mental picture is created in their minds that gives them *enough* information. But Yolŋu hearing these words get only minimal information from them. In many cases, Yolŋu not only suffer physically and emotionally because of the lack of information; they are also blamed for being lazy or irresponsible.

So what is wrong? Why don't Yolŋu get the same information English-only speakers do when they hear these English words?

The Foreign Language Learning Process

For readers who don't speak a second language, it must be said that there is no such thing as a literal translation of languages. In other words, a word in one language does not always have a direct equivalent in another language. Exceptions are words like 'yes' and 'no', and words like 'sun', 'moon' and 'tree' that name tangible things. The encoding of tangible things in the mind is influenced by what the eye sees, and people from all cultures see the same tangible objects. So these usually have direct equivalents.

On the whole, however, there are no direct equivalents for words that explain or name intangible things. Here the encoding of meaning in the mind is influenced by many other factors, including the other physical senses, the social, physical and technical environment and the people's experience of the particular subject. As a general rule, the more complicated the content of a concept or word, the fewer the number of direct equivalents. This is particularly so when the languages being used come from different regions of the world where the people have had different histories.

So what happens to a Yolŋu person when they hear a new English term that has not already been linguistically analysed by them or someone else?

At present, a few incomplete dictionaries exist for Balanda who are learning Yolŋu Matha. These arrange Yolŋu Matha words in alphabetical order and give their English meaning. But only one very limited dictionary of nineteen pages exists for Yolŋu to look up an English word and get its Yolŋu Matha meaning. This is totally inadequate when you consider that the Oxford English Dictionary contains some 500,000 words, and the total modern English vocabulary, including dialect expressions and scientific terms, has been estimated at more than one million![91]

Without a good English-to-Yolŋu Matha dictionary, the people are stuck whenever they come on a new, intangible English term. There is no easy-to-use linguistic tool to help them. They enter 'uncharted language' waters.

To better understand the difficulty of this problem, let me explain the trouble I have learning a new Yolŋu Matha word that has not already been analysed and recorded. There are no short cuts to understanding the meaning behind such a word. I can't just go to an existing Yolŋu Matha-to-English dictionary. So I follow a natural, informal method of learning language—the same method children use all the time when they are learning a language.[92]

When Yolŋu want to teach me a new word, the first thing I concentrate on is the word's sound, or *phonology*. I want to be able to say the word and recognise it when my Yolŋu instructors use it again. It would be very embarrassing if my teachers used the word and I didn't recognise it. The syllable sounds in the new word might be very strange, so I will use a lot of energy and concentration to get the sound of the word right.

As I'm doing this, without thinking I will soak up the *syntax and morphology* of the word—the information about where it is used in a sentence, its grammar, and if it has a suffix or prefix. This will happen as I hear where and how the word is used.

Next I will concentrate on the *context* in which the word is used, because this will give me a pointer to its meaning and where I can use it. First I will learn what subject area the word fits into—economics or law, for example, or something related to disease. I will learn whether the word has some restrictions on it, as it might have if it is a legal or gender specific term or is used in some way to talk about a subject indirectly. I will concentrate very hard on this contextual information, because once again, I don't want to be embarrassed by using the word in the wrong place and sounding stupid or rude.

All this is a lot of information to take in, but the chances are I will still not know the *semantics*, or meaning, of the word. If it is an intangible word, this aspect will be the hardest of all.

There is no easy way to understand meaning. My Yolŋu teachers cannot just say, 'Oh, it means such and such in English', because they don't know what it means in English. They don't even know if English has a word for such a concept. Many times one of my teachers will say, 'I think the English language might be inadequate and not have this word.' Then we will talk and talk, testing different ideas until we discover the meaning behind the word. This might take weeks, months or even years, depending on the level of familiarity that my instructors and I have with each other's language and our knowledge around the particular subject. Of course, once it has been done and the word recorded, it does not have to be done again.

Knowing but Not Knowing

Understanding this process helps explain how Yolŋu can know and use English terms but not know their meaning. They can learn the phonics of words and use them in the right place in the sentence, and most of the time in the correct context. They can even pass exams by using these words because the grammar and context are known. But still they might have no understanding of what the words really mean. They can use these 'hidden' English terms but not really understand them.

Sometimes the context can be a bit 'out'. It is rather like children using a word which is not quite in context, or me using some Yolŋu Matha word I don't fully understand. A Yolŋu Matha first-language speaker will pick it up straight away because it sounds silly! Of course, Yolŋu might think they know the meaning of these English words, and in truth they will have some understanding. But whether this understanding is correct or not, it will constitute for them the *whole* meaning of those words.

If those of us who speak English as a first language have a question about the meaning of an English word, we go straight to a dictionary to check its meaning. But imagine if we had no dictionary and had to rely on our peers to check the meaning—peers who also did not understand the word. We would all stay ignorant of the true meaning. In fact, the word would take on a new meaning— the meaning we all thought it had.

This is the situation Yolŋu are in. Many times as a cultural group they will come to an understanding of an English word and will teach each other that meaning.

But without a standard like a dictionary to test their understanding, they will continue in their belief that it is correct. In fact, it may be disastrously flawed.

While this is a major problem with medical terms, it is also a dilemma in economics, law, technology and many other areas. Professionals from the dominant culture assume that Yolŋu who use English words know what they mean, but as long as English remains an uncharted language for Yolŋu, many of these intangible terms will remain 'hidden' and therefore will be used incorrectly.

The Importance of the People's Own Language

In 1952 Beulah Lowe arrived at Milingimbi in north-central Arnhem Land as the first trained schoolteacher. Then in 1958 she moved to full-time language work.[93] Beulah developed language courses that became mandatory for all mission staff. This language learning was undertaken and, with varying degrees of competency, achieved.

With the end of the mission era, however, there was a slow drain-off of dominant culture staff who spoke Yolŋu Matha. Some other Balanda have tried and are still trying to learn Yolŋu Matha, but it is no longer being done in an organised way. Only a few really learn. This places a massive load on Yolŋu to do all the linguistic work.

Strangely, in some ways it is easier for a Japanese businessman visiting the Northern Territory to communicate with government representatives and others in the local dominant culture community than it is for Yolŋu citizens of the Territory! The Japanese businessman will have an interpreter provided by the government, and he has the advantage of good Japanese-English and English-Japanese dictionaries. But a Yolŋu clan or community leader will have no interpreter provided for him in the same circumstances.

The failure of the dominant culture to recognise the importance of languages leaves Yolŋu in a very vulnerable state. I am constantly approached by people from various organisations and companies who have been given jobs that involve educating or consulting with Yolŋu. The questions are always the same: 'How can I really hear what the people are saying?' or 'How do I know if the people are hearing what I am trying to teach them?' My response is also always the same: 'Without language and without understanding the worldview of the people, it is impossible. Yes, you can go out and get some responses; but you will never really hear the people, nor they you, unless you can communicate intellectually with them in their own language.'

Most Balanda just walk away from these experiences blaming the people instead of looking for rational reasons why the problem exists.

In a world that is keen to make sure plant species are not destroyed in case some genetic material is lost, little attention is given to the loss of intellectual ability that occurs when languages disappear. Yolŋu Matha and other Aboriginal languages are complex, sophisticated languages, something acknowledged by the

House of Representatives Standing Committee on Aboriginal and Torres Strait Islander Affairs in 1992:

> Contrary to popular misconceptions these [Aboriginal] languages had complex grammars, rich vocabularies and subtle ways of describing the world around them—a world in which they had lived for tens of thousands of years.[94]

As a speaker of Yolŋu Matha, I know these languages have the ability to empower thinking in a modern world. More importantly, they have the intellectual capability to empower Yolŋu for the next thousand years in a complete way, with rich thinking and learning power. This ability will die unless the dominant culture can seize the day and initiate, in partnership with the people, the linguistic research necessary to analyse the presently uncharted Yolŋu Matha languages completely and fully.

These languages could even be the means for Yolŋu to learn English in a truly effective way. That is Yolŋu, like Asians and other English-as-a-second-language students, could work straight from concepts in their own language over to English concepts, by simply using English to Yolŋu Matha dictionaries and other such tools. Such tools together with properly trained teachers and competent learning methodologies could equip Yolŋu for a brighter future.

Yolŋu dream and therefore construct knowledge in Yolŋu Matha. Yolŋu Matha is then the language of their 'mental computer'. Any new learning will have to construct knowledge in the language of their computer until they start to use English or another language to think in. The transition to that other language will need to be done in a way that does not destroy their capacity to think dynamically, as is now happening. Language *must* be taken seriously.

6
CHAPTER

Thirteen Years of Wanting to Know

World-view—as Important as Language

Health promotion supports personal and social development through providing information, education for health and enhancing life skills. By so doing, it increases the options available to people to exercise more control over their own health and over their environments, and to make choices conducive to health.

Ottawa Charter for Health Promotion[95]

For Yolŋu patients to receive information about their health so that they can exercise more control over their lives, the information needs to make sense to them. Medical people should not assume that Yolŋu patients understand what is said to them, even if they seem to understand English. Cross-cultural/cross-language communication is much more complex than this. Apart from language, there is another essential element needed to communicate successfully in a bilingual, inter-cultural situation. This is *an awareness of world-view*.

To explain world-view and its effects on communication, I will tell the story of David.

David was a Yolŋu man who for over thirteen years had an illness he could not understand. By analysing David's problems in communicating with the medical system we will see what world-view means, and how world-view differences can block people's chances of getting the information they desperately need to exercise control over their health and even save their lives.

I only knew David casually when I became involved in his case, although later he became a very good friend. Once he finally understood his sickness—diabetes—he wanted to join my colleagues and me in teaching his people about this medical complaint. He knew that many of his countrymen suffered from this condition, and also from the problem he had faced: not being able to get information that made sense to them from 'the system'. We had just started putting together material for a mass education program when David contracted a severe tropical infection and died.

I have changed David's name and some minor details to disguise his identity. Other than that, his story stands as a testimony to a wonderful, humble man.

David's Thirteen-Year Search

David was in his mid-forties when he approached me one day asking for help. He had been told thirteen years earlier that he had 'bad kidneys'. He said the doctors had also told him his heart was enlarged, but when he asked them why, he couldn't get an answer that made sense to him. The doctors also told him to give up things like salt, sugar and cigarettes, but he found it hard to uncover the reason. He remained confused and therefore unable to comply with their instructions.

David had a very good knowledge of English. He had been the elected member on a government commission for many years and was at one time on the executive of that commission. This meant he travelled to Canberra many times. When government people visited his community, David did much of the interpreting. Yet he still had great difficulty understanding what the doctors were saying to him about his own condition.

David explained he had just been to Darwin to see a specialist about his heart. The specialist had said he couldn't tell why David's heart was enlarged. This had David very confused. 'If he's the specialist and he can't tell me why my heart's enlarged, then who can?' he asked.

I had some idea why David's heart was enlarged and why the doctors had told him to give up sugar, salt and cigarettes. But not having formal medical training, I delayed talking with him about it because I didn't have all the information, especially the information from the specialist. I also knew it would be better if David heard the story straight from a doctor. I could act as facilitator and discuss points in Yolŋu Matha with David where necessary.

The doctor happened to be visiting the community and David had an appointment to see him the next day. I asked if he wanted me to go with him. 'Would the doctor allow that?' he asked. I assured him it was his right as a citizen to have anyone he wanted with him when he saw the doctor, but he still seemed unsure. I suggested that if he liked I would go and check with the doctor whether it was okay.

I went from my meeting with David to the local clinic and told the doctor the story. A nursing sister, overhearing the conversation, challenged me. Why was it necessary for me to help David, she asked. David had come back from the specialist in Darwin and told the clinic staff the same things the specialist had written in his report. So from her point of view he had the whole story. Besides, she said, David's close relatives were health workers. He could get information about diabetes any time he wanted.

I agreed with the sister to avoid more of an argument, then said, 'But who do I listen to? You're telling me David understands; David's telling me he doesn't understand. Who should I listen to?' I paused briefly then turned to the doctor. 'It's David's right to have anyone he wants in the consultation, isn't it?' The doctor confirmed this and said he would be happy to have me there.

The next day David and I went to the clinic together. The doctor asked David if he had any questions.

'Why is my heart enlarged?' he asked.

The doctor told him that the specialist could not *conclusively* say what had enlarged his heart. 'They can't really tell you without sticking an injection into your heart and testing some of the heart muscle,' he said.

At this point I intervened. I knew the doctor was seeing one picture and David another. I explained to David in English that the doctors could not definitely say what had enlarged his heart *unless* they tested it by doing a small operation. This involved using a special thing like an injection, but it was different from an injection because the instrument would be put into the heart muscle and would bring a little piece of muscle out. That piece of muscle would then be tested under a microscope to find out what might have caused the heart to enlarge. I got the doctor to confirm that this was somewhat dangerous because they could hit a vein and cause bleeding.

I said to the doctor, 'But you have a good idea why David's heart is enlarged anyhow, don't you?'

'Yes,' the doctor said to David. 'I think it's because of your diabetes. But it could be hereditary. I can't tell for certain.'

David turned to me and asked how the doctor could tell this. Switching to Yolŋu Matha I said, 'It's because the doctor knows the *gakal* (literally, the action or the symptoms of progression) of diabetes and kidney failure.'

David was thoughtful. 'What is the *gakal* for diabetes and kidney failure?' he inquired.

I asked the doctor to explain diabetes and especially the kidney failure side of things. He said that only two per cent of David kidneys were operating. I had to stop him again and explain what two per cent meant because percentage is a concept Yolŋu just do not understand. So I drew a kidney shape on a piece of paper and shaded in about two per cent. 'That's how much is still working,' I told David. 'The rest is, like, "dead".'

This was a shock to David. He double-checked that both kidneys had the same problem. The doctor confirmed this. 'Because your kidneys are so bad they are not working properly, so your blood is very thick. This makes it hard for your heart to pump, so it's getting large.'

I went over this again with David, drawing out the role the kidneys play in the body. The kidneys are like a filter in a car that takes the water and rubbish out of the diesel or oil, I explained. The doctor reiterated this: 'Your blood is now very thick, David, with lots of rubbish in it because the kidneys are not working. The blood is so thick that it's hard for the heart to push it around the body.'

I checked whether David understood this. He asked about thick blood. We discussed this back and forth because I didn't know a Yolŋu Matha word for thick liquids. I tried different ways of explaining thick and thin liquids, then he saw it and he taught me two words in Yolŋu Matha to explain thick blood. He wanted to know whether the doctor was talking about congealed blood or non-congealed but thick blood. When we were both sure we were talking about non-congealed but thick blood, we went on to discuss how the heart finds it hard to push the thick blood around and so the muscle tissue expands. I said this in Yolŋu Matha and showed it with my hands.

'Yes, I can see that,' David said finally. 'So why do I have to give up sugar, salt and smoking? These are three things I love in life.'

The doctor explained that the sugar was not being used up in his body because of the diabetes. Instead it was carried to the kidneys and was helping to destroy them. I asked for clarification on how sugar hurts the kidneys and the doctor responded, 'It's like it rots out the filters.' I questioned him further but he said, 'It's a complicated process, and to say it rots the kidneys is close enough.'

I wasn't sure how to explain this because I knew David would have problems trying to understand how sugar might rot the kidneys. So I gave an explanation I had used with diabetics about sugar in the blood and its relationship to skin ulcers. Bacteria (which David knew about) love to find sugar in places like sores and kidneys because the bacteria see the sugar as good food. It gives them lots of energy to grow strong and propagate. This leads to the kidneys being destroyed by the bacteria. (I have since upgraded my understanding of the full kidney/sugar relationship so I can more accurately explain this process.)

David saw this without further explanation and said, 'What about the salt?'

'That's hard,' said the doctor. 'How do I explain osmosis?'

'Let's use something from David's experience that would explain it,' I said. I thought for a moment. 'If we get some salt and pour it on this chair here, then come back in the morning, what would we find?'

David replied in Yolŋu Matha that it would be 'melted'.

'That's right,' I said. 'The salt would become *gapumirr* (watery). That means if we have salt in our body, the salt becomes watery in our bodies and we get fat.'

The doctor added: 'The salt and sugar cause more problems for the kidneys and your heart, making much more work for them to do.'

We talked next about smoking. Nicotine, the main chemical in cigarettes, causes all the veins in the body to constrict, making it hard for the heart to pump blood around the body. I talked this through with David in Yolŋu Matha because it is a story that the people have never heard. David saw the problem straight away and said that that was going to be the hardest thing to give up.

The doctor told David that because his blood had a lot of rubbish in it, he was very worried about it. If it stayed like that, David would have to go to Darwin and be put on a dialysis machine because his kidneys would fail.

David glanced at me, looking for an explanation. I outlined dialysis to him. He said he wanted to stay on community and didn't want to live in Darwin. The doctor responded that a time would come when he would have to be on a dialysis machine. He said he would make an appointment for David to see the specialist in Darwin so they would be ready for him when the time came. 'But it is up to you,' the doctor said. 'If you can look after yourself, you might be able to stay on community for a while.'

David had no more questions. We left the clinic and went back to his office. He was quiet and I asked him if there was anything wrong. 'They've been telling me about my kidneys for thirteen years, and only today have I understood what they meant,' he said.

A week or so later I received a phone call from the doctor. The conversation went something like this:

Doctor: What did you do?

Me: What do you mean, what did I do?

Doctor: With David. His blood levels are almost back to normal.

Me: What do you mean?

Doctor: When I saw him last, his blood and urine tests showed there was a lot of rubbish in his blood. I thought I would have to hospitalise him before the month was out. But now his blood levels are back to normal. If he can keep them like that, he can put off the Darwin visit. He won't need dialysis for a while. So I was wondering, what you did to get him to stick to his diet?

Me: Nothing. You were there when I talked it through with him. I only spent about twenty minutes with him after we left your office. We talked a bit about the diet. He asked for clarification about the types of drinks that had sugar in them. I told him to drink only pure fruit juices and fresh water, because I know a lot of Yolŋu are confused about what are good or bad drinks. I emphasised the need to drink fresh water because not many Yolŋu drink it these days.

Doctor: Well, whatever you did is a miracle.

Me: I wouldn't call it that, doctor. More like good communication.

How can a twenty to thirty minute consultation make such a difference in a person's understanding of their medical condition? The answer lies partly in the fact that this was the first time David had been able to discuss his condition in Yolŋu Matha. If English speakers talking to David had kept to the 'three F's'— family, football and fishing—he would have been judged a very good English speaker, but his experience shows how incorrect this assumption would have been. Yet language was not his biggest difficulty. His major problem was the difference between his understanding of the world around him and the understanding of the world held by the professionals in the dominant culture health system. The problem was a *difference in world-views.*

From Experience to World-view

Let's look further at what I mean by the term 'world-view'.

A people's world-view is the product of a host of environmental and historical factors. Western culture, for example, from which the dominant Australian culture developed, grew up under a variety of influences. Some of these include:

- *The development of centralised villages.* This created an experience of living within a permanent dwelling and needed all sorts of adaptations for survival.

- *The development of cities.* This experience was, in general, horrific—streets ran with sewage and other waste, crime proliferated, poverty abounded.

- *The experience of the bubonic plague* in the fourteenth century. Up to seventy-five million people died.

- *The industrial revolution.* The harnessing of mechanical power through the steam engine and other technical innovations, creating a change from agricultural to manufacturing-based economies.

- *A shift in thinking.* From 'sickness was created by spirits, bad air or the influence of the stars' to an understanding that most sickness is caused by 'little animals', later called 'bacteria' and 'viruses'.

- *The development of public health facilities.* Services like sewerage and rubbish collection, along with disposal methods to meet these new understandings and conditions.

These developments took place over many centuries, and out of sheer necessity Western culture adapted and changed to meet the new challenges.

The same necessity did not occur for Yolŋu. Living in Arnhem Land, in a different environment isolated from the social changes and the microbiological pool that developed in Europe, they knew nothing of these great historical shifts. Over the centuries Europe became a cesspool of disease through its trading network and the development of cities, but Yolŋu have really only experienced this microbe invasion in the last century. Today, in a single lifetime, they are having to live through the stages of development that took Europeans many centuries.

Experiences like these have created a world-view among dominant culture Australians that is very different from the world-view of Yolŋu.

How can we describe these differences? Let's return to David's story. His experience vividly illustrates eight world-view problems and two language conflicts. I will look at each of these in turn, analysing the divergences between Yolŋu and dominant culture world-views and identifying the confusions and complications these bring.

The Effects of World-view on Communication

World-view Problem 1:

David was not sure if he would be allowed to have anyone with him when he visited the doctor.

The Yolŋu world-view.
This is a common problem. Yolŋu do not know their citizenship rights on these issues. This could partly be because the people have never had a contract relationship with doctors, where doctors are paid servants of the people. But the real genesis of the problem comes from the fact that, when Yolŋu visit a clinic or see a doctor, it is to them an extension of the mission era and therefore of the welfare system.

Under the mission/welfare system, the doctor or sister commanded and the patients obeyed. People were forcibly taken to hospital. Mission medical staff, backed by the full authority of Commonwealth Welfare Department patrol officers, would take babies from crying mothers' arms (when deemed necessary) and send them to hospital. Many old people were also taken from their loved ones, only to die alone in hospital while their families at home grieved. As one mourning relative said to me in February 1997, 'Why did they take our grandmother to Darwin from Nhulunbuy hospital if they knew she was going to die? Why didn't they return her to —— [her home community] so she could die with her loved ones? Did they take her to Darwin to practise on her?'[96]

Many years of this practice have left deep scars in the memory of the people and a bad understanding of their rights as citizens.

During the welfare days, whenever Yolŋu walked overland to visit Darwin they would be rounded up by force and returned to the missions on the next mission lugger. If Yolŋu didn't do what the Welfare Department and mission told them to do, they were punished. And to Yolŋu, not a lot has changed today. Common practice in Darwin and Gove hospitals until not so long ago saw medical patients who had run away rounded up by police and returned. The people still see the health system as akin to a 'police state', as it was in the welfare era.

During 1998 I was asked to help a Yolŋu family understand the medical condition of one of its members. The man leading the meeting introduced me and said, 'You can relax. Wämut understands our fear of hospitals and that we don't like our relatives sent there.' This fear is so real that many people, especially men, will only use the health system as a last resort. Often they seek help far too late. At times the people try to hide their old ones from the system for fear that a sister or doctor will send them to hospital, never to be seen alive again.

David's problem was a little different, but the same fear was there. He saw the medical system as authoritarian. Unsure of his rights, he was unsure if the doctor would allow anyone to accompany him during his consultation.

The dominant culture world-view.
The Balanda involved in this case would probably not know that David had any of these concerns. Balanda come from a different historical perspective; they

usually know their rights and assume others do too. But the complication caused by this difference in world-view meant that I had to go to the clinic and check if it were all right for me to accompany David. If David had known his rights, we could have arrived together the next day and avoided my confrontation with the sister.

World-view Problem 2:

The sister believed that David had the whole story because she had heard him repeat 'accurately' what the specialist had said. Those words gave a clear picture to her so she assumed they gave a clear picture to David.

The Yolŋu world-view.
The memorising of words and phrases is a common Yolŋu learning methodology, even when the meaning of what is said is not understood. This is further complicated by the uncharted nature of English for Yolŋu Matha speakers, as discussed in chapter five. Besides this, Yolŋu traditionally memorise information they don't understand because they know that later information will probably reveal the meaning of the unclear statement, word or phrase.

As a mostly oral society, Yolŋu are taught from an early age to carry and repeat messages *accurately*. When a message-carrier delivers a message they don't understand, they will not ask for meaning because it might be something they should not know about. Many times I have been given a message to pass on to someone in another community, and usually the message makes no sense to me. But when I give it to the recipient in the exact format, in which it was given to me, it is understood immediately and makes good sense to him. Sometimes the meaning has been revealed to me, other times it has not.

The dominant culture world-view.
Balanda operate quite differently. Whereas committing statements to memory in their exact form and order is the Yolŋu way, Balanda try to get the *meaning* of what is said to them and remember that, rather than the actual words and word order. Or they write the message down so they don't forget it.

It is obvious from this that culturally it was quite normal for David to be able to repeat what the specialist had said to him without understanding what it meant. The Balanda nursing sister, not knowing the Yolŋu way, was understandably confused about how this could be so.

World-view Problem 3:

The Balanda nursing sister said that David could ask his relatives, who were health workers, for any information he wanted to know about diabetes.

The Yolŋu world-view.
The world-view problems David had about his health were shared by the health workers. In this case, I checked with David's health worker relatives and they were as confused as he had been about his condition.

Another difficulty for David was that he was an older male, making it very hard for younger female health workers to give him medical information, even though one was a very close relative. In fact, this close relationship itself presented other cultural blocks which made it impossible for him to get information from her even if she did know it.

The dominant culture world-view.

The problem that the Balanda sister had is a common one. She didn't realise that many of the world-view problems causing David trouble also cause difficulty for many health workers. Balanda sisters and doctors assume that because health workers have had some training in a dominant culture institution, they therefore know everything about diseases like diabetes and renal failure. Many Balanda medical staff arrive on community not knowing where the people or health workers are up to, and without language training they are unable to accurately assess the health workers' knowledge.

One sister, while attending a training program on community education, commented, 'I have been in Arnhem Land for many years now, working in health clinics with Yolŋu health workers and the people. I never realised before that the people did not understand many of the things that I assumed they knew.' When I asked her for an example, she said, 'The health workers many times will come and ask what procedure they have to do next when treating a patient. Then the next day they will ask the same question again, as though they had not asked the day before. Now I realise that they don't understand the causation of disease and sickness and their effects on the body, so the clinical diagnostic procedures don't make any sense to them.' She went on, 'Now I have to find out what they know and don't know so I can work from where they're at.'

Language Problem 1:

The use of the word 'conclusively'.

It was here that the whole conversation between the medical professionals and David fell down. The doctor said the specialists could not tell 'conclusively' why his heart was enlarged. This was a language problem embedded in world-view problems.

David did not understand the word 'conclusively' in its English sense and probably did not use it when he repeated the findings to the sister. 'Conclusively' is one of many intangible English words with which Yolŋu have great difficulty. I think it would be hard to find a Yolŋu health worker who understood the meaning and implications of the use of this word in a sentence.

So what was David hearing? When working in a foreign language, if you don't know what a word means, you try to work out what is being said by the other words in the sentence. The word you don't understand becomes a sound with no inherent meaning. So David was hearing from the specialist: 'We can't tell *blahblahblah* why your heart is enlarged.' And this is why he told me the specialist could not explain his enlarged heart.

Language and world-view are inseparably linked. When communication between David and the medical professionals failed around the word 'conclusively', it sent them down two completely different world-view tracks.

These differences surrounding the word 'conclusively' create a constant problem between Yolŋu and the Western medical world. For example, in March 1997 I accompanied a Northern Territory government committee to three of the major Yolŋu communities. In each community, Yolŋu asked the committee members if they had ideas of what the Balanda doctors knew about the effects of kava. Some Yolŋu said, 'We want the Balanda doctors to tell the communities clearly how kava is affecting the people.'

The committee replied that not enough was known about kava and its effects on the body. 'We need to do more research,' said a researcher travelling with the committee. I know this puzzled the people because they could see for themselves how kava affected the abusers' skin, made them thin, at times threw them into fits and so on. They thought the doctors also must have been seeing something . . . if they were any good as doctors, that is.

Of course, the doctors were seeing many side effects, but their world-view led them to state cautiously, 'We cannot say *conclusively* that kava is causing heart, liver and maybe kidney problems.' In other words, it's not good science to say kava is having this or that effect unless it can be proven 'conclusively'. This really confused the Yolŋu, many of whom were looking for support from the committee, and gave ammunition to the pro-kava lobbies in the communities which were saying, 'Kava doesn't kill, people kill' (meaning people were dying because of sorcery, not from the effects of kava). Yolŋu health workers confirmed the problem: 'We go out and try to educate our people about the bad effect of kava abuse but they will not listen to us. We need someone to come and help us.' But the 'conclusive' nature of Western medical culture prevented this.

In David's case, because of these different world-views, it was easy for the sister and doctor not to factor in the reason why he was really concerned. From David's point of view, on the other hand, it was impossible to appreciate their cultural concern for being medically and scientifically accurate in the information they gave.

For me, the key cultural word in the conversation was 'conclusively'. I knew David was probably not hearing it, yet it gave me a lot of information from the dominant culture side. Putting this together with the Yolŋu world-view, I was able to move the conversation forward, knowing that the doctor might not know 'conclusively' why David's heart was enlarged but would know that the progression of David's kidney failure was the *probable* reason. I also knew that the doctor could explain this process and that this information would satisfy David, for two reasons: one, because it was coming from the doctor—that is, from someone who had knowledge in the area of Balanda sicknesses—and two, because David's own experience of his sickness would validate the doctor's explanation.

World-view Problem 4:

The implications of not being able to explain the enlargement of David's heart.

The Yolŋu world-view.

When David thought the doctor could not tell him why his heart was enlarged, he had another problem. According to Yolŋu thinking, if a sickness, a disease or a death has no clear physical cause then someone must be doing sorcery. In other words, if the enlargement of his heart could not be explained in physical terms, David would suspect sorcery.

In the Yolŋu world-view, sorcery is both *real* and *illegal* according to the *Maḏayin* traditional law. It is seen as a lawless and disgusting practice. No self-respecting Yolŋu would ever admit publicly to being a sorcerer or being involved in an act of sorcery. It would be like admitting to being a murderer—and a cowardly one at that.

However, sorcery, although illegal, is taught secretly to some people by knowledgeable members of individual clans as a sort of secret weapon. Lawful Yolŋu refuse to learn sorcery because of its illegal status. But human nature being what it is, some people learn the trade. (This is not much different from nations that have a secret chemical warfare capacity. Everyone knows, for example, that the Americans and Russians have got it, even though they deny it emphatically. And so it is with Yolŋu clans.) When something happens in Yolŋu society that is unexplained—sickness, disease, accident or death—sorcery is seen as the cause.

David did not want to believe that superstitious stuff. But after he had asked the doctors over and over again and they kept coming up with 'We can't tell *blahblahblah* why your heart is enlarged', he started to believe that even the doctors were thinking it must be caused by 'something else'. 'Something else' to David meant sorcery. He was starting to think that maybe some individual or group had let an assassination contract on him. The contracted person's job would be to make sure the deed was done in such a way that no one would know who either the contractor or the contracted person was. This is why David kept asking if the Western medical system had any answers for him.

Remember that David's condition had existed for thirteen years. Over that time he had started to think down the line of sorcery. In fact, he spent many of his waking hours trying to work out who was trying to kill him and why. Maybe he had offended some person or clan. If so, who could it be? Was it someone he lived or worked with? Was someone gloating over their handiwork right now, as they saw him get sicker and sicker? Was it one of his closest friends? Was that killer asking him for a cigarette every day or sharing a meal with him?

The suspicion of sorcery can only be ruled out when a clear intellectual reason can be seen as the cause of the problem. Any fuzziness is cause for suspecting foul play.

The fact that David could not get a clear story from the specialist only made his fears worse.

The dominant culture world-view.

There are two dominant culture world-view problems in this situation.

The first is the dominant culture medical world-view. When the word 'conclusively' is used in this medical context, it carries a lot of cultural information that even English-first-language speakers sometimes have trouble understanding unless they have a medical background, let alone people from a completely different language/cultural group. This is because of the nature of medical science. Within the culture of medicine, no-one likes to make a statement unless it can be 'conclusively' proven. David did not have this understanding, whereas for both the sister and the doctor it was second nature.

Secondly, in the dominant culture world-view, sickness and disease are understood to be caused by identifiable physical causes such as viruses, bacteria and poisons, or other factors such as diet, lifestyle, trauma and so on. Sorcery is usually not considered a factor. If it were raised as a factor, the dominant culture would still misunderstand the Yolŋu concept of it, passing it off either as 'superstitious rubbish' and 'primitive' or as a 'groovy new way of thinking'. Witches are in vogue now—kids' stories about your friendly neighbourhood witch abound. So if even the hint of sorcery is raised at the professional medical level, it is usually dismissed as childish, immature thinking. Not many dominant culture people know how to handle this subject. But for Yolŋu it is serious business—as serious as international espionage to the dominant culture.

World-view Problem 5:

David did not feel able to ask the doctor about the questions he was thinking in his mind.

I had to lead the discussion and ask the doctor, 'But you have a good idea why David's heart is enlarged, don't you?'

The Yolŋu world-view.

In Yolŋu society, it is a cultural 'no-no' to ask questions. The reasons for this are very complex, but in short it is part of the mechanism used in oral societies to keep information accurate. This is done by making certain types of information valuable. The way most societies make something valuable is by controlling the supply. In Yolŋu society, information has been made valuable by making it secret, so only the 'owners' of the information can give permission to newcomers to learn particular things.

The cultural mechanism used is this: if you mistakenly ask a question in an area where you don't have the owners' permission to receive the information, the person answering the question will be evasive. On hearing the evasive answer, the questioner will realise that he is on 'holy ground' and has no right to be there. If he continues asking questions in this area, he could be in serious trouble. If I had not asked a leading question at this point, the conversation would have stopped because David felt he had no right to continue the questioning.

The dominant culture world-view.

Most Yolŋu are not assertive when it comes to asking questions. The doctor, on the other hand, came from a culture where assertive questioning is the name of the game. He was probably waiting for a prompt from David to show he needed more information.

Due to these different cultural mores, communication between Balanda and Yolŋu is blocked and both parties just sit there and look at each other. This is not the fault of either party; in fact, both are unsure why communication is not happening.

World-view Problem 6:

Percentages were used. (The doctor said that only two per cent of David's kidneys were operating.)

As mentioned previously, percentage is a concept that Yolŋu have great trouble with. As a cultural group they just do not understand it. Even people with seemingly good Western education standards have problems with it.

To use percentage as a quantitative measurement and expect to convey an accurate concept to Yolŋu is very dangerous as far as their health is concerned. It was equivalent to saying to David, 'You have only two *wup-wups* of kidney working.' It gave him no picture at all but simply added to his confusion. David would not even have realised that percentage is a measurement of quantity. The *concept* is just not understood, so it is very difficult for a patient to frame and ask questions about it.

World-view Problem 7:

When we started talking about the kidney itself, the doctor assumed that David would have some idea of the role that kidneys play in the body.

The Yolŋu world-view.

Yolŋu have a very good understanding of the shape, size and place of body organs. This is probably due to their long history of working with animals. Most Yolŋu have dissected many animals in their lifetime. In preparing a meal, the organs are sometimes cooked and eaten separately from the rest of the animal. So in this area of knowledge, Yolŋu are way in front of the average Balanda. (Some younger Yolŋu now growing up in communities are losing even this knowledge.)

But although the people can quickly identify organs on x-rays and in books, and can name them in their own language, they do not have much knowledge about the purpose and function of various body parts.

The only organ whose function most Yolŋu have some idea about is the brain. Most Yolŋu will say, 'The brain is involved in the thinking process.' But if asked about the heart, for example, most Yolŋu would say they are not sure what its function is. They know the heart is full of blood and connected by veins and arteries to the other parts of the body; however, they do not know it is the central pump for blood circulation. This is the case even with the traditional doctors. Now because of this lack of knowledge David had no idea that his kidneys cleaned up the blood in his body.

The dominant culture world-view.

As a general rule, Balanda have some idea of the body's major organs and how they work. In AD 150, the Greek doctor Galen suggested that the blood flowed back and forth in the body like the tide, and this was accepted until 1628 when William Harvey wrote that the heart was a central pump and the blood circulated around the body.

At that time he was challenged for this thinking. It was when pumps were built to shift water and people could see the relationship between shifting water and shifting blood around the body that Harvey's theory was accepted. Later that century, the development of microscopes allowed the Italian physiologist Marcello Malpighi to discover the existence of tiny capillaries in the body which allow blood to move from the arteries across to the veins. As a cultural group Balanda now have this knowledge.

Language Problem 2:

When David and I discussed the concept of 'thick blood'.

David had problems understanding the idea of thick blood. He could see a clear picture of congealed blood, but that gave him other problems. He knew congealing usually occurs when someone is dead or when the blood is spilled out onto the ground in an accident or such.

This was also a language problem. When communicating at this level, it is essential to know what language the person is thinking in, because you are operating in concept areas, like viscosity of liquids. For me, this was the most difficult part of the discussion. In the end, David saw the minor qualitative differences and was able to go on.

World-view Problem 8:

When David asked the doctor why he was being asked to give up sugar, salt and smoking.

The Yolŋu world-view.

In their traditional education, Yolŋu are taught from childhood to work out for themselves the reason behind what they are being told to do. This is a Yolŋu educational methodology. As young people are trained they are only given a certain amount of information; the rest they are supposed to deduce. This is to teach them to be creative thinkers, always working on unsolved problems. Consequently, if information is given to a Yolŋu person and they find it does not add up intellectually, they will continue to think about it.

Because of this highly refined culture of education - giving Yolŋu a limited amount of information, that does not sit together with knowledge they already have within their cultural group, will cause major problems for them. Although Yolŋu find it very difficult to ask questions, for Yolŋu teaching Yolŋu this is not a problem. Because the teacher and student come from the same world-view, the teacher will not lead the student down a blind alley—that is, they will only give information from which the student can deduce the next step. But when a person with a different world-view gives the information, the blind-alley syndrome occurs all the time. This sends Yolŋu virtually crazy trying to work out what is really being said to them. They need to understand intellectually what is going on.

In David's case, he had to know *why* sugar, salt and smoking, three things he loved, were being banned. When he could not see an intellectual reason, he tried to guess why. Many Yolŋu in the same position come to the conclusion that the doctor is punishing them for some reason, or playing with them. Consequently, they refuse to comply. To dominant culture people this can look like arrogant stubbornness, but from the people's point of view it is an attempt to maintain a sense of integrity in a system that holds no intellectual meaning for them.

I know that David had been trying for years to find out the reasons why he had to cut these things out of his lifestyle. The system was unable to answer this basic question in a way that made sense to him, so he remained confused, out of control and non-compliant.

The dominant culture world-view.

Dominant culture patients, as much as Yolŋu patients, want information from their doctor that makes sense to them. In most cases they receive this because their language and world-view are similar to the doctor's. Sometimes, Balanda doctors simply tell Balanda patients to give up sugar, salt and smoking with little explanation, yet patients will try to cut them out because of their respect for the doctor.

Often another component of the dominant culture world-view affects communication at this point: the idea that Aboriginal people are simple and therefore need simple solutions. Balanda do not, as a whole, consider traditional Aboriginal people to be highly intellectual and therefore they give only basic information. But even if a doctor wants to give intellectually competent information, the poor communication factors stop it.

Trained Professionals Are Essential

David's story illustrates that an understanding of world-view as well as language is essential for good communication. In fact, an understanding of world-view is essential *even if language is not a problem*. If educators and other professional personnel employed to work with Yolŋu were trained in these areas, many millions of dollars would be saved and Yolŋu would not have to suffer the way they do.

Another way to tackle this problem would be to provide professional facilitators and educators who could play the role I played with David. Such people could work beside medical professionals, even at the end of a telephone, so that Yolŋu patients could understand and therefore be in a position (as this chapter's opening quote put it) to 'exercise more control over their own health and over their environment, and to make choices conducive to health'.

If this had been the case for David, he would not have had to spend thirteen years wanting to find out knowledge that should have been easily available to him. He could have done something about his condition much earlier—before it became critical. Instead, he and many other Yolŋu leaders have suffered very premature deaths and have become mere statistics in this long war of words.

7
CHAPTER

'You Can Hear the Grass Grow'

Understanding the People's Cultural Knowledge Base

It is true that Balanda sometimes use bad words for us and have bad opinions about Aboriginal people. The reason for that is often that Balanda have not very much knowledge about our way of living. Our way is very much different from the European way.

Jack Mirritji[97]

We have looked at language and world-view, but there is a third element that is vital for good cross-cultural communication: understanding a people's 'cultural knowledge base'.

An understanding of 'cultural knowledge base' is especially important when one culture is trying to share unfamiliar or new information with another culture. If those trying to share this information are not conscious of the effect that someone's cultural knowledge base has on the acquisition of new and 'strange' information, then attempts to pass on such information will fail. In fact, it is quite likely the new knowledge will be rejected because it does not 'stack up' against pre-existing knowledge in the receiving group's cultural knowledge base.

This happens continually when Yolŋu try to gain new knowledge or information from the dominant culture (whether from doctors, sisters, teachers, trainers or others). It leaves many Yolŋu highly frustrated and confused. Many blame themselves for being unable to understand what the dominant culture person is saying. They don't realise that they have fallen into another of the many traps in cross-cultural communication.

Pre-existing Knowledge

Most teachers are trained to teach 'from the known to the unknown'—that is, to build on the knowledge that a student already has. Sometimes this is called 'scaffolding'. In a classroom, a teacher will try to establish the pre-existing knowledge that a given class has and use it as his/her starting point to impart new knowledge.

The pre-existing knowledge of different groups of students will vary according to the experiences they have had in their local living area. There will be distinct groups of knowledge even in the same ethnic community. And what is true of groups of students is also true across whole cultures. When a cultural group has a history and language completely unlike that of other groups in their country, their pre-existing knowledge will be distinctly different. For Yolŋu, this is because their culture and dominant Australian culture have roots in unrelated parts of the world. This pre-existing knowledge held within a particular culture is what I call its 'cultural knowledge base'.

The cultural knowledge base is the core knowledge and information accepted by the majority of people in a cultural group as being *true knowledge*. The cultural knowledge base is what shapes the world-view of the group. Some individuals may have specific knowledge that the group as a whole does not have, but often they will keep it to themselves because the majority of the group will not acknowledge it as true knowledge.

For Yolŋu to acquire new knowledge, this new knowledge must build on existing knowledge within their cultural knowledge base. If new facts and concepts are taught which do not fit into what they already understand to be true, then this new information will make no sense or its truth will be questioned. Either way, it will usually be rejected.

Having a different cultural knowledge base from Balanda culture gets Yolŋu into trouble in two ways. First, they are almost constantly misunderstood by dominant culture people when they try to share information from Yolŋu culture. Frequently they tell Balanda something deep from their law or cultural knowledge, but after working through the subject it soon becomes obvious that the Balanda do not understand (even if the Yolŋu are speaking English). The Balanda, on the other hand, can make no sense of what they are told, so they reject it as nothing. Both parties are left not knowing what to do, and Yolŋu are tempted to despair because they cannot make themselves understood about things that are central to who they are.

Secondly, the differences in cultural knowledge base mean Yolŋu have trouble receiving new information or knowledge from the dominant culture in a way that makes intellectual sense. To illustrate this, here is a story from my early days in Arnhem Land.

Get Behind, Brother

On my arrival in Arnhem Land in 1973, I spent the first three months at Milingimbi. There I started to learn Yolŋu Matha. When the three months were up, I learnt I was to move to the mainland to help build the new town of Ramingining.

Along with a group of about twenty Yolŋu, all previously unknown to me, I crossed the three kilometres of open sea in a small dingy. We were dropped off at a barge landing on the mainland where we were met by three Yolŋu men driving a tractor. Behind the tractor was a large flat-topped trailer—our transport for the twenty-five kilometre trip inland. I was new and felt very alone.

We started out but had only gone a kilometre or so when a wheel fell off the trailer. I could see that we would not be repairing it there. The group started to walk, with the children riding on the tractor. Then the tractor stopped. *Water in the fuel*, I thought; but with no tools, the whole group was soon walking. The sun was starting to go down and the people were eager to hurry on—we had a long journey ahead. As I walked into Arnhem Land that night, with the only knowledge of civilisation behind me (the mission station at Milingimbi), I once again felt very alone.

It was then I became aware of my Yolŋu companions. The people organised themselves with an air of confidence as they shared the burden of load and children. The tractor and trailer were broken—so what? We could still walk!

As we filed out across the tidal plain, heading for the woodland ahead, I joined the leader up the front like a 'good Balanda'. We were following the two tracks in the grass made by the vehicles on their journey out. The people were on one track behind the leader and I was on the other, beside the leader.

We walked for a while then my companion said, 'Brother, walk behind me here.' Not knowing what he had in mind, I did as I was told for a while; but then I rejoined him, walking on the parallel track. Again he beckoned me to walk behind. This made me very uncomfortable. I could hear him say in Yolŋu Matha, 'Walk behind me', but I could not understand the other things he said which presumably explained the reason for this instruction. *Maybe it's because he's the boss and doesn't want anyone else up front with him*, I thought. After a kilometre or so my cultural instincts overtook me and I moved up beside him again.

This time he stopped. The whole line of people came to standstill as he motioned me back behind him. I was starting to feel a bit stupid. *What is going on in this guy's head?*, I asked myself.

Just then I found out. We had only gone another thirty metres or so when a large snake came out of the middle of the track and headed for cover, travelling right across the path I had just been walking on. The word '*Bäpi!*' rang out from everyone's lips. After the group calmed down and they were sure the *bäpi* had gone for cover, we continued on.

I was a bit stunned. *So that's what he was trying to tell me*, I thought soberly. If I had still been on that track, the snake would have been wrapped around my legs. He was not only concerned for me; he was just as concerned for himself because I could have disturbed the snake and frightened it into his legs.

I learnt three things that day: that the Yolŋu Matha word for snake is *bäpi*, that I should always trust the people while in their environment, and that Yolŋu as a group of people have knowledge that Balanda don't have.

Over the next eleven years I learnt much from Yolŋu. Some of it made no sense according to my Balanda cultural knowledge base. But when I discovered the other knowledge that Yolŋu had to support their view, the new knowledge made good sense and I was able to retain it.

Some things, though, took some working at. I remember the day my adopted Yolŋu uncle first told me you can hear spear grass grow in the Wet season. My Balanda brain, working from my Balanda cultural knowledge base, had real trouble believing him.

I had asked him for the name of the frog that calls out a long mournful sound in the Wet season. He waited for the sound. 'That one?' he asked with a laugh (as if to say, 'Don't you Balanda know anything?') 'That's not a frog—that's the spear grass growing!'

'The spear grass growing?' I said with a smile. 'You're trying to trick me.'

'No,' he said seriously, 'You can hear the spear grass grow. Everybody knows that.'

Now, years later, I *do* believe you can hear the spear grass grow, even though many people from my own cultural group will not believe me until someone 'qualified' does a documentary or study on it. Then it will become accepted knowledge within the cultural knowledge base of the dominant culture. Until that happens, my Yolŋu friends and I will be considered a little weird because when it comes to hearing grass grow, our cultural knowledge base is different from that of the dominant culture.

The Role of a Cultural Knowledge Base in the Learning Process

For Yolŋu, the knowledge about how to live with snakes and the fact that you can hear spear grass grow is ordinary, everyday knowledge. Yolŋu, like Balanda, possess a mountain of knowledge dealing with all aspects of life. When this knowledge is accessed piece by piece, it can be used as the starting point for the sharing of new information in a way that makes sense to Yolŋu.

How is this done? First, information around a particular subject is sought from the people. This includes:

- learning what the people already know about a subject;
- seeing if there is any comparative example or supportive pre-existing knowledge in their cultural knowledge base; and
- determining what 'gaps' exist around the subject.

The gaps in knowledge are usually what the people want answers for. It is these gaps that leave them confused and vulnerable.

The following story illustrates a gap in the Yolŋu cultural knowledge base and one way I have used to deal with it.

Using the Cultural Knowledge Base to Bridge the Gap in Knowledge

'What are bacteria?' a health worker asked me when we discussed this subject at a workshop in Gove in 1997. 'I've been a health worker for twenty-five years, but I still don't know what bacteria are. I have all the names for them but in my mind I don't know what they are.'

In other words, she did not know if these 'bacteria' had shape or size, whether they were inanimate or animate, whether they were spirit or just some type of force. She definitely did not know they were living, breathing, reproducing creatures.

Another day a Yolŋu colleague related a similar experience. He asked some Yolŋu health workers what sickness was. 'We're not sure what sickness is,' they replied.

'Well, what is scabies then?'

'If the people come in with scabies skin then we give them a particular medicine.'

'I didn't ask you what medicine you used. I asked you what *is* scabies? What is its shape and size? How does it get onto our bodies and propagate?'

'*Yuw!* (Don't know!) When people come in with scabies skin, we give them a particular medicine.'

We asked ourselves: How could it be that nursing sisters and educators have been teaching Yolŋu about bacteria and scabies for over thirty years yet they still don't know what they are?

I decided to analyse the problem further and discovered that what we feared was true: the people only knew the names or words for such things as bacteria and scabies. They had no mental image of what bacteria and scabies looked like. In fact, they did not even know there were living things that could not be seen with the naked eye.

At first this was alarming. But then I remembered that Yolŋu have an in-depth knowledge of the life cycles of all living fish, birds, insects and animals—information that could provide a basis for extending their knowledge about the microbiological world.

I now knew what information was required to overcome Yolŋu confusion about bacteria. I needed to show them these living creatures through a microscope. But to use a microscope I would have to teach microscope literacy. This meant I needed to understand what knowledge Yolŋu already had in their cultural knowledge base about things like microscopes.

Fortunately I had previously analysed this and had discovered some useful information. First, the people knew very little about microscopes, thinking they were like a video camera, just replaying something already put in them—'some sort of Balanda trick'. They did, however, know that reading glasses make things appear larger, and this could be good supportive knowledge on which to build. The gap in their knowledge was that they did not know microscopes could let you see something invisible to the naked eye. They also did not realise that even doctors and nurses used them as a tool in medical diagnosis.

So to teach the people how microscopes work, we began with their understanding. First, we pulled the eyepiece out of the microscope and let people look through it. At the same time we held a pair of reading glasses over an object. This way the people saw that the microscope had 'glasses' in it that made it possible to see small things more easily.

Then the people found an ant and put it under a dissection microscope. Yolŋu already know a lot about ants, but when they saw the ant's teeth under the microscope, they were surprised and excited. They had always wondered how such small insects could inflict such pain! In this way, 'playing' with the microscope not only built on their existing knowledge, giving them new understandings of the insects, but simultaneously familiarised them with the microscope and how it works.

Once the people were convinced that a microscope could show them things invisible to the naked eye, it was time to move down a level. Stagnant water was good for this. If the people found the water themselves, they would know there were no tricks in it! We let the people try to see living things in the water with their naked eye, and of course they couldn't. So we placed the water sample under the dissection microscope with the ant. They were shocked to find 'things' in the water!

We then moved to the compound microscope. 'Now we're going to look at *very* small things, smaller than we have already been looking at,' we said. We mounted a hair on a slide and put this under the microscope. We started magnifying x10, showing the people how big this made the hair. We then moved through x40 and x60 up to x100. This gave the people a good picture of the comparative sizes they were going to look at.

Finally, we showed them bacteria in both water and spit. Only when we got down to this level were they ready to learn about specific bacteria. (Scabies, of course, could be shown to people straight after they had seen the ant. It was just a matter of finding some!)

At this stage we began to teach the life cycle of the particular bacteria or parasite the people were interested in. In the life cycle information we included the reproduction times and methods, the method of entry to the body, and how the infant and adult act within the body, causing the body to get sick.

The people got very excited about this type of education. Health workers began to tell me they had learnt more in one hour using this method than in years at college. It was exciting for them because it built on their cultural knowledge base and was delivered in their language and through their world-view. We have used this educational methodology many times since, with great success.

The Effects of Different Cultural Knowledge Bases on Learning

Dominant culture people might say, 'I've never seen bacteria, yet I know what they are.' Yes—but who taught you about them? It was probably someone like your mother or another influential person in your cultural group. Educators tell us that seventy-five per cent of what we learn comes from the influential members of our family. If members of a particular cultural group or family unit are confused or lack information about the world around them, the same confusion and lack of knowledge will be transmitted to their children. In other words, the cultural peer group maintains and teaches what that particular group sees as real knowledge and truth within their cultural knowledge base (see chapter 12).

Yolŋu have knowledge of the spirit world but no knowledge of the little creatures that are invisible to the naked eye: the microbes that live and breed and sometimes make us sick. The influential people in Yolŋu culture can't pass this knowledge on because they just don't have it.

It is good to remember that, although Anton van Leeuwenhoek[98] first discovered bacteria in 1675, it took over 200 years for Western culture generally to believe in the relationship between bacteria and sickness. If we were to wait at least 200 years then the Yolŋu might have absorbed this knowledge and be able to teach it to their children, just as Balanda teach it to theirs. But Yolŋu need this information *right now*. Effective cross-cultural education methodologies must be employed to equip the people for survival.

The example of bacteria exposes the fallacy that traditional Aboriginal people are unable to understand this type of information. In reality, this is the sort of knowledge Yolŋu deal with every day. They consider it commonplace. Within their cultural knowledge base, Yolŋu adults have a vast amount of information about their natural environment and the creatures that live in it. They know these creatures as intimately as a professional biologist from the dominant culture knows the creatures he works with. For thousands of years this knowledge has been necessary so the people could farm these creatures and at times protect themselves from them. It has been taught from generation to generation through the Yolŋu educational processes. So it was not strange to discover that Yolŋu were very interested in bacteria and their relationship to sickness. This is the kind of information that they consider important to know about their environment.

Another example of understanding and building on the people's cultural knowledge base relates to the role of the heart. As already mentioned, Yolŋu know the size, shape and position of all the organs of the body much better than many Balanda do, but they don't know the functions of these organs (other than the brain). The heart's role in blood circulation is definitely not understood. Yet all Yolŋu know they have a pulse, and many of them can point out all the pulse points on the body. They call the pulse *ŋir'* (the breath, life force) and it is thought this pulse is caused by the *ŋir'* (breath). Almost no Yolŋu know that the pulse is caused by the heart pumping blood around the body. The Yolŋu understanding is that the blood is just there in the veins. The pulse is seen as a separate force.

This has massive ramifications for explaining information about blood pressure, heart disease, stroke, high and low blood pressure, and all sorts of circulatory problems. At the moment, when a Yolŋu person is told they have high blood pressure, it makes no sense to them. One picture they get is that there is too much blood in their body. Low blood pressure may be seen as not enough blood in the body.

On many occasions I have had to explain a heart attack. Knowing the people's pre-existing cultural knowledge base, I talk first about blood circulation and the role of the heart as a 'pump' and then go on to talk about the other aspects of heart attacks. This can be tied together with *ŋir'* or breath by saying, 'Yes, Balanda doctors also see the blood carrying the *ŋir'*. Doctors call it "oxygen".' In most cases the Yolŋu patient becomes very responsive to this information because it starts with what they know. Many go on to comply with the treatment necessary to correct their condition.

Education and the Cultural Knowledge Base

From the perspective of education and training, the same rules apply. If Yolŋu were to receive education and training in their own language, taught through their world-view and with knowledge built on their pre-existing cultural knowledge base, they would more than competently learn and understand.

This may seem simplistic to some, and in a way it is. But because these elementary things do not occur in contemporary education and training centres, Yolŋu education is in an appalling state. The disastrous failure of communication around the elements of language, world-view and cultural knowledge base is matched by the failure of Balanda education. Yolŋu have heard the promise, 'If you learn Balanda ways you will be able to run your communities'—but they, along with those in the education department and government, are frustrated because nothing seems to work. I will explore this dilemma further in the next chapter.

My colleagues and I believe there is nothing Yolŋu cannot learn. The only limitation is *the capacity of the teacher to teach*. Unfortunately, dominant culture teachers and trainers currently come to Arnhem Land with almost no preparation in intercultural education. If the dominant culture trained its professionals in the Yolŋu language, Yolŋu world-view and Yolŋu cultural knowledge base—and it is possible to do so—then Yolŋu would not have to do all the hard work to cross the cultural knowledge barrier. They could then receive the vital information they need to survive.

8
CHAPTER

Is the Age of Knowledge and Thinking at an End?

Why Cross-Cultural/Cross-Language Education Is Failing

I was educated in the '70s. I got a better education than my daughter here. I know how to read and write and talk English. I can talk to you, to anybody, to Land Council. I don't want more excuses that we are blackfellas. So the education department I reckon is going backward and is always coming up with excuses. . . . Maybe you don't want us to be educated properly because you don't want us to do your jobs. Educate us properly so that we can come back and be bookkeepers, and things like that, run this place. . . . We're worried now. It is getting worse. This is the first time in 20 years that someone has come and talked straight to us about what is going on in our schools. We are wasting time sending our kids to your white schools. Teach us properly, to speak like you. I don't savvy [understand] why you don't.

Learning lessons.[99]

In societies across the world since ancient times, the quest for knowledge has been elevated to a high-level discipline, even an art form. In Yolŋu society, knowledge has always been considered valuable—almost more valuable than life itself. Traditionally Yolŋu were prepared to pay much for information from other clans. Over the years they have also tried to obtain dominant culture knowledge wherever they could.

When I first came to north-central Arnhem Land in 1973, I soon discovered how much the people wanted to learn. I spent my first two years working with two brothers, old men of the Murruŋun Wolkpuy clan who spoke Djinaŋ. In fact, there are about eight different Djinaŋ dialects and these men knew them all, along with six or so other languages.

One of these men was a traditional 'mailman'. When he was younger, before radios and vehicles, he ran many hundreds of kilometres up and down the *dhumbarpar dhukarr* (trading highways) that stretched across Arnhem Land and beyond. As a 'mailman' he carried letter sticks with messages on them and also *madjapala* (formal orders/contracts for services and/or products) to and from distant clans and nations. This meant he needed to know the ancient writing on the letter sticks and have a good knowledge of many more languages than his brother.

These men started teaching me two forms of Djinaŋ and much other knowledge. They were supposed to be working with me in the workshop, but many times we found ourselves in teaching sessions—I taught them about the Balanda world and they taught me about their world. I was astonished to discover their vast knowledge and the way they applied themselves to learn from a young twerp like me.

Most Yolŋu I know have spent many of their waking hours in a quest for learning. Their hunger for knowledge is insatiable. This is not what my culture led me to believe about these ancient scholars.

The Degeneration of Yolŋu Education

In the 1960s and '70s many Yolŋu went through to higher education and on into full-time employment. Now young people arrive at school leaving age with no chance of entering any form of full-time employment. Many will not even get a driver's licence because their literacy levels are so poor. School attendance is low, as though the people see no sense in education. Blame is heaped on them for their non-participation and their supposed academic failure.

In 1999 the Northern Territory Department of Education held an independent review of Indigenous education in the Northern Territory. It found 'substantive evidence that Indigenous educational outcomes are deteriorating from an already low base'. Some of the measures of this decline, according to the report, are:

- *An overall decline in attendance at the same time that enrolments have been increasing. . . .*

- *Advice from employer bodies that, more than ever before, they are unable to find people who meet basic literacy and numeracy entry criteria for employment and training.*

- *A repeatedly stated observation from Indigenous elders that their children and grandchildren have lesser literacy skills than they do.*[100]

So why don't Yolŋu learn, and why does there seem to be less motivation to attend schooling than there was even in the 1970s?

A great many things can affect the desire for education. One is the level of meaningful work in which Yolŋu adults are involved; another is whether the people actually learn anything from the education process. High on the list is the quality of education offered. Could it be that the dominant culture education delivered to Yolŋu is so ineffective that almost no education occurs, and Yolŋu are left thinking that the age of knowledge and thinking is at an end?

In approaching the issue of Yolŋu education, we first need to be clear *which* schooling system we are talking about. Is it the dominant culture schooling that operates in community schools run by the Education Department? Or is it the traditional Yolŋu schools and universities that the dominant culture call 'ceremonies' or 'corroborees'?

It is the dominant culture schooling system that is failing. The traditional schools and universities still operate very effectively in some places despite dominant culture opposition and lack of support. They continue to teach ancient knowledge in a very efficient manner—and the attendance rate is fantastic! These institutions are 'Yolŋu-friendly', using the people's language, communication mores, educational methodologies and ways of constructing knowledge. As well, the traditional Yolŋu teachers (not those with Western mainstream certificates) use well-refined 'scaffolding' methodologies, building new information on students' pre-existing knowledge.

Many Western-educated Yolŋu teachers lose almost all these culturally appropriate teaching methodologies when they attend mainstream training institutions (even those designated 'Aboriginal'). This is because their instructors have a dominant culture mind-set and do not know the 'Yolŋu-friendly' methodologies. Many of these institutions do not understand the principles of good cross-cultural/cross-language education.

With Yolŋu communities awash with dominant culture-trained teachers and trainers who use typical Western methodologies designed for a mono-cultural/mono-language setting, almost no contemporary learning occurs.

Unfortunately, when the people are constantly bombarded with seemingly unintelligible information, they withdraw, feeling harassed and frustrated. They know they do not learn as well from contemporary schooling and training systems as Balanda do. They see Balanda go on to become doctors, accountants or airline pilots while they remain unemployed, and they start blaming themselves and seeing themselves as 'inferior' and 'unintelligent', even as less human. This is not strange—Balanda would have the same feelings and learning problems if they had to pass grades in a traditional Yolŋu educational structure.

The Need to Know 'How the New World Works'

Many Balanda argue that Yolŋu should be left alone because contemporary knowledge will only destroy their traditional ways. And in a sense they are right. Yolŋu elders themselves sometimes comment, 'It would have been good if Balanda had never come and we still lived according to the old ways given to us by *Waŋarr*, the Great Creator.' However, they then add, 'But Balanda are here now taking over our lands, resources, jobs, everything. We must know their ways so we can survive.' The time for the romantic notion that Yolŋu can live in isolation is well past.

Western influences and behaviour now impact on Yolŋu from every direction. There are almost as many Balanda living in Arnhem Land as there are Yolŋu. A large number work for mining companies and other related industries. Some do the work that Yolŋu themselves once hoped and dreamed would be in their domain on their own communities. Others run their own businesses and trade where Yolŋu once traded. Clearly Yolŋu need contemporary knowledge if they are going to be able to compete and regain some control over their lands and lives. Traditional knowledge versus contemporary knowledge is no longer an issue.[101]

There are two questions that Yolŋu ask me all the time: '*How* does the Balanda world work?' and '*Why* is this or that affecting us?' For people who have been brought up to learn everything about their environment, it is an intellectual insult not to be told the reason behind everyday occurrences.

With regard to health, Yolŋu patients want to know about modern disease so they and their loved ones can live long, happy lives. New introduced sicknesses and lifestyle diseases have outrun the people's own knowledge. They need access to new knowledge. They want to know the reason behind their medical treatment. When they are told and understand, they can act responsibly and comply with any intellectually competent advice. They can intervene in culturally appropriate ways to halt or control diseases or illnesses affecting their health.[102]

I suggest that it is not dominant culture education per se that will destroy Yolŋu ways, but dominant culture education that is *ineffective*. Ineffective education results in confusion, not cognition.

The High Cost of Ineffective Education

Someone has said that even the worst colonial education is better than none. I strongly disagree, because this statement seems to suggest that:

1. the people had no previous education — as though education did not exist before the colonials 'invented' it, and

2. formal Western education, such as the aquisition of literacy, may in itself increase the students' thinking ability.

I believe all cultural groups on the face of the earth, including Yolŋu, have their own very effective traditional formal and informal educational procedures. As well as this, good research exists that tells us that literacy aquisition in itself may not increase the students' thinking ability.[103] In fact when a group of people like Yolŋu continually experience *ineffective* Western education, it can have far-reaching negative effects, leaving them confused about the modern world and *even about the nature of knowledge itself*. This is because the educational experience gives students no rational, objective knowledge—that is, no knowledge that makes intellectual sense to them. Instead of receiving positive learning, the people are left intellectually crippled.

Let's look in detail at the effects on Yolŋu of ineffective education.

Because of ineffectual education, Yolŋu learn to feel inferior and unintelligent.

In 1998 a group of Yolŋu schoolteachers asked to speak with me. They said someone had told them that I had been criticising Yolŋu teachers. I replied that I had never criticised Yolŋu teachers, but I had criticised the modern education system because it was not teaching Yolŋu properly. They asked what I meant.

I went straight to the heart of the matter. 'Let me give you three English words: value, liability and mortgage. Do you know them?'

'Yes,' they replied.

'Can you spell them?'

They spelt them all accurately, including the 't' in mortgage.

'Now, do you know what these words mean?'

There was a long silence.

I asked for examples of the word 'value'. 'What picture do you get in your mind when you hear the word?'

'I see the word 'value', that's all,' one replied.

'It is a big important Balanda word,' said another.

'Okay,' I went on. 'If I say to you, "This is a very valuable thing in my hands", what would it mean?'

'It would mean the thing in your hand is a very important thing.'

'But do you know why it is important?' I persisted.

'No.'

Next I asked if they used the words 'value' or 'valuable' in the curriculum at school. They said they used them all the time.

'So what do you say to the children if they ask you what these words means?'

'We just tell them it's a big important Balanda word.'

'And what do the children learn from that?'

One of the teachers looked at the ground. 'That Yolŋu are dumb,' she said.

In Arnhem Land today, ninety-five per cent of Yolŋu have no understanding of terms like democracy, citizen, state, republic, referendum, atmosphere, environment, hire-purchase, credit, tax, grant, superannuation, insurance, production, trade, constitution, community, council, proposal, prosecute, defence, guilty, germs, bacteria, virus, scabies, pneumonia, tumour or antibiotics. Some of the people can spell and use these words, but they don't know what they really mean. And these words make up only a tiny fraction of 'secret' or 'hidden' English.

What is schooling about if Yolŋu teachers themselves do not understand these concepts? Imagine being a teacher and having to use terms and concepts on a daily basis that have no meaning for you. Then imagine how a class feels when they see that their teachers have no understanding of these 'big important Balanda words'. This happens not only to Yolŋu teachers but to the whole adult Yolŋu population. Yolŋu come to believe that the meaning of these 'secret' English terms is beyond their ability to comprehend. Indeed, whole subject areas of dominant culture knowledge do not make sense to Yolŋu, leaving them feeling inferior and unintelligent.

The damage caused by ineffective cross-cultural/cross-language education can be seen in the number of Yolŋu who have gained various levels of Western education but are now involved in alcohol and substance abuse. One middle-aged Yolŋu man told me he is the only one of a group of twenty Yolŋu who went to high school together who is not dead or drinking themselves to death. This is common. If you visit the Yolŋu drunks in the long grass in Darwin or Nhulunbuy, you will find that a large proportion of them have had college or tertiary education. This education has left them feeling inferior and unintelligent to the point where they need to 'drink to forget who they are'.

Because of ineffectual education, Yolŋu discount their elders and traditional knowledge.

Let's continue the story of the three teachers. Next I gave them a Yolŋu Matha word, *miŋurr*, and asked them if they knew it.

The young teacher who had led the discussion up to this point, the one with the most Western education, did not know it. She was about to tell me there was no such Yolŋu Matha word when one of the older teachers said, 'Yes, that is *gurraŋay matha* (intellectual language).'

I affirmed this and asked her to give an example of what it meant. She responded, 'If I buy something new I will not want others to use it, because *miŋurryun ŋarra ŋuli* (value/it I always).'

Now because *miŋurr* has been analysed—and I have checked it many times over a fifteen-year period—I was sure it held much the same meaning as the English word 'value'. I told them this. It shocked them that it could be so simple to understand a 'secret' English term.

In about ten minutes we worked through the two other English words, liability and mortgage, using the direct Yolŋu Matha equivalent of 'liability', *rom maraŋgum*, and unpacking the word 'mortgage' (we have still not found a term in Yolŋu Matha for this). I was not surprised that the younger teacher also did not know the term *rom maraŋgum*. It is becoming common for Western-educated Yolŋu not to know much of their own intellectual language. Many consider their traditional ways and knowledge 'old hat', with no real value in the modern world.[104]

The pressure to cast traditional knowledge aside has come from both the dominant culture's direct instructions and its ineffective educational methodologies. First, dominant culture personnel have told Yolŋu repeatedly, 'Forget your old ways' and 'You need to think for the future'. Secondly, 'modern' education does not use traditional knowledge or *gurraŋay matha*, and the neglect speaks volumes. 'Actions speak louder than words.'

Many educators and even linguists have participated in this discounting of Yolŋu elders and traditional knowledge by naming *gurraŋay matha* the 'language of the old people' and not bothering to seek understanding of it. Yolŋu who work with them often do not know their own intellectual language and will also call *gurraŋay matha* the 'language of the old people'. It is dismissed as an antiquated, almost unnecessary language of the past. Because *gurraŋay matha* is not understood by either Balanda or many of the Yolŋu involved in this dialogue, its intrinsic value to knowing is lost.

Discussing this with me in December 1998, a clan leader observed, 'You know, *Wämut*, these Balanda-educated Yolŋu do not know our *gurraŋay matha*, nor do they know the English *gurraŋay matha*, do they?' He was correct. Many Western-educated Yolŋu have little understanding of either.

Because Yolŋu construct knowledge in Yolŋu Matha, losing these Yolŋu Matha terms means losing the intellectual capacity to know and think about the concepts. This is not to say the people cannot learn the terms in English; they can. But it may take many generations for this to occur naturally. In the meantime, generations of Yolŋu will live in intellectual deprivation.

This is already a massive problem because these terms, words and concepts *are the basis of what education itself is about.* They are the terms that drive economic, political and legal systems, that teach citizens their responsibilities and rights, that pass on good etiquette and manners, that create diverse and powerful thinking in subjects like philosophy and human dynamics. This clan leader said, 'It is the *gurraŋay matha* that contains all our history and our law. Take away our *gurraŋay matha* and you take away all our knowledge—even our knowledge of who we are.'

Because of ineffective education, Yolŋu lose the 'cause and effect' relationship in their thinking about how the world operates.

As discussed in the previous chapter, most people from the dominant culture have some idea that sickness and disease are mainly caused by little creatures invisible to the naked eye. We call these creatures 'viruses', 'bacteria', 'parasites' and so on. We also know something about lifestyle diseases. Most dominant culture people understand this 'cause and effect' relationship to one degree or another, and if someone does not know these facts, there are many within dominant culture who can explain them.

This is not so for Yolŋu. The Yolŋu understanding of life is still basically pre-microscopes. Yolŋu are now, as it were, at the 'Black Plague' stage of understanding disease which Europe held in the 1400s. It is instructive to remember that the English word 'malaria' came from the Italian *mala aria*, bad air, and that 'influenza' was so named because it was believed epidemics were caused by the influence of the stars. The root meaning of these commonly used medical terms points to the fact that the dominant culture's cultural knowledge base was also once void of knowledge about the causes of diseases. Now, as the twenty-first century dawns, Yolŋu still have insufficient knowledge in their cultural knowledge base to help them understand most diseases. For a cultural group without this knowledge, it is impossible to even start thinking in the right direction.[105]

When we add to the confusion about bacteria a further confusion about Western medicines, we can start to see the negative effects on Yolŋu understanding of 'cause and effect' in relation to disease. Traditionally Yolŋu knew all their own medicines—that is, they knew which plant was a cure or treatment for which complaint. There was no mystery about the origins of their own medicines. But there is real mystery about the origins of Balanda medicines.

One of the people's most powerful experiences of Western medicine occurred in the late1940s and early 1950s. At that time, missionaries or government patrol officers visiting people on their traditional estates or meeting Yolŋu on missions and settlements carried with them phials of penicillin for the treatment of yaws. This nasty disease, originally from Asia, was transferred skin to skin and in the tertiary stage created massive ulcers, destroying large areas of the nose, bones and joints and leaving sufferers scarred or disabled. However, after a patient had received penicillin shots, the ulcers healed over in a few weeks. Soon people were being brought great distances for these 'injections'.

Although many Yolŋu alive today have never seen the debilitating effects of yaws, the power of the 'injection' and the seemingly magical effects of 'penicillin' are firmly implanted in their cultural knowledge base. But they still wonder where Balanda get this and other powerful medicines from. They saw the results of the medicine, but nobody answered their puzzlement about it in a way that fitted with their pre-existing knowledge. Many Yolŋu have told me, 'We know what an injection is, but we have no idea what the "medicine" inside is.' They know that penicillin is a white liquid that comes in a bottle and is drawn into a syringe, and there the information stops. Few Yolŋu have any idea that Alexander Fleming discovered penicillin by chance in 1928 when he found mould growing in a culture dish and saw it killing bacteria in the dish. Nor do they know that other workers later found a way of getting purer penicillin and discovered it was poisonous to many dangerous bacteria but not to animals and humans. When Yolŋu are given this information, they are shocked that the powerful Balanda medicine penicillin comes from such a humble origin as mould.

When the people do not know that sickness is caused by little invisible 'animals' and that medicines are 'specialised poisons' that kill these 'animals', the 'cause and effect' relationship is lost. And if people do not understand 'cause and effect', then dynamic, critical thinking around this subject is not possible.

This loss of 'cause and effect' has very serious ramifications. Imagine a Yolŋu person going through some form of dominant culture medical training but not having the 'cause and effect' relationships of bacteria, disease and medicine established in their thinking. On returning to their community to practise medicine, the former student thinks along these lines: 'What I must do is give this medicine for this particular condition.' All they know is the name of the condition, perhaps some of its symptoms and the name of the medicine used to treat it. No real cognition has occurred in their training. The complicated dynamics of the disease and medicine relationships are not understood. If the name of the medicine changes, the student is again confused. Issues like resistance to some drugs make no sense. Over- or under-prescribing becomes a major problem. The 'grieving mother' in chapter 5 is another example of this reality. She did not give the correct medicine at the critical time because she was not sure what it would do. With all this confusion, Balanda medicines, when they work, are seen as mystical or magical.

The loss of the 'cause and effect' understanding even affects people's view of housing. A Yolŋu community member said to me in 1997 after I had shown his family bacteria on a microscope: 'They have never seen bacteria so they think it's what type of house they live in that makes them sick or not. If it is a Balanda house then you won't get sick. They don't know it is bacteria from the rubbish and other things that make you sick. That's why people always want new houses.' So even the Balanda house can be seen as some form of mystical cure for disease. This is why many Yolŋu push for new Balanda-style housing even though their existing house might be only a few years old. They are convinced the house itself, not the unhealthy bacteria in it, is the reason why their family gets sick all the time. Once again, without 'cause and effect' understanding, the people start to think it is the shape and/or material content of something that stops them getting sick.

Similar confusion exists around many subjects other than health—money, for example. Many Yolŋu believe that 'all Balanda are filthy rich because the government gives them lots of money'. Earlier, many thought money came from God or the Queen or somewhere else that only Balanda knew. Whenever the people receive confusing, seemingly unintellectual information from the dominant culture, then 'cause and effect' is lost. This compounds to the point where it starts to affect the whole domain of knowledge.

Because of ineffective education, Yolŋu come to believe that dominant culture knowledge is of a superior, mystical quality and unattainable.

When people lose 'cause and effect' thinking, such deep confusion results that they can lose touch with reality. It is then only a small step to believing that Balanda operate by some form of mystical power, and that the real knowledge of this power is unattainable to Yolŋu.

The people see Balanda with powerful, superior things that Yolŋu do not understand. For example, for 100 years the origins of gunpowder and its destructive effects have left Yolŋu puzzling, 'Where do the Balanda get this great power from?' They are shocked when told that Balanda 'stole' the idea from the Chinese! Yolŋu assume this powerful black powder must have been the invention of *goŋ-nyanyuk* Balanda (Balanda with the ability to invent and create), or that it came from the land where Balanda originally came from, a land where many sophisticated, mystical forces influence and empower the dominant culture world. Yolŋu don't know how Balanda developed this or any other modern technology or commodity.

When a cultural group like Yolŋu become confused about the things that come from an alien dominant culture, the objects they are in awe of become mystical. Balanda medicines that obviously have superior qualities to their own medicines, for example, are viewed as having almost supernatural qualities. People see them as some sort of Balanda magic. Some Yolŋu even think that perhaps Balanda got this medicine straight from *Waŋarr*. It's not *what* people know that is the problem, but what they *do not* know.

After many years of this type of experience, the people start to see *all* dominant culture knowledge as mystical—even English itself. One Western-educated Yolŋu leader said to me in July 1999, 'I used to believe English was magical, that if I just knew the English words and how to use them, even without really understanding their meaning, [good] things would happen for me.' An elder, also Western-educated, said to me one day, '*Wämut*, can you teach me the right way to pray to God in English so I will not be sick any more?' I asked him what he meant. 'Well,' he replied, 'Yolŋu are sick because we do not know the proper English to talk to God so he can heal us. If you could teach me this English then we will be healthy like Balanda'. He was very surprised that there was no special 'magic' English language.

In the end, Yolŋu are forced to conclude that dominant culture 'education', and the 'knowledge' it relates to, is probably just some form of religious activity rather than a process of true cognition. This is because in general Balanda cannot and have not explained the 'how' and 'why' of their world to Yolŋu. The people come to believe that if you use certain terms in certain ways around particular subjects, you will get a certificate; and when you get this certificate, you will be recognised by the dominant culture and all your needs will be met. A job, housing, a vehicle will all be provided—not because you now have knowledge and are productive, but simply because you have a certificate. True mastery of mystical Balanda knowledge, however, seems impossible for Yolŋu to attain.

Because of ineffective education, Yolŋu learn that ritual, rather than productive action, is all-important in the dominant culture world.

When dominant culture knowledge, and therefore life in the modern world, becomes mystical, Yolŋu are led to another conclusion. Mystical forces need *rituals* to sustain them, so maybe it is rituals that run the dominant culture world. Maybe people come to power, obtain riches and live a long life by the correct observance of rituals rather than by responding to real life forces and events.

A number of features of dominant culture education reinforce this conclusion.

First, the *content* of education is usually determined by the dominant culture. From a Yolŋu perspective, this means that most education starts in a different place from where Yolŋu thinking is at in relation to particular subjects. So the construction of the new knowledge makes no sense to them.

Secondly, the *style* of education concentrates on aspects of learning that ignore real meaning. When, from the point of view of Yolŋu students, dominant culture educators seem to be satisfied with students learning only:

• the sound of words and their correct spelling,

• how the words are used correctly in the sentence structure, and

• what subject the words relate to,

but seemingly give little or no attention to the real meaning of the words or concepts, then the students gain no real knowledge but only an understanding of the 'ritual' relating to that particular subject. In more technical terms – when the dominant culture educators seem to concentrate on the phonology, syntax, morphology and the context of the subject, but largely ignore the semantics, the students are left to conclude that they are being taught some form of ritual related to the subject, not the 'how' and 'why' of the subject matter. Therefore only the learning of ritual around the particular subject occurs, not true cognition.

Thirdly, Yolŋu continually see the dominant culture putting more emphasis on the 'ritual of learning' than on actual cognition. Yolŋu are always being told by teachers and well-meaning Balanda friends: 'If you just get your certificate you'll be okay'—as though the certificate itself had some innate force. Then much pomp and ceremony is expended on the giving of certificates, many dignitaries come and people are convinced to have some form of traditional Yolŋu ceremony. Often all this expense and effort is outlaid while the students are still confused about what they have been studying. Further, the demands of maintaining numbers in training institutions means that students can also be 'minced through the training machine' to keep the institution afloat financially, confirming the people's belief in ritual rather than true cognition as the real purpose of dominant culture education.

There is one other factor that reinforces this 'ritual' view held by Yolŋu of the Balanda world—what I call 'Irish sarcasm'. This permeates dominant Australian culture and runs through most of informal discussion between Yolŋu and dominant culture people when Yolŋu are really looking for answers to serious questions.

'Irish sarcasm' is the end result of many Irish convicts and immigrants forced by hunger and British tyranny to leave Ireland for a new life in Australia, especially in the first century of colonisation. Almost all of these early unwilling settlers were strongly anti-establishment. This contempt for government and authority has invaded contemporary Australian culture. Everything is the government's fault and nobody thinks twice about slinging off against the government, the politicians and the system.

This seems very strange from a Yolŋu perspective. Traditional Yolŋu governments are perceived as holy, not just because of their religious function, but also because of the holy function of maintaining a civilised, peaceful society. 'Irish sarcasm' leaves Yolŋu confused and alienated because they know the government is powerful yet its 'citizens' seem to have no say in it and resort to sarcasm. Yolŋu conclude that there must be no mechanism such as the 'rule of law' or citizen's rights in Balanda government, and therefore it must be some form of dictatorship or rule of the powerful over the powerless. From this Yolŋu perceive that the dominant culture does not run on forces which ordinary people can determine or shape, as does their own culture, so it must be run by rituals of some sort.

All this confusion is compounded because true intellectual dialogue between Yolŋu and Balanda culture fails when communication is not taken seriously. So the people have to rely heavily on observation and on the distorted knowledge they receive through superficial dialogue and many sounds (words) that for them have no meaning.

Because of ineffective education, Yolŋu lose all interest in gaining knowledge.
When knowledge loses meaning, it kills the people's curiosity to learn. If someone tries to understand something but is given more and more confusing information about it, it is not long before they give up trying to learn about that thing. When this happens again and again and you never seem to learn anything, eventually your curiosity is strangled.

Many who experience this blame themselves, naming themselves 'stupid', 'unintelligent' and many other things. When it happens to a whole cultural group, the result is devastating. The people start to question whether it is worth trying to learn at all.

This even affects the way the people look at their own traditional knowledge. For many Yolŋu, traditional knowledge does not work anymore. Traditional trading and economic knowledge is an example of this. At one time Yolŋu produced and traded locally, nationally and internationally. All this has stopped because of the dominant culture's intervention. Yolŋu are now dependent on an economic system they do not understand and that an ineffective education system cannot teach them about.

In this way, knowledge, both contemporary and traditional, becomes confused. The traditional is seen as outdated and irrelevant; the contemporary as mystical and unattainable. This confusion literally kills the people's curiosity. It all seems so useless.

Inappropriate Responses to Given Situations
To bring all this down to earth, let's look at some concrete examples of how ineffective education leads Yolŋu to make inappropriate responses to given health situations.

A Visit to the Doctor
Yolŋu go to the doctor or clinic because they are sick and hope to be given some Balanda medicine to make them better. Sometimes they receive a bottle of medication—say, tablets. On leaving the clinic, some will take one or two tablets and throw the rest in the bin. This is because they see no relationship between the medicine and the condition. They reason: 'If the doctor really wanted me to get better he could give me the right medicine. If I took it just once then it would make me better immediately.'

Here the only knowledge the patient has comes from their cultural knowledge base, including knowledge of the treatment of yaws with penicillin and other experiences where Balanda medicines displayed almost magical effects.

I remember visiting one old man who had been in hospital with chronic scabies. He was sent home with instructions to apply the scabies cream in two days' time, then wait another two days and apply it again. When I visited him, he asked, 'Why can't I just put the cream on now and again tonight? Then I won't have to worry about it anymore.'

His question was quite reasonable from his perspective. He saw no relationship between the 'cause' of his condition and the 'effect' of the medicine or treatment. He did not know that scabies was a living, breeding creature; all he knew was its name. He was thinking that the medicine and its application was some form of magic.

So I told him about scabies. Drawing pictures as I went, I showed him the life cycle of the parasite. I started with what he already knew.

'How do turtles lay their eggs?' I asked.

'In a hole the turtle has made in the sand, a big mob all at one time.'

'And how does a bird lay its eggs?'

'One a day until there's a handful or two.'

I then told him that one scabies female has lots and lots of eggs, which it lays in a hole it burrows under a person's skin, two or three each day. It takes the young scabies a few days to hatch and come out of the burrows—maybe three to five days. I explained that the 'medicine' cream was a poison to these scabies, but it might not kill off all the eggs that are down the burrows in the skin.

As soon as I had said this, the old man responded. 'I can see it now. I have to wait for the eggs to hatch out before I put the next lot of cream on.' He was now happy to comply with what the doctor told him because he could see the reason why.

Some time later, when the old man got the parasite again, a nursing sister showed him scabies taken from his own bed sheets under a microscope. When he actually saw the creatures, he said to her, 'Quick! Where's that medicine?' Seeing is believing!

'Cause and effect' had returned to his thinking about scabies. Without this understanding he would have continued to make inappropriate responses to his health situation.

But Our Children Grew Bigger . . .

One day in the early 1980s I asked a group of Yolŋu mothers why they thought many of their babies and young children were suffering from malnutrition. The very old women present explained.

'When we first came to the mission from our traditional estates, we fed our babies and children on Balanda food like white flour, golden syrup and white sugar,' they said. 'The babies and children grew really big, bigger than any Yolŋu children had ever grown before. So we thought it must be this Balanda food—it must make people grow big and strong. Then we noticed that Balanda and their children always seemed fit and well, so we thought: *Maybe if we feed our children* **only** *on Balanda food they will be even fitter, bigger and stronger.*'

So the women now fed their children only on Balanda food. But they were very confused. 'Why are our babies and little children now so small and sick and crying all the time?' they asked.

I questioned the old women about how much Balanda food and how much traditional food they ate at the time they first came to the mission. What they had failed to take into account was that they were still eating many of their traditional foods in those early days. Balanda food was used mainly as a supplement when they could not get to their estates or during seasonal variations when their estates were in a lean period. So access to *some* Balanda food gave them a continuous supply of food. Eaten in this way, it didn't create a problem—in fact it was very good.

However, with the coming of welfare benefits (mainly unemployment benefits), the women thought they would have money to buy Balanda food all the time to make their children fit and healthy. Some families even left their homeland estates when they began receiving unemployment payments and moved as close as they could to the community store so they could buy Balanda food.

It is clear that, like all caring parents, these Yolŋu mothers were deeply concerned for their children's welfare. They wanted to know what food was best. But the only information they received about this issue came from their own observation, and these observations led them astray.

Interaction with Balanda about this issue was hard and generally unhelpful. The people saw that when Balanda were offered traditional Yolŋu foods, they turned up their noses and made noises of disgust. (After many bad experiences of Balanda responses to their food, Yolŋu are now very reticent to offer any of it to Balanda.) Balanda named Yolŋu food 'bush tucker', implying it was somehow inferior to Balanda food. Then in the 1960s the Balanda set up home-care centres where the people were encouraged to cook Balanda food. From all this, the people concluded that the sophisticated Balanda deemed their food to be worthless rubbish. In contrast, Balanda food came in fancy packaging from unknown, maybe mystical origins.

With this thinking, the people made a cultural adaptation to eating the supposedly more sophisticated Balanda food and began naming their traditional food *wakiŋu ŋatha* (food that is profane or inferior, forgotten and left behind). In the 1980s some Yolŋu would eat no traditional foods on principle. Today many community-based/mission-influenced Yolŋu will still call their traditional foods *wakiŋu ŋatha*, though now they do not attribute all the negative aspects to it.

Because the people received very little objective evidence about the true value of their own foods, and no objective knowledge about Balanda foods, they made inappropriate decisions in the area of good eating. This problem continues today.[106]

Sweet Equals Good Food?

In April 1997 I was asked by the council of a Yolŋu community to facilitate a meeting between Balanda supervisors and community leaders. One of the Balanda, who had lived on the community for years and worked in a take-away shop, asked, 'Why do Yolŋu mothers always buy their children Coca-Cola and lollies? Don't they know they are rubbish? Sometimes all the money the mother has goes on Coca-Cola and lollies.' He went on, 'My heart cries when I sell them this. They could be buying something else with good food value in it.'

I introduced this question to the Yolŋu in the group. 'What do you think of Coca-Cola when you see the adverts on TV? Do you think it is good or bad for you, in terms of food value?'

The majority of Yolŋu responded, 'We think it's good for us. We see all the healthy kids and they do all those healthy things—sometimes fantastic things—in the advertisements.'

I then asked them, in both Yolŋu Matha and English, if they knew that Coca-Cola was a 'false'[107] juice and had drugs in it which could be addictive. Only two of the ten Yolŋu in the room said they knew this. The rest were greatly surprised.

Next I asked someone to explain why many Yolŋu buy lollies for their children. 'Because it is sweet, the people think it is good food,' one Yolŋu replied. I explained to the Balanda present that all traditional sweet foods were good food. Yolŋu assume that sweet Balanda food must be the same. They do not know about such things as artificial sweeteners, artificial colours and imitation flavours. Because the Yolŋu cultural knowledge base is not complete in this area, discernment is impossible.

This is further complicated by the fact that much of the dialogue about food with the dominant culture is transmitted through TV advertising. Because many Yolŋu have lost the private enterprise mind-set they had before dominant culture intervention, having been institutionalised through mission and government settlements, they see the ownership of property and goods as resting mainly in the hands of 'government'. This includes the TV station and the products it advertises. Many assume it is the government telling them to drink Coca Cola, eat confectionery and so on. When they learn that products like this can contribute to diabetes, renal failure and chronic heart condition, many Yolŋu say, 'That's funny, the government is complaining that they are spending so much money on health while at the same time they're killing us.' Again, the lack of objective knowledge about the world is leading the people to make inappropriate responses to a given situation.

Is Knowledge and Thinking at an End for Yolŋu?

For many Yolŋu, 'knowledge' and 'thinking' *is* at an end. All they have left is confusion from long years of conflict, war and the non-recognition of their lands and resources. Their languages and intellectual knowledge are not taken seriously. Balanda teachers do not understand their world-view or show any interest in their cultural knowledge base. Strange communication mores and 'secret' English make it almost impossible to understand what dominant culture educators are talking about. So both formal or informal attempts at learning from the dominant culture continue to prove futile.

The cognitive life of the people is negated because the dominant culture sees its mainstream educational processes as the *only* educational reality. It is as though education is seen as some sort of mechanical process or magical event, where a teacher talks in a foreign language and somehow the children learn through 'verbal osmosis'. Of course, when education is done this way, it constantly fails.

The 'catch-up' in knowledge that Yolŋu need can only occur when the dominant culture and Yolŋu work *together* to achieve it. A level playing field needs to be created so that Yolŋu do not have to do all the work to obtain this knowledge. They need dominant culture people who already know this knowledge to come as teachers or trainers. People who are *experts in communication*, prepared to first listen to Yolŋu, learn their language and world-view, and then start from where they are at.[108] Then together through dialogue the trainers and the people can truly fill in the knowledge gaps that at present leave Yolŋu exposed and confused. As Paulo Freire wrote,

> Only dialogue, which requires critical thinking, is also capable of generating critical thinking. Without dialogue there is no communication, and without communication there can be no true education.[109]

This kind of effective cross-cultural/cross-language education is impossible without specialised training. Until this training happens, ineffective education will continue to waste human potential and resources in the mono-cultural, monolingual march forward, leaving the Yolŋu, through no fault of their own, straggling far behind - convinced that the age of knowledge and thinking is at an end.

PART THREE

THE COST OF BEING DIFFERENT

Yolŋu culture is very different from dominant Australian culture. This difference creates all sorts of trouble for Yolŋu as they try to relate to the world that now surrounds them.

In Part Three I talk about the cost of being different. Yolŋu pay a heavy price for this difference that can be measured in the quality of life they experience daily. When not understood by *both* cultural groups, this difference leads to massive confusion.

To talk about this confusion I will focus on three different areas:

Chapter 9 examines how traditional health and healing systems conflict with the contemporary dominant culture system of health and healing. Ancient Yolŋu health wisdom has been progressively marginalised as 'primitive' and 'superstitious', but the result is that the very people with authority in these matters in Yolŋu society are no longer able to contribute to the care of their people.

In *Chapter 10* I look at one of the most destructive influences on Yolŋu: the dominant culture welfare mentality. Welfare has effectively imprisoned Yolŋu. The people's economic life, once so wide-ranging and vibrant with commerce and trade, has been reduced to sitting around waiting for social security cheques. Welfare has created a 'living hell' where the people live with a constant sense of hopelessness.

Other factors besides the welfare mentality help us understand the heavy cost of being different.

Chapter 11 looks at different psychosocial phenomena that weigh heavily on Yolŋu, including culture shock, future shock and the multigenerational legacy of past trauma. These phenomena have been well-analysed in other contexts, but their presence in Yolŋu experience has been scarcely noted.

9
CHAPTER

'Witch Doctor is the Real Doctor?'

Health, Healing and Traditional Authority

I have only recorded and analyzed phenomena, claims and beliefs. My object has been to show, first, that Aboriginal medicine men, so far from being rogues, charlatans, or ignoramuses, are men of high degree, that is, men who have taken a degree in the secret life beyond that taken by most adult males— a step that implies discipline, mental training, courage, and perseverance; second, that they are men of respected, and often outstanding, personality . . . In brief, Aboriginal men of high degree are a channel of life.

A. P. Elkin[110]

Before European contact Yolŋu had a health system that took care of most of their health needs. They had health professionals and a rich cultural knowledge base that gave them the ability to maintain healthy living. Today a casual observer could mistakenly think the people have no traditional health knowledge and no health professionals in their ranks. With the disease and general morbidity rates through the roof and getting worse, it could be concluded that the people's cultural heritage was deficient.

Like A. P. Elkin I know this is not the case. So what has happened to this wealth of ancient knowledge and to these warrior-health professionals who once were so revered?

It seems the years of contact with dominant Australian culture have left Yolŋu so confused about what knowledge is real knowledge and whether their traditional doctors are evil or not, that they no longer know 'witch doctor is the real doctor'.

Traditional Yolŋu Health Matters

Traditionally health and healing for Yolŋu covered a wide range of subjects. These included knowledge of:

- *Philosophy and fables pertaining to healthy lifestyle*, for example: 'The ones who rise early and immerse themselves in the mist of the morning will grow strong and tall quickly.'

- *Food pertaining to good health*: Yolŋu have always had knowledge of food groups and taught the need to eat from these groups in a balanced way. The people also know special foods—they know, for example, that the brains and livers of animals, fish and birds are good food for babies, sick people and the elderly. Pregnant mothers are required to follow certain food restrictions. Some shellfish have a cleansing affect on the body and blood, and so on.

- *Disease and sicknesses themselves.*

- *The pharmacological effects* of herbs, fauna and aquatic life. These include leaves, bark, wood and herbs, together with parts of fish or shellfish, ash from fires and so on. Traditionally these were processed together in a particular way according to the law to create medicines.

- *Poisonous and non-poisonous substances.* All known substances that existed in the people's world prior to Balanda arriving had been classified into poisonous and non-poisonous groups. Only a few post-contact substances have been classified to date.

- *Known unhealthy areas within Yolŋu estates,* generally called in English 'sickness country' or 'sacred areas', but called in Yolŋu Matha *dhuyu nuŋgat wäŋa* (holy restricted places) or *Madayin wäŋa* (law places).

- *Medical procedures to eliminate or treat physical ailments.* Many of these procedures are completely unknown to Western medicine.

- *Procedures to stop the transference of disease from the dead to the living.* This is the concept of *goŋ-wukundi*, which says that when people touch a dead body their hands are considered untouchable; they can't feed themselves and so on until a ceremonial washing process is carried out.

- *The life force within—märr* (spiritual power/strength), and how a person's *birrimbirr* (spirit), *ŋayaŋu* (soul/personality/emotional base/inner-person) and *rumbal* (body) can be kept healthy or even increased in strength by the expenditure of sweat and releasing of this *märr*.

- *How to identify attacks of foul play or sorcery.* The knowledge of how to check a body or clothes of a deceased or sick person for sorcery.

- *How to care for dying relatives.* A whole system of care for very sick and dying people allowed the close relatives space for quality time.

- *Investigative procedures* to ascertain the cause of death of a clan member.

All this knowledge and the correct procedures pertaining to health and healing is encapsulated in the Yolŋu law, the *Madayin*. The *Madayin* is much like the laws of other ancient cultures, similar to the Muslim's Koran or the Jewish Torah (Mosaic law). Within the Koran or the laws of Moses there are laws relating to politics, economics, social organisation, health and theology. And so it is with the *Maḏayin*. The knowledge of the *Maḏayin* is taught to all Yolŋu. They are also taught that if you live according to this law you will have a long, happy, healthy life.

Of the many aspects of health law in the *Maḏayin,* we will concentrate on two: the classification of food and the role of traditional healers.

The Yolŋu Classification of Foods

Traditionally Yolŋu divided foods (*maranhu*) into two main groups, with five or six sub-groups. These groups are *murnyaŋ'* (carbohydrate foods) and *gonyil* (protein foods).

Table 2. The Yolŋu Classification of Foods

MARANHU (foods)	
Murnyaŋ' (plant or vegetable food) Alternative names: **Dhäkaḏatj, Ŋayaŋay', Buku-bira'**	**Gonyil** (meat, shellfish, eggs) Alternative names: **Matha-yal, Merrpal', Matha-bira, Ŋänarr-yal**
1. Borum—fruits	**1. Warrakan'**—land animals and birds
2. Guku—bee products	**2. Miyapunu**—marine mammals
3. Ŋatha—root foods	**3. Maranydjalk**—rays and sharks
4. Maŋutji Ŋatha—seeds	**4. Guya**—fish
5. Mudhuŋay—cycad foodstuffs	**5. Maypal**—shellfish, crabs
	6. Mapu—eggs

© ARDS Inc. 1996

The old people would talk about the need to eat from both *murnyaŋ'* and *gonyil* foods groups and the need to supplement their diet with *gapu* (fresh water). While this balance was maintained, the people knew they were eating correctly.

Every day the people would try to find suitable food from both groups. If only one group was readily available, they would seek out food from the other group, even if it meant travelling to another clan's estate and obtaining the needed food from them under *buku-djugu'* (verbal contract). For example, if one clan had a lot of *gonyil* food on their estate and no yams (from the *murnyaŋ'* group), they would go to a neighbouring clan and establish a *buku-djugu'* for the exchange of *gonyil* food for yams or other *murnyaŋ'* food. This *djugu'* might last right through a season, allowing the first clan to regenerate their own *gärul* (yam garden) for the next season.

Marrŋgitj—the Authorised Healers and Doctors

In the past health knowledge was taught to the whole clan as a general subject, so that all had some knowledge. Some, however, were selected for special training and instruction. These people were chosen from within the clan because they displayed a special gift in the area of retaining knowledge and/or in the area of healing. These 'apprentices' were nurtured with great care by their tutors. When their healing knowledge and skill was seen to be effective, they were recognised in their clan's legal system as herbalists, midwives and healers/doctors. As in all societies, the people who could practise these great skills were rewarded for their ability through payments in kind, and with privileged status within the clan and indeed across the whole of Yolŋu society.

Yolŋu called these medical experts *marrŋgitj*. The word *marrŋgitj* carried connotations of healer, person of great knowledge, doctor, professor. Men and women who reached the state of *marrŋgitj* gained extensive amounts of knowledge. Rather like doctors in Western society, the healers were considered to be in a class above ordinary citizens. They were consulted on all matters relating to health and healing.

These *marrŋgitj*—that is, the few who are still left—know medical methods currently unknown to the Western world. I personally have had an illness successfully treated by a *marrŋgitj* when the Western health system had no answers for my condition. I have also witnessed Yolŋu patients who, having attended the community health clinic and getting no satisfactory solutions to their health problems, have gone to their clan's *marrŋgitj* and had their health issues resolved that same day.

There is a gender division among these healers/doctors. The *marrŋgitj* women are skilled midwives. The men, on the other hand, learn how to manipulate the body to heal. Both know the art of being herbalists/chemists, although many of the women excel in this area.

Herbalist practice and the manipulation and healing are both conducted in public, but the knowledge of birthing and its associated practices is totally the women's privilege. This is kept secret from the male population even today. Similarly, men have privileged knowledge in the area of politics and law. Traditionally the male *marrŋgitj* would also get involved in resolving disputes or misunderstandings and were the main people involved in carrying out investigative procedures after the death of a clan member. Their words in these cases held great sway, as there was no greater earthly authority.

Unfortunately, these great *marrŋgitj*, both men and women, have lost their status today. Only a few remain and their profession is almost forgotten.

Confusion in a Balanda-Controlled World

Much has changed for Yolŋu since Balanda came to their lands. Besides wars and conflicts, Balanda brought new thinking and practices in many areas, including health and healing. Yolŋu are confused about whether or not their old health ways are any good.

This confusion is hard for dominant culture people to appreciate. To Balanda it seems strange that Yolŋu would let outside influences invade their culture. But this invasion has been very subtle and in most cases unintentional. It is the result of two cultures colliding.

To make it easier to appreciate how this has happened I want to discuss a number of issues around the themes of the traditional food groups and the traditional healers/doctors in the hope of creating more understanding.

Old Knowledge Rediscovered

Although in recent years my colleagues and I have spent much time in dialogue with Yolŋu on health matters, only gradually has the issue of traditional food groups surfaced. This knowledge is very significant, but because of the denigration of traditional ways and the rejection of them even by many Yolŋu, it is in danger of disappearing.

The information finally came to light when an old man saw his own live blood under a microscope while we were teaching a group of Yolŋu about their immune systems. He could see his blood cells were very different from everyone else's—the red cells were like little shattered stars (echinocytes) instead of the normal round, doughnut shape.

'Why is my blood like that, *Wämut?*' he asked.

We took another sample to make sure we had not traumatised the first one, but it was the same.

"What do you normally eat?' I asked.

'Only tea and damper.'

'Why?'

'Because I have no teeth left and I find it too hard to chew things that are hard.'

'But uncle,' I protested (he was my uncle in relationship terms), 'you need to *mel-manapan ḻuka* (eat the eyes out of all different types of food).'

He nodded his head. 'I will get my wife to make me some soups so I can *mel-manapan ḻuka.*'[111]

About three weeks later, he approached our female educator while she was working with a group of women. He asked her to put a drop of his blood under the microscope to see what his red blood cells were like. To his great delight, the cells were a good doughnut shape. 'Now I can see what food is for!' he exclaimed and went home a happy man.

A month later this man was talking to the executive officer of our organisation, himself a Yolŋu man, and started to tell him about these traditional food groups. Our executive officer got very excited. 'Now the old man can see the reason for food, and he's gone back into traditional law to make sense of the results,' he said. 'He sees that our traditional law has told us how to live in a healthy way from the beginning of time.'

While the concept of eating a balanced diet was once common knowledge for Yolŋu, it is not so today. For many years Balanda did not know Yolŋu had this knowledge, so they talked to them about *five* food groups in a balanced diet, not two. Yolŋu saw no relationship between this idea and the knowledge in their cultural knowledge base. If dominant culture educators had first learned about the people's food groups and *then* integrated the five food groups information into this existing knowledge, I believe the people's understanding of what makes for a balanced diet, as well as how they feel about their own foods, would have been very different.

This is easy for me to say now, but in the past I was no better. When dieticians visiting Ramingining in the late 1970s and early 1980s asked me for advice on teaching the people about balanced diet, I was no use at all. I knew nothing about the traditional food groups. We tried everything to improve the people's diet, from getting them to add raisins and dried vegetables to their dampers to plain, old-fashioned harassment. But at no time did it occur to us that the people would have traditional knowledge to unlock the problem.

As in so many areas, without this vital information communication has foundered. Most existing food charts are illustrated exclusively with Balanda foods; only a very small number of charts in recent years have shown traditional foods. An advertisement on Northern Territory television during 1997/98, aimed at getting Aboriginal people to eat more fresh food 'because it is good for you', ended up giving Yolŋu the wrong message because the only fresh fruit and vegetables shown were Western. The people then assumed their own foods must be not as healthy. This kind of approach in effect educates the people to denigrate their own foods and to believe that only white-fella food is good and healthy. The advertisement needed to show both traditional and Western fruit and vegetables.

Tragically, many Yolŋu, especially young people, have cast aside their traditional information as 'old hat', unsophisticated, or irrelevant in the modern Western world. Many also see their traditional healer/doctors in the same light.

An Encounter with the Local 'Witch Doctor'

I will never forget my first encounter with a traditional Yolŋu doctor. About six months after my arrival in Arnhem Land, the Ramingining community fell into the grip of a 'Hong Kong' 'flu. Three old people died in one week (in those days people died in their 80s, not their mid-40s as they do today). We had a clinic about the size of a small bathroom, and I was in there one afternoon helping the health sister break up aspirin—our supplies were running short and we had 300 patients.

While we were doing this, a baby girl was brought in with an extremely high temperature. The sister did everything she could think of, but the baby grew hotter and hotter. In the end she started convulsing. When this happened, the sister broke down and ran out of the clinic, screaming and in tears. I was left with the shaking child and the terrified mother standing at the door. I continued swabbing the baby with a wet washer as I had seen the sister doing, but I was horrified. I had never seen convulsions and I had never seen a human being die, but I was sure that I was going to see this beautiful little girl die that day.

As I stood there for a long, desperate moment, my mind raced back to my childhood, wishing I had read more of my mother's medical handbook, which I had glanced through only occasionally. *If only I'd spent more of my idle moments really reading it, perhaps I'd be able to help these poor primitive people now,* I thought. My desperation deepened as the child continued convulsing, and I starting praying frantically, asking God to send me some help.

Suddenly a big, black hand was placed on my shoulder. It pulled me back out of the way. A large, powerful man took control of the situation, manipulating the baby's legs and arms with quick, flicking strokes. Within seconds the baby coughed and lay calm. I reached my hand over and felt her; she lay quietly as though asleep.

I looked up in absolute shock at the man standing beside me. His primitive look disappeared and I knew I was looking at a man of great knowledge and integrity. He said nothing but just looked back at this stunned white fella. Then, with a hint of a smile, he left.

The sister came back in. Seeing the baby lying calm, she took her temperature. It was close to normal.

I found my voice. 'Who was that man?'

'Oh, he's one of the local "witch doctors",' she quipped over her shoulder.

This shocked me. *Why would God send me a 'witch doctor'? Don't they work for the opposition?* The sister echoed my thoughts. 'It's a bad day when their evil work shows up the limitations of Western medicine. It's one of our jobs here to get the people to have faith in Western medicine rather than the superstitious dealings of the "witch doctors". Otherwise the people will always live in fear.'

She's right, of course, I thought as I went on with my job of breaking up willow bark extract (sorry, aspirin). Or was she?

Traditional Practices—Holy or Evil?

What has influenced people like this sister to think this way? It seems that when Europeans travelled all over the world in their quest for trade, they met many different tribal people who had 'strange practices'. And practices we find strange we easily misinterpret.

One such practice was the keeping of the bones of deceased loved ones. Many cultures shared this custom. The bones kept were usually the skull and the two femurs (thigh bones). These would be cleaned meticulously and stored. Yolŋu also practised this art, wrapping the bones in the paper bark of the melaleuca tree for safe storage.

When Europeans saw these bones carried by various tribal peoples, they tried to understand the practice. Not being able to communicate clearly with those they met, they concluded, from their own history and experience, that these bones were carried for evil purposes. Somewhere in European history, these bones became symbols of evil—the 'skull and crossbones'. Today if you draw these three bones on a whiteboard and ask Balanda what they mean, they will answer, 'Danger, pirates, poison, death.' But if you ask Yolŋu to be really honest and not respond to the peer pressure of the mixed group, they will say, 'Holy, very precious, something that we love'—the very opposite of the Balanda understanding. In fact, Yolŋu used the bones to remind them of their loved ones, sometimes carrying them for a number of decades before performing the final funeral ceremony. There was *never* any suggestion that these precious, holy bones could be used for evil purposes such as sorcery.

The roles in Yolŋu culture of the *marrŋgitj* (healer) and *galka* (sorcerer) are completely different. Some *marrŋgitj* may get involved in illegal activities, just as some Balanda doctors do. But if a *marrŋgitj* is caught doing *galka djäma* (sorcery), he is treated as a murderer and will be prosecuted as such under the *Maḏayin* law. When these two are confused, and great *marrŋgitj* are named as 'evil' by the dominant culture, all the knowledge they would usually nurture and teach is also named as evil.

It could be that Balanda observers have confused these two roles because they have seen that all *marrŋgitj* have knowledge of sorcery, and have concluded that sorcery is central to the traditional doctor's role. In fact, *marrŋgitj* know about sorcery and how to detect it in the same way that dominant culture doctors know what drugs and procedures can kill a human being. This knowledge is necessary so that any danger to the healing process can be detected. They must know if they themselves or someone else is causing harm to a patient. Similarly, the *marrŋgitj* learn knowledge of sorcery so they can detect if someone is trying to kill, or has killed, another person.

When I was taught about the *marrŋgitj* art of healing, my Yolŋu teacher also taught me how to look for and guard against signs of sorcery. To teach me this, he actually explained to me how sorcery was done. But I was also taught in the same lesson that it was a vile, repulsive, illegal act. Many Yolŋu see it as worse than homicide because the killer does not have the courage to face his victim. I was told over and over again that to practise sorcery was against the *Maḏayin* and would not be tolerated by anybody.

So What Has Happened to the Traditional Doctors?

Traditional Yolŋu society treated the role of the healer/doctor as central to all issues of health and healing, but this is not so in Arnhem Land today. The *marrŋgitj* role has been usurped, forced underground and almost eliminated. This devaluing of traditional health practice and its practitioners has serious ramifications.

Chief Medical Officers Locked Out

Now that the male *marryŋitj* have been named by dominant Balanda culture as 'witch doctors', many of the people themselves have come to believe that their traditional systems actually *are* what they have been named. This is especially true for Western-educated Yolŋu. This naming has dragged the 'Chief Medical Officers' of traditional Yolŋu society down to the level of evildoers who must practise their trade underground, like criminals.

In the mission days, this thinking meant that the *marryŋitj* were locked out of the medical clinics on most communities. Even in the late 1970s, when the Ramingining council asked the Northern Territory Health Department to employ two male *marryŋitj* in the community clinic, the officer-in-charge for the region responded, 'Only over my dead body.'

With this loss of status, the *marryŋitj* have also lost the trust of many of their people. Now Yolŋu must trust dominant culture doctors who have a strange way and a foreign language.

The Midwives Also Lose Control

As already noted, in Yolŋu society the traditional midwife role is carried out solely by women. Their women's traditional universities centre on this knowledge and practice. Because of the secret nature of this subject, I will only record here what is general, public knowledge (it is the dominant culture, not Yolŋu, that has forced this once-secret information into the open, because the dominant culture sees birthing and all related issues as public knowledge). I would be happier if I did not have to say these things, but the cultural clash makes it necessary so we can see the mistakes that have been made and look for ways to correct them.

When the time comes for any woman to give birth, especially for the first time, she wants to be close to the people she trusts. Traditionally Yolŋu women put their trust in the senior women of the clan, who cared for her throughout this life-changing adventure. This built bonds between them that would remain for life.

At these times in a younger woman's life, the senior women displayed great skill in this area of great mysteries. When the young mothers returned from their traditional 'hospital' setting to their families with the newborn infant, they were not only justly proud of their newborn; they were also proud of being Yolŋu and proud of their senior women. Many would dream of the day when they in turn would be the midwives of their clan, able to walk tall as they helped the younger women in their time of need.

This bonding created a relationship that allowed the young mothers to go freely to the older women for advice on womanhood and motherhood. There was, of course, no communication problem between these women, so skills were effectively taught in a culturally appropriate way.

This was all to change—first on the missions as more babies were born in the controlled setting of the clinics (something which became mission policy on most stations), then in the late 1970s when all mission clinics were transferred to the Northern Territory Health Department. From that point it became policy for all expecting Yolŋu mothers to be sent to Nhulunbuy hospital so their babies could be delivered in a safe environment.

Thus the esteem given to the female *marrŋgitj* has been slowly replaced by dependence on 'experts' from the dominant culture. The message is clear: Yolŋu are not intelligent or knowledgeable enough to be involved in this 'mystery of life' any more.

Of course, hospital birthing was seen by the dominant culture as necessary to decrease infant and maternal morbidity and mortality rates, and it has successfully done that. But the policy has had other disastrous consequences. For one thing, because of communication difficulties, the new mothers find it almost impossible to learn anything from the dominant culture professionals. Even more seriously, the exclusion of the female *marrŋgitj* destroyed both the status of these senior women and the knowledge that they used to teach the younger women about womanhood and motherhood. The intellectual and emotional bonding that occurred between the young mothers and these elite elders is now impossible. The policy may have saved a few lives, but it now sends Yolŋu children back to live in knowledge-deprived, dependent communities.

I believe this in turn has contributed to the high rates of 'failure to thrive' and 'malnutrition' in children now seen in many Yolŋu communities. Back in the 1970s leading Yolŋu women said that taking away their birthing rights—the central event in the female domain—would lead to some of the young women having difficulty keeping their babies and children healthy, and they were right.

There are only a handful of these professional old women left. Some Yolŋu women prefer the new way; others wish the old ways were intact. We have divided the people on this subject. Many of the old women who have died did so without passing on the ancient knowledge that kept their clan strong for generations. The Yolŋu women's university, which was built around the art of midwifery, is under massive threat, putting all the associated knowledge of womanhood and motherhood at risk.

The implications are far-reaching. Now many Yolŋu mothers today are untrained and unmotivated to learn, and their children seem destined to a poor and crippled future. Young women no longer look forward to being senior elders but live in a world where the status and honour that once accompanied old age has been replaced with the glorification of youth—the getting of certificates in the mainstream education system. 'Specialists' from the dominant culture have usurped the position that once came after a lifetime of practice and learning.

The Cultural Clash

Because this mystery of life and the information that goes with it is women's business, men will have nothing to do with it. This restriction is so strong that Yolŋu men will not even allude to the existence of the information. Consequently Yolŋu women have had to suffer insults and shame in complete silence. (The same may be said for Yolŋu men when they have not been able to talk about the secret/sacred nature of their political law.) They have not even been able to call on Yolŋu men to help them fight for their rights.

However, because Balanda are also cultural beings, they find it almost impossible to work within these Yolŋu restrictions. Let me illustrate the problem this creates.

In 1997 at a conference in Darwin, I was asked to give input on the subject of communication between medical officers and Aboriginal patients for whom English was a second language. Many of the Balanda specialists present worked in paediatrics and were concerned about the 'failure to thrive' syndrome among Aboriginal children. I decided to use an illustration from their field to show how health information can fail to communicate and is culturally inappropriate as well.

I focused on a poster produced by the Territory Health Services depicting an Aboriginal woman smoking. The smoke was shown going down into her womb where the baby was breathing it in.

The first problem with the poster, I explained, was that it was culturally inappro-priate because it showed a pregnant woman and the baby in the womb. Such information is sacred for women and therefore men should not see it. Yet the Health Department was displaying it in hospitals and clinics across the Northern Territory (and later, in early 1999, even in a television advertisement). Any Yolŋu man seeing the poster would be offended and would probably think he had just entered a sacred women-only area. Yolŋu women would also be offended by its existence.

The second problem was that the poster actually gave Aboriginal women a totally wrong picture. Many Yolŋu women thought the smoke was going into the baby's lungs. This, of course, is medically incorrect; but more to the point, it did not convince Yolŋu mothers that smoking was bad for their babies. They saw no problem with smoke going into their own lungs, so why would it be a problem for their babies?

Of course, I explained, if Aboriginal women were asked by dominant culture people if smoking was bad for them or their unborn babies, they would usually say, 'Yes, it is bad'. But this would either be because they were one of a small number who now believed smoking was bad, or because they had been told many times by medical people that smoking was bad and answered 'yes' to avoid being shamed. At the same time, they would not be intellectually convinced and would continue to smoke.

After checking that there were no Aboriginal people who could be offended in the room (health workers or others), I told the specialists how they could get the true picture across to Aboriginal mothers (in the privacy of a consultation). They should *use the correct medical information*. This would convince Yolŋu mothers because it fitted with their world-view. 'Simply tell them the truth about the chemical affects of nicotine on the biology of the baby's internal feeding system,' I said. I knew from experience that when Yolŋu mothers hear this information, especially in their own language, they are horrified because they see immediately that they are starving their babies.

This example was a clear illustration of the cultural clash between Balanda and Yolŋu over restricted information, and a problem which occurred soon after that, drove the point home.

The very next day the same specialists gathered again. But this time the group had changed—a number of Aboriginal people, both male and female, had joined us. Apparently oblivious to the presence of two Aboriginal men, one of the specialists addressed a question to an Aboriginal woman: how many Aboriginal women knew the truth about the information I had shared the previous day? This information had been conveyed in a closed and privileged situation. The answer he received was not clear, perhaps because the woman wanted to avoid the culturally insensitive question.

It seems that when dominant culture people are told that certain information is privileged or of a sacred/restricted nature, they find it hard to comprehend the importance of this and have extreme difficulty treating it as private. This kind of cultural violation occurs on a daily basis for Yolŋu women. They suffer it in silence.

The Disappearance of Knowledge

Some Balanda ask, 'If the traditional healers/doctors had so much knowledge, why don't they just stand up and teach their people?' But it is not that simple.

For Yolŋu, as for most oral societies, there is a cardinal rule about the handing on of knowledge: *knowledge of high value is not taught to those who do not appreciate its value.* Another teacher said 2000 years ago, 'Don't throw pearls before swine.' With increasing numbers of Yolŋu accepting the dominant culture view that their traditional ways are rubbish or even evil, the *marrŋgitj* of Arnhem Land have great difficulty finding interested and trustworthy students. Sadly, this means the remaining *marrŋgitj* will probably take their secrets to the grave.

I do not know of one *marrŋgitj* employed in a health clinic in Arnhem Land. I know one herbalist who is employed as a cleaner and only one Aboriginal health worker who has learned both the traditional healing profession and Western medicine. Some say, 'The people need to change, leave the ways of the past and get on with the future'. But the painful complexities of the Yolŋu health crisis will not be solved by such 'lecturing'. We need to help Yolŋu find a way to combine their traditional medical systems with the contemporary. Only when the two are working together, complementing each other, will we see advancement in the people's health.

The Question of Law and Authority

Some may think that the place formerly occupied by *marrŋgitj* in Yolŋu society can now be taken by Aboriginal health workers, but the cold, hard fact is that health workers usually receive more authority from the dominant culture to practise medicine than they receive from the *Maḏayin* law. This creates a traditional legal minefield that health workers must negotiate daily.

To fully explain the question of law and authority and its effect on the people would take volumes, but I will say a few things here.

Confusion About Dominant Culture Systems of Law

It must be said that Yolŋu are very confused about the real state of law in contemporary Australia. From the comments of Yolŋu leaders, it seems they accept that Balanda and their law are here to stay. But the shape and content of this law is a complete mystery to them.

Some time before 1953, a Murinbata Aboriginal named Muta quoted the following verse to anthropologist W. E. H. Stanner:

> White man got no dreaming,
>
> Him go 'nother way.
>
> White man, him go different.
>
> Him got road belong himself.[112]

If we change the word 'dreaming' to 'system of law', we get a better picture of what this old man was saying:

> White man got no system of law,
>
> Him go 'nother way.
>
> White man, him go different.
>
> Him got road belong himself.

It seems that Muta believed 'white men'

• do not have a system of law;

• live in a way different from Aboriginal people;

• are not ruled by law, but are a law unto themselves.

This is the Yolŋu perspective as well. To Yolŋu there is no real process of law in this country and therefore no protection for its citizens under a system of law. To illustrate: in March 1998, the Northern Territory Minister for Health visited some of the communities in Arnhem Land to talk about the kava issue. During this visit the question was raised in nearly every community: 'When will kava be banned? When will new laws controlling the use of kava come into force?' In the people's minds, the Minister could just 'say' and the police would 'do it' that day. In other words, they saw no rule of law in the Balanda culture—only a rule of powerful individuals who can change the rules of the game as they want.

So Yolŋu are caught between two systems, one based on a clear 'rule of law' and the other seemingly capricious, vague and incomprehensible. Dominant culture people who say, 'Yolŋu should just decide what law they live under' or 'Yolŋu just have to accept things and change' need to understand the depth of this problem. When you are a citizen of a nation, you are not free to decide whether you will live under its law or not, and this is especially so for Yolŋu regarding their *Maḏayin* law, which to them is supremely important and holy. Yolŋu still assent by a ceremonial process to the ancient *Maḏayin* law of their clans, but neither they nor their forefathers have ever assented to contemporary British/Australian law!

To make matters worse, there is no political alliance between traditional Yolŋu parliaments and the Balanda parliaments of this land. This has enormous ramifications. Imagine Australia without clearly defined legal alliances between the separate states of the Commonwealth. Without clear understandings established through the correct processes of law, our nation would disintegrate. Nothing would work. States would not only have angry words with each other; they would probably go to war (as was actually suggested before Federation).[113] Similarly, it is impossible to imagine the arrangements for trade and defence between Australia and other nations without such alliances. All these processes depend on legally enforceable alliances that have passed through the proper channels and been encoded in law.

If you can visualise the chaos for Australia without such alliances, perhaps you can see why Yolŋu have lost so much control. Their communities are in a state of legal crisis because there is no formal recognition by the dominant culture of the traditional legal processes that have existed on these lands for thousands of years.

This legal nightmare impacts on everything we are discussing in this book. The non-recognition of Yolŋu law is a deep underlying cause of the malaise we see in Arnhem Land. It is the *root cause* of most of the social problems and leads to continual frustration in the area of community management. It also impacts heavily on health and healing.

Imagine trying to run any organisation or government department without clear legal demarcations. It would be impossible. Yet this is the current legal situation for Yolŋu. No-one knows who has what authority to do what anymore.

'Who Ever Asked Us?'
The following story illustrates how this legal confusion affects the health of a community.

One day, when my boss and I were visiting one of the Arnhem Land communities, we were asked to attend a meeting with a group of traditional leaders of the clans on that community. They wanted to talk about a recent confrontation at their community clinic. They had started to discuss the problem when my boss, a Yolŋu clan leader himself, said to me, '*Wämut*, tell the leaders here what the policy of the Health Department is in relation to the Aboriginal Health Workers.'

So I told the leaders in Yolŋu Matha that the Territory Health Services (THS) saw the health workers as the primary health carers and educators.

At this they all laughed.

I was shocked. 'Why are you all laughing?' I asked.

One old man said, 'Whoever asked us, as clans, who we want as our primary healers?'

'No-one,' a number said, almost in unison.

'Well, they [the THS] *think* that you've been asked,' I said.

'How?'

'When the Health Department talks to the community council, they think your clans have given approval through the council.'

The elders shook their heads. 'The council is for Balanda business. If someone wants to know what we think as *bäpurru* (clans), they will have to come and talk to us, the political leaders of our clans, not the council.'

Some time later (July 1997) I told this story at a workshop in Darwin. Some Darwin-based THS staff members were perplexed. One said, 'But I thought the community members would have chosen their health workers. The story you just told us indicated that isn't the case.'

I explained that the health workers who are now employed would have come to their positions in many different ways, but probably none of them would have been chosen through a *traditional endorsement* process.

'Some of the long-term health workers came from the old mission training system, others through a community council nomination. A number would probably have been "recruited by —— College in an attempt to keep their numbers up" (as some community health sisters have told me). Then there are those who would have come to the job through the health centres themselves— that is, by an interested Yolŋu person approaching a health centre staff member who sent their name off to council for endorsement. Some have been assisted by well-meaning Balanda or Aboriginal people from outside Arnhem Land who see a bright young Yolŋu person with 'good English' and want to help them apply for training. So there are a number of ways that health workers are recruited, but almost none come through a traditional endorsement process.'

This shocked the THS staff members. 'If we're not doing that right, then what are we doing right?' they wondered.

Pseudo Schemes and Structures

In this confusion there are two players—Yolŋu, who are totally confused about dominant culture organisational and legal systems, and the dominant culture, which is totally confused about Yolŋu organisational systems and law. The dominant culture's confusion is no less intense than that of the Yolŋu.

This is why the various health programs devised by governments and others never seem to work. Schemes like the Aboriginal Health Worker Program, the Aboriginalisation of schools and 'community-controlled' health centres have been tried; the latest idea is Community Health Boards. But all these programs are much like the community councils, housing associations and community industries set up over twenty-five years ago to transfer assets and authority to Yolŋu (see chapter 2). That is, they get their authority from the dominant culture system of law, not Yolŋu *Maḏayin* law. Therefore, Yolŋu see them as pseudo-schemes with pseudo-positions and pseudo-structures. They have no authority in the eyes of the people.

From the Yolŋu point of view, you do not make something legal just by putting the word 'Aboriginal' in front of it or even by using a traditional Yolŋu Matha term as a name. No, an organisation or program is only legal and has authority according to *Maḏayin* law if it is developed out of *Maḏayin* statutes and processes.[114]

The Yolŋu clans and nations are like a 'nation' within the dominant culture nation. The citizens of the Yolŋu nations do not understand in any real way how the political and legal system of this dominant culture works, but they know the ancient *Maḏayin* law as well, or even better than most Balanda know their own law. The strange, or what Yolŋu call *mulkuru* (foreign), system of Balanda law is to them the epitome of lawlessness. This is not to say Yolŋu cannot learn to understand Balanda legal processes. They can. But they will only do so when the problems discussed in Part 2, such as the 'charting' of legal English and Yolŋu Matha terms, has been done. That is a long way off.

Because the people do not see any intelligible system of law operating in the dominant culture, they also see no authority connecting them to organisations or positions that receive their authority from the dominant culture. The only legal system they understand, and therefore the only system from which they see authority coming, is the traditional *Maḏayin* law.

The Effect on Health Workers

This lack of traditional authority is central to the effectiveness of the health worker program. The more a health worker's authority comes from the dominant culture and the less it comes from the people, the less functional he/she becomes.

From the dominant culture point of view, it is Yolŋu health workers who should be leading the way in health intervention in their communities. Yolŋu health workers are told this again and again in their training by both the Balanda and their Aboriginal peers in the community health centres. Unfortunately, in many cases we are setting these Yolŋu health workers up to fail, making them the meat in the sandwich between their people and the dominant culture medical system. This is especially so on communities where there are only one or two health workers but many different clans. In such cases the health workers find it even harder to delegate the appropriate health worker to a particular client in a way that even partly meets the traditional legal requirements.

The situation that Yolŋu health workers face is a bit like overseas doctors not being accepted in Australia because the dominant culture does not think their training is up to standard and therefore refuses to give them accreditation. According to Yolŋu law, the health workers have not been recognised as *marrŋgitj*.

If health workers have no traditional authority then they have real problems being the 'front line' of health intervention and prevention. For example, issues arise when someone is critically ill or dying. At these times it is very difficult for health workers to be close to or treat the patient. Unless they have rights as family members, it is almost impossible for them to be involved. In fact, they can suffer harm under traditional law because they are operating without authority. I personally know health workers who have left the service, some ending up in Darwin as prostitutes and alcoholics, and when I ask them why, they say, 'Because I was blamed for the death of one or two patients at —— [their home community] and now I fear for my life.'

Community health systems such as health clinics also have no authority under traditional law. This is the major reason why Yolŋu men do not attend these clinics. Depending on the community, between seventy-five and ninety per cent of clinic users are women and children. The men, being clan leaders, see the community health system as an extension of the mission clinics where the people's law and legal control were not wanted.

Despite everything that is against them, some health workers have gained great respect from their communities, several having worked in this role since the mission days. Now some of the more recently trained health workers who have 'certificates' are challenging these older health workers. This causes further division and confusion. It is as though the harder the dominant culture pushes accreditation, the worse the problem becomes and the greater the level of dysfunction.

The dominant culture can set up council-type structures, elect Yolŋu through Balanda-style democratic processes to various boards and associations, and train Yolŋu through nationally-accredited programs until the cows come home, it will make no difference. When these chosen few return home, they still have no authority from their own people to make decisions or to practise. This is true not just in health but in other fields as well. Of course, if this process continues for another twenty or so years, there will be nothing left of the traditional systems and the people will be totally lost in no-man's-land.

Dying with Dignity

There is one further subject associated with traditional health and healing that must be dealt with: the issue of death and dying. This subject is too important from the people's point of view for me not to mention it.

Many Yolŋu families are traumatised because the dominant culture lacks understanding of death and dying as Yolŋu see it. This happens when—as Yolŋu believe—the health system 'steals' their elders and sick countrymen from them at the point of death. Of course, these incidents are never intentional. But they are usually the direct result of hospital and nursing personnel making decisions in a vacuum of knowledge.

For Yolŋu, the period near death is a very important time. It is a time when the dying person wants to be with his or her loved ones. It doesn't matter how sick they are or even at times how much pain they are in. Dying in Yolŋu society is a family affair. The whole family will gather to sing the clan story to the dying person. People in a special *gutharra* (grandchild) relationship to the dying person will look after their every need, twenty-four hours a day. The dying person will also see that all their legal responsibilities are handed to the right people. (This is why Yolŋu like to be told if their condition is terminal and approximately how much time they might have left.)

The caring process continues until the person passes away. Sometimes the dying person will refuse food and later water as they ready themselves for the adventure ahead. The family will allow this, as it is the ultimate right of the dying person under law.

The songs that are sung before death and after death are different. Those sung before death are to make the person feel good about themselves and how they fit into their clan and the world around them. Sometimes this singing will make the person better again. Many dominant culture people mistake this singing for some form of sorcery. Some nursing sisters, having witnessed a person being 'sung' to and then dying, conclude that Yolŋu visitors have sung the person to death. This is totally wrong. The singing that occurs while the patient is sick and weak is to make them feel better. This singing is like reading a book about the history of the person, their clan and clan estates and how they fit into the scheme of things. It continues until the person gets better or passes away.

At the point of death the singing changes to help the spirit move on to the traditional place of rest.

The dominant culture view of death and dying has some things in common with the Yolŋu view. The big difference is that Balanda usually expect their dying relatives to die in hospital, where medical staff can look after them. In a way, this is the same as Yolŋu having people in a special *gutharra* relationship to look after the patient, giving the immediate relatives space to grieve and spend quality time with their dying ones. Balanda use hospitals in much the same way. So it is that most Balanda, including some health personnel, feel they are doing the right thing for Yolŋu by keeping dying Yolŋu patients in hospital. The problem is that when the dominant culture imposes its way of doing things on Yolŋu, it creates hurt and trauma.

There are many stories that demonstrate the hurt Yolŋu feel over this issue. Here are just two.

The first occurred in Darwin not long after my return to the Northern Territory in 1992. I was sitting with a group of Yolŋu friends, telling them about a visit I had made to the Darwin hospital to help another Yolŋu man from Arnhem Land. They said to me, 'You should have helped our sister in the next room too.' I asked why. They said, 'She was very sick and her death wish was that she had the strength to get out of bed, get a stick and kill some of those hospital staff before she died, for keeping her from being with her loved ones at the time of her death. Instead she was in a foreign place, with foreigners all around her, in a freezing cold [air-conditioned] room. She died the next day.'

What was seen as compassionate and humane treatment by the hospital staff was seen as something akin to being imprisoned by the patient and her family.

Then in February 1999 I was called upon by another Yolŋu friend for help. He had been with a sick relative in hospital and was unsure what the doctor had been saying to him, even though his grasp of English was very good. His relative had a form of cancer and was being put on chemotherapy, but the English word 'cancer' had apparently not been used—the doctor had used a more particular medical term. My friend was not sure if the condition was really serious or not. Every time he asked the doctor a clarifying question he got mixed messages. Eventually he had rung his home community and told the family that everything would be okay—the doctors were going to give the patient some medicine and that would make her better again. After the phone call he felt uneasy, wondering if he had told them the truth, so he rang me.

I organised a three-way phone link up between my friend on a mobile, the doctor at the hospital and myself. I knew from the information my friend had given me that his relative was probably critically ill. Now the doctor told us her condition had deteriorated and she might not see out the night. My friend was shocked.

After we had finished talking with the doctor, we tried to work out what had gone wrong with the communication. It seems three things had occurred:

My friend had not understood the seriousness of the disease from the names the doctor used.

The doctor had been trying to tell him gently about his relative, so my friend had been unable to 'read between the lines' of what the doctor said.

My friend was not able to ask the right questions to get the full story from the doctor.

In cases like this, medical staff need to know that Yolŋu want to hear as clearly as possible what the real situation is. My friend had to make hurried phone calls and completely change the information he had given to the family back home. If he had not told them the real story, his relatives would have been very upset with him, as any relatives would be in similar circumstances.

Yolŋu want to know the full truth about their personal condition or that of their relatives. If this information is not given in its fullest form, the people will be deeply upset, especially if it means they are unable to help their relative in their time of great need.

People need the full story so they can die with dignity, with their family members fully involved. Of course, this information needs to be delivered in a sensitive way. This is another area where dominant culture people need specialist training in cross-cultural/cross-language communication. I find that asking people what they want to know, and when they want to be told it, is a good way to let them drive the process.[115]

The Unhealthy Cost of Being Different

The cost of being different has been so heavy on Yolŋu that there is a real question whether they will make it as a social group through the next century. The people's 'different' knowledge, health practices and legal systems, which have enabled them to run their society effectively for thousands of years, have been grossly devalued. These ancient human forces are not being employed to deal with the very problems they were designed to combat. They remain an enormously unrecognised, untapped resource.

There is great confusion out there. The dominant culture plans and implements, then waits for things to change—but nothing does! Could it be that the health programs set up to empower Aboriginal people are not understood by the very people they are designed to help? These programs end up being merely cosmetic and do not empower the people in any way at all. In fact, I believe they are a major part of the whole health problem themselves—a misdirection of resources that at times works against the people.

Clichés like 'self-determination' need to be re-examined. What chance do the people have to be truly self-determining while the dominant culture continues to assault their traditional ways and no real thought is given to how you merge two very different social and legal systems? Another cliché is 'culturally appropriate'. Do we mean 'culturally appropriate' according to dominant culture perceptions or according to the traditional world-view of the Yolŋu of Arnhem Land? Or perhaps according to the Western-educated Yolŋu world-view? Or according to the pan-Aboriginal world-view? How we answer these questions will have far-reaching consequences for the policies aimed at giving control—real control—to the people.

I believe the way forward is to build on the already established traditional health and healing processes, or what is left of them, and the people's legal and social systems. If these systems can be employed, they will not be out of step with health and healing initiatives from the dominant culture. Otherwise, the cost of being different will continue to wreak havoc, and the people will be left to ponder: which doctor is the real doctor?

10
CHAPTER

'Living Hell'

Welfare and Dependency and their Effect on the People

Dependency is the biggest disease that is killing Yolŋu today.

Rev Dr Djiniyini Gondarra[116]

One afternoon in 1995, I was sitting with an old colleague, friend and teacher, John Djatjamirrilil, talking through the meaning of some Yolŋu Matha terms. After working on several words I asked John to give me the picture he had in his mind when he thought of the word *wulula*—the name of the people's traditional hell (an island to the east of Arnhem Land, north of *burralku*, the heaven island).

Djatjamirrilil responded without hesitation. 'Living in the community is like *wulula.* We sit with sad faces, with nothing to do except watch the Balanda running around doing everything for us. Yolŋu and Balanda don't say hello to each other any more like in the old days. We just sit around with nothing to do. That's what *wulula* is like. It's like living in a [present day Arnhem Land Aboriginal] community.'

We sat there for a while discussing this. I wanted to see if he was having a go at me. The more we talked, the more depressed I became. I already knew that things had changed drastically for Yolŋu in the previous fifteen years, but our discussion that afternoon reinforced this. The people were deeply depressed because of their dependency on Balanda. The old warriors' dreams from 100 years before of remaining independent had not been lost in the wars they fought face to face with the pastoralists and others. No, their dreams had been lost in the myriad of well-meaning welfare programs of the last two to three decades.

Once those wars were over, the people had come to the missions to survive and had learnt the 'art of Balanda labour'. Then came the era of self-determination, full of uncertainty and hope. Now, twenty years later, this hope had become hopelessness. Dominant culture people did almost all the work to 'help' the people while Yolŋu just sat and watched.

As Djatjamirrilil said, this change has turned life on modern Yolŋu communities into a 'living hell'.

A New Way of Living?

Already in this book we have examined several things that contribute to the crisis facing Yolŋu. In this chapter we will look at another insidious factor: the *welfare mentality*. This mentality pervades the thinking of many dominant culture people in their approach to 'helping' Yolŋu. It leads to programs that end in debilitating dependency for the people and ultimately death.

In 1978-79 people working in development programs around Asia came together for a series of workshops run by the Christian Conference of Asia. Their topic: how to decide whether a program, however well intentioned, was really 'developmental' or not. They concluded:

> Charity and Welfare—the Social Service Approach—is the most traditional approach [in helping the 'under-developed']. It constitutes a valid role as a strategy of action in crisis, caused by natural calamity or the devastation of war.
>
> However it is:
> a. Temporary
> b. Confined to particular affected people
> c. Auxiliary to the ongoing life of the people.
>
> Where the people's problems are chronic, vast, and written into the social economic and political structure, the social service approach cannot solve the problems. It can never tackle root causes.[117]

In Australia welfare is usually organised by the government. In fact, it is often said that Australia has one of the best welfare systems in the world. This welfare takes many forms, from family allowances to old age pensions, disability pensions and unemployment benefits. But many other programs that provide services or goods cost free or highly subsidised could also be classed as 'welfare'.

The Yolŋu experience of welfare began several decades ago when missionaries and patrol officers started telling Yolŋu leaders, 'You must leave your old ways and come to the mission where you will learn *a new way of living*.'[118] These old warriors thought it truly strange that they should have to leave their productive estates and stop trading between clans. They wondered what this 'new way' could be.

Out of necessity, some started to go to the missions to trade, staying longer and longer each time. This was made easier by the gifts the missions gave to family groups to convince them to stay. The missions also offered rations for work, paid usually in stick tobacco or cans of syrup. These items became a 'currency' on many missions. In some places cooked food was also provided to 'mission Yolŋu' every day.

This first welfare experience under the mission system was truly life-changing. Missionaries and Welfare Department patrol officers thought they were telling the people to give up the nomadic, hunting and gathering lifestyle so they could learn the 'work ethic' and live 'more productive lives'. But Yolŋu heard them saying they must give up their self-sufficient production and trade on their estates to live on the missions and be fed by Balanda. As so often happened, miscommunication got the people into trouble.

Some Yolŋu spent their entire adult lives on the missions. They kept watching to see what the 'new way of living' entailed. They saw two things:

• a Balanda man from outside Arnhem Land—a 'superintendent'—had *supreme authority over everyone*, including the other Balanda (even the gun-toting trepangers, pearlers and crocodile shooters);

• a new economic order where 'rations' were the cornerstone of life.

This left a deep impression, and many Yolŋu still believe that the 'new way of living' is a political system based on dictatorship and an economic system based on rations/welfare.

After the mission experience, Yolŋu had their second encounter with welfare when they received a level of independence through self-determination and self-management in the 1970s. At this time Yolŋu became eligible for government benefits. They were entitled to these under Australian law, it was said. But following the collapse of their traditional economic system and then the mission-welfare experience, Yolŋu felt vulnerable and confused. This new form of welfare came from the seemingly all-powerful, very rich government and was paid directly to the people. Most Yolŋu did not understand that it was what Balanda call a 'safety net'. They saw it as a further development of the new economic order: the government provided money, houses, wages, everything, for everybody in Australia. This confusion is still the dominant understanding held by Yolŋu today.

Once Yolŋu were economically strong and self-sufficient. They seeded and traded pearls through Macassan traders that probably reached Europe. Trepang traded with Macassans certainly reached China. All this international trade was lost in 1906 when the Macassans were refused trepang-fishing licences. Now dominant culture companies control the pearling industry. At that time some Yolŋu moved into the crocodile skin trade. This too was stopped in 1972. Again, dominant culture companies now control the crocodile skin trade. Virtually the only economic activity that Yolŋu have left is welfare.

Welfare is no longer an auxiliary to the ongoing economic life of the people. It has become almost their total economic existence. Even their contemporary calendar they have named (in Yolŋu Matha) around welfare payments. They have become hopelessly dependent on the dominant culture and its welfare system.

Welfare—A Yolŋu Perspective

So we can see this dependency from the people's point of view, I want to tell a story. I first heard it from Tony Binalany Gunbalga, a man I worked with in the Community Development Office at Ramingining in the late 1970s.

We were in the office one day when a government official arrived to tell the community about unemployment benefits. The Ramingining Council already had a strong position on unemployment benefits: it did not believe they were right for their community. The old men on the council said, 'If the young people get paid for doing nothing, it will kill them.'

These men remembered the old Yolŋu economic ways and wanted their young people to remain self-reliant, dependent on nothing but 'their own ability to sweat [work]'. There was plenty of work in Ramingining in those days. Alternatively, the people could paint and do craft work for money (some who did are now the great artists of the area). Also, land rights had made the people owners of hundreds of hectares of land. As the people struggled for greater independence, the elders were determined to keep their young people strong and disciplined, even stopping them from sleeping on foam mattresses. 'You have to be able to sleep on the hard ground, anywhere, like Yolŋu—not become soft like Balanda,' they said. This same resolve was reflected in the council's strong stance against unemployment benefits.

The government officers could not believe it was the people's decision to knock back unemployment benefits. They thought that somehow I was manipulating the council. So a government officer came into our office one morning to work on me. I told him that although I agreed with the council, it was not my decision but the people's. He kept talking directly to me, almost ignoring Tony. 'It's the people's right to have unemployment benefits and you should be advising them that way,' he said.

After a while Tony interrupted politely and asked if he could tell us a story. The officer agreed. This is the story.[119]

The Fish and the Shadow

'A long time ago, somewhere near here, there was a billabong. It was very beautiful, with calm, clear water and water lilies growing across the surface. In the water lived some fish families—mother and father fish, old fish, young fish. They were very happy and loved their home.

'Every morning the fish woke up and went about their work. The mother and father fish went off hunting for food, working hard all day. The young fish went with them, learning everything they could from their parents: where to find the best food, how to catch it and how to be on guard against sea eagles, ducks and other enemies. Their parents taught many things about life while they worked together.

'In the evening all the fish came together and shared the different types of food they had found during the day. They also told stories about the day's activities. If any fish had done something funny during the day, other fish acted it out, making everybody laugh. At night the fish went to sleep early, tired from their day's work.

'The old fish taught the younger ones discipline of mind, body and soul, giving them direction and advice on all aspects of life. The young ones listened in awe to their wise counsel, hoping not to miss or forget even one word. The fish all shared responsibility for life in the billabong. They lived well and were very happy. They didn't depend on anyone else or leave their work to others.

'Then one day about four o'clock in the afternoon, the fish saw a shadow fall across the water. Something stood near the billabong. The fish had not seen anything like it before. The shadow threw something white onto the water. The fish saw it land on the surface, sending rings out across the billabong. They all shrank back, fearful as the white stuff sank to the bottom.

'After a while a couple of brave fish—there are always a couple in any mob— swam up gingerly to the white stuff. They nibbled it, finding the taste funny at first. But they nibbled it again and again until there was none left. When the white stuff and the shadow had gone, all the fish went back to their hunting and other work.

'Four o'clock the next day the shadow came again with the same white stuff. A few more fish joined in the nibbling.

'The third day the shadow came again. This time, because all the fish had been talking about the shadow and the white stuff, many more came out of hiding to taste it.

'The shadow came again and again at four o'clock every afternoon. Now the fish quickly grabbed at bits of this white stuff, trying to eat as much as they could because it was free for the taking. The fish found the taste bland but it filled them up. As time went on they named the white stuff 'bread'. The shadow threw bread to the fish every day, giving it freely.

'Slowly the life of the fish started to change. They waited for the shadow to come every afternoon. At first they still went out in the morning to gather some tasty food for themselves and returned in the afternoon ready for the shadow. But when the shadow saw that lots of fish were interested in the bread, it threw more and more into the billabong. Soon the fish were not going out in the morning any more. They just waited around for the shadow to feed them.

'For the first time in their existence, the fish found themselves bored at night. There were no more interesting stories to tell about the day's experiences and they were not tired because they had done no work. Many stayed up most of the night because sleep would not come till the early hours of the morning. They started to find other ways to take up their time, gambling and things like that. This caused many arguments. Soon the fish were getting up late, but this was not a problem because they only had to wait for a while before the shadow came. The bread was still bland, but it was easy food and the fish had grown too lazy to care.

'Trouble, however, was brewing. Some fish, completely forgetting their old co-operative ways, raced to get to the bread first. 'We were the first to taste the bread when you were all scared, so the shadow's bread belongs to us. You mob go away and find your own shadow,' they argued. Others said, 'The shadow comes to our end of the billabong. That means the bread belongs to us.' They fought and jostled each other out of the way. Fish got hurt, which caused arguments between families. Sometimes these arguments went on for a long time, causing bigger fights. The fish had stopped thinking about each other; they only thought about themselves.

'Then the old fish became very sad because the young fish had no respect any more. They did whatever they liked, following their undisciplined desires. It was all too hard to deal with. Many old fish became so sad that they died.

'More and more the fish's life changed. They didn't teach their young ones the old ways any more. And they took and kept the bread for themselves, wanting it desperately, their hearts held by it. Many fish mistakenly thought the bread must be good for them because it made them all very fat.

'Then the shadow began to change. Usually it came right on time and the fish were happy. But sometimes the shadow came a little late. This made the fish angry. 'Why is it keeping us waiting? It knows we've been waiting all day,' they cried. Then the day came when the shadow forgot to bring bread at all. As this became more frequent, the fish got really mad, swearing at the shadow and even threatening to hurt it in some way. But these threats only made the fish feel very weak because they knew their threats were hollow. They could not hurt the shadow; it was too powerful. It lived outside the billabong where no fish had ever lived. And only it knew the source of the bread on which they had come to depend.

'There was now a deep feeling of emptiness and shame within the fish. They didn't value or even think about anything other than bread any more. They lived badly, unhappily, with their hearts and spirits bound. Their lives became powerless and meaningless. They got sick because of their troubled thinking and couldn't sleep at night. They had no peace of mind and felt deeply insecure, not knowing who they were or where they belonged.

'Then came the time when the shadow no longer fell on the water. Maybe the source of the bread had dried up. All the fish grew skinny and lamented its passing, because they were too weak to go hunting for themselves or didn't know how. They had forgotten the way of the *ŋurrŋgitj* (black charcoal)—the time-honoured way of their ancestors.'

When Tony finished telling this story he pointed to the government officer and simply said, '*And you're the shadow—get out!*'

Administering the 'Last Rights'

The officer left a little peeved that day, but it wasn't the end of the matter. The next time the people heard anything on the subject was when six Social Security officers from Canberra turned up in the community. Tony and I were away at the time. These officers signed up the whole community, workers, artists and all, for unemployment benefits.

On our return, the chairman of the council told me the story. He was almost in tears. I asked him why they hadn't stopped the officials and told them the council's position.

'We tried, but they wouldn't listen,' he replied. 'They said they were from Canberra and that the government had sent them to do this job and no-one was to stop them. After that we felt we had no power and so we let them do it.'

'How did they go about their job?' I asked.

'It was like the old mission days. We were forced to line up like horses or cattle. The three Balanda men asked all the Yolŋu men to line up over here and the Yolŋu women were asked to line up over there with the three Balanda women. They had to stay in line until their forms were filled out. They even sent vehicles to the homelands to pick up the people there to make sure they filled out their forms too.'

I asked him what the people thought about it. Some were happy, he said, because the Balanda from Canberra had told them, 'The Government would give them money every two weeks so they would not have to starve any more'. Others were scared because they didn't know what it all meant. The old people were worried because they knew the young men and women would just sit down and not be interested in work. 'They'll become weak and die,' the chairman said.

'But you can get other forms and say that you don't want this unemployment benefit,' I explained.

He smiled in surprise. 'Can you?' Then his smile turned to a frown. 'No, we can't do that; the young people will rebel. They have heard the words of the Balanda from Canberra and they're listening to them now, not to us old people. They want the easy money. They don't want to work.'[120]

In a way, events like this were the final straw for communities like Ramingining. In the years that followed we saw many changes. People moved into town from their homeland estates to be close to the store so they could spend the cash they now had. Alcohol started to flow, with unemployment cheques being pooled and taken to Darwin to buy grog. Within three or four years, many of the young men who had refused to listen to the old people were dead from alcohol-related conditions or because of fights.

In Ramingining, the first real cases of children with malnutrition occurred within two months of the first unemployment cheques being paid. This happened because people played cards night and day, and when someone won all the money, they took it off to Darwin, leaving the others without money to buy food. At the inquest into the December 1990 death of a baby at Ramingining, the coroner stated in his report:

> No direct relationship between the heavy consumption of kava at Ramingining and the child's death was established on evidence. Notwithstanding the obvious depletion of financial resources within the community by reason of the heavy consumption of kava—the dissipation of money otherwise available for the purchase of food—food programs aimed at combating malnutrition were activated but were met with general apathy within the community. Therefore it is too simplistic to attribute the incidence of malnutrition to the consumption of kava.

The underlying operative factor is to be found in the community's lack of understanding of the importance of nutrition and in the low priority accorded to personal health and well-being. *The problem is essentially one of community attitude.* The heavy consumption of kava appears to be a symptom rather than a cause of that attitude. I suspect that the present attitude of the community would persist whether the substance being abused was kava or alcohol and, possibly, if the use of both substances was removed from the community.

Furthermore, cognizance must also be taken of the high incidence of card-playing at Ramingining which affects the financial resources of individual members of the community and which, like the consumption of kava, is accorded priority over matters of personal health. *Once again card playing is symptomatic of the community's underlying lack of appreciation of the importance of nutrition and personal health.* (My emphasis)[121]

Many programs have been initiated to deal with the malnutrition problem, from meals on wheels to feeding programs. All have failed almost as soon as the dominant culture person involved stopped active participation. In fact, every attempt to solve the problem with outside ideas has sent the malnutrition rates higher. Welfare-type programs simply send the people into greater depths of dependency, which increases feelings of confusion and hopelessness. Old people as well as children are not being cared for.

During 1999 the children received a free breakfast at the school and some people were talking about giving them free lunches as well. So now the government feeds the people's children, as well as builds their houses and provides all levels of welfare for them. What is there left for them to do but go off and drink kava or gamble?

Learned Helplessness

The administration of Aboriginal affairs by the Australian government has evolved from the 'protection era' through the 'assimilation era' to the so-called 'self-management era.' The result of exercising control over Aboriginal affairs has been that a once self-sufficient people has learned dependency and helplessness.[122]

When we see a group of people displaying high levels of dependency, it is easy to blame them as though it were their own fault. In fact, the dependency of Yolŋu is a direct consequence of policies and attitudes that have taught people a 'learned helplessness.'

A story told by another Aboriginal person, Roy Yorrowin, illustrates this better than I could explain it. Roy is now deceased, but I have permission from his family to use his name in this story as a dedication to this great old man.

I first met Roy in March 1977 when my wife and I found ourselves at Belyuen (then called Delissaville) on the mainland across the harbour from Darwin. We were sent there as part of a community development training course.

We travelled to Belyuen in the company of two Balanda from the Commonwealth Department of Aboriginal Affairs (DAA). They drank whisky on the ferry all the way over from Darwin and slurped it down under cover of their briefcases in the back of the vehicle driving into the community. The task of these two intrepid travellers was to close down the community kitchen, which had been set up by the Northern Territory Department of Welfare in earlier days. The trouble was, the people in Belyuen were now totally dependent on the kitchen for all their meals.

I walked about the community when we arrived. It was a strange place and it took me a while to work out what was wrong. I was used to Arnhem Land communities where everywhere you saw Yolŋu preparing food, cooking and eating it in family groups. In Belyuen, the homes of the people had no cooking fires and no cooking utensils, not even a billycan to boil water for a cup of tea.

There were other odd things about the community. Most of the men were drunk by nine o'clock in the morning. You could see them gathered on one side of the community. The women lived in their homes with the children, but most of the men lived by themselves in a group so they could get drunk together. People from the community's administration office had said they were going to close the pre-school because there were no more children being born. To see a community in this state shocked me.

The next morning I walked around looking for someone to talk to. I met a middle-aged man who knew an old friend of mine back at Ramingining and spent about an hour-and-a-half with him. Then I sat down with two old men—the only ones I could find that were sober. They were happy to meet a Balanda who showed an interest in what they thought.

We sat on a sheet outside their home and talked for almost an hour. Then one of them asked me what time it was. I said it was twenty minutes to ten. We talked some more and again they asked me for the time. It was fifteen minutes to ten. This unnerved me a bit and I asked if they were too busy to talk further. 'No, no, we're not too busy,' they assured me. So we continued. We had just got talking again when once more they asked me for the time. I told them it was about eight minutes to ten. Two minutes later they asked me again.

I now noticed they were stretching their legs as if getting ready to stand up. This made me ready myself too. Less than a minute passed before they asked me for the time again. This did it for me. I told them that it was five minutes to ten and started to rise.

They beat me up. In one leap they were on their feet and taking big strides down the road. 'Come on, young fella,' one called over his shoulder, 'the bell [siren] will ring any time now and we only have three minutes to be there before they lock us out.'

'Get where?' I asked, hesitating.

'To the kitchen for our cup of tea,' one of them bellowed back from fifty metres down the road, not breaking stride.

I was still standing there watching these old men disappear down the road when the siren sounded. I think they made it easily because my watch was two minutes fast.

I didn't follow the old men. The whole idea of a community kitchen repulsed me, especially when I remembered that the authorities were going to close it down that very week. How were these people going to look after themselves when they depended on the kitchen even for morning and afternoon tea?

I was deep in thought as I turned back to the administration centre. As I sat on the verandah reflecting on what I'd seen, another old Aboriginal man came out of the office and sat down beside me. I introduced myself and he said, 'Yeah, I know you. I was the one who answered the phone when the college organised for you to come here.'

We sat for a while looking down the road in the direction of the kitchen. Finally I broke the silence. 'Have the DAA drunks left yet?' I asked.

The man exploded into laughter. I turned to him with a smile because I wasn't sure what he found humorous.

'You're a funny white fella,' he said.

'Why's that?' I asked, turning my hand over in the Yolŋu questioning mode.

'Because of that,' he said, pointing to my hand motions. 'And because when white fellas like you come in here, they always talk about the Aboriginal people being drunk. But you talk about those two white-fella government blokes that were drunk here yesterday. What are you, Aboriginal or what?'

I told him I had lived with the people in north-central Arnhem Land for (at that stage) five years. I told him that the people had taught me many things, the main one being that I didn't know as much as I thought I did. I felt since I had been living with Aboriginal people that I was really only just starting to learn.

The old man reached out his hand. 'My name's Roy Yorrowin. Glad to meet you,' he said.

We sat for a while drinking in the world around us, then I cleared my throat. 'Is it okay, old man, if I ask you something that's really bothering me?'

'Yes, what's your trouble, young fella?'

'Well, I've already told you I've lived with the people at Ramingining for a while and I know some of the ways of Aboriginal people. But what I'm seeing here really hurts me. The people are so broken. What has done this to you?'

There was silence as Roy considered the appropriate response. Then he told me the following story.[123]

Roy's Story

'Many years ago, before the white man came to this area, our people were very different. All the Aboriginal people around here lived on their own land, making a living from their own work. Everyone had a job, a role to play in the family group, things to be proud of and a reason to live.

'The women had the job of collecting food like root vegetables and the seeds from grasses and grinding them into flour. Then they had to cook the food. They also had to look after the children. They made the small carry-bags for food and they helped in collecting material for building houses and things like that.

'The men had the job of catching the bigger animals for meat and protecting the whole family from trouble. They also made the big things like rope, traps, spears and houses.

'Everyone felt needed because each person relied on everyone else to pull his or her weight. Everyone felt proud knowing they were all needed.

'Then the white people came to the Belyuen area. They rounded up the Aboriginal people on horseback, with whips, herding them into this settlement. If anyone tried to run back to their own home areas, they sent men on horseback to find them and drive them back to the settlement. In the end the people gave up and stayed, even though they didn't want to.

'The Balanda bosses here at Belyuen built a community kitchen where the people were fed like cattle. We had to get all our food there. This stole the jobs from both the women and the men. The Balanda also took away the job of cooking the food. Soon the people had only the job of listening for the bell. They couldn't think of getting their own food any more. They couldn't even choose what they would like to eat.

'From this the people learned that you don't have to worry about *thinking* and *planning* what you and your family will do in the future, because from now on the government will do everything for you.

'The Balanda also built houses for the people and told them to live in them. If the people built their own traditional houses, which they liked better, the Balanda would come and tell them to pull them down. They would say things like: 'You can't live in that rubbish dump any more, you have to live in a proper house.'

'We were prisoners here. Everything had to be done the way the Balanda wanted. We were not allowed to make any decisions. They even stopped us using our own law. The superintendent was the law. If we tried to do any of our ceremonial business we were stopped. Some of the old men got very angry about being pushed around all the time. But if they made a noise about it or didn't do what they were told, the Balanda saw them as troublemakers. If the people didn't behave themselves, they were arrested and taken to gaol in Darwin.

'After many years of living this way, the people forgot about doing things for themselves. They had no role left. The only ones who still had a role were the mothers. Babies were still being born and they had to feed them; then as the babies grew into children they lived with their mothers. The men, though, wondered why they were even born; they had no business in their family any more.

'It was even worse when the mothers got child endowment from the government. The men felt they were not needed now and the government would do everything. Maybe the government was even the father of the children now.'

Roy stopped, swallowed hard and sat quiet. 'So you're saying,' I said after a long pause, 'that the men get drunk because they feel they have no role in life.'

'Yes,' he said, 'they just feel they're nothing, like dirt. But when they get drunk they're someone—they can pretend to be strong and important, or they can just have fun and forget. When they get drunk every day they also have a role to play, something to plan for and achieve: they have to get the money to buy the grog, then work out who's going to buy it and so on. It gives them something to do. They can be someone—a drunk.'

We sat in silence again and thought how stupid the whole situation was. The government was paying out money to kill these people, all because the dominant culture did not understand that they were human beings and needed to be treated as such.

'How come you're not over there with the men?' I asked Roy, motioning towards the other side of town where the men were drinking. 'It must be hard being the only male Aboriginal person in the office.'

'Yeah. I used to be a drunk. For many, many years I couldn't stand living without grog. Then one day a bloke named Wali Fejo, who was working here in the community, said to me, "Roy, when are you going to give up the grog and help your people?" His words sort of hit me and I haven't had a drink since.'

We continued talking about the community kitchen and the fact that the DAA was going to close it down in a week. 'How are the people going to cope?' I asked. 'I don't know,' Roy said in a long, low tone, shaking his head.

I don't know what happened at Belyuen after that. I haven't been back since. But the situation there was typical of what has happened to Aboriginal people all over Australia, and is still happening to people like Yolŋu today. Welfare-type programs have taught them helplessness. And when people's lives become as institutionalised as they were at Belyuen, life loses all meaning.

Dependency and Its Effect on the People

The two stories above give us deep insight into the dysfunction that plagues current Yolŋu society. In 'The Fish and the Shadow' a whole community is affected. In 'Roy's Story' it is the men in particular who are trapped.

It's important to try to understand what dependency really is and how it destroys people. As we have seen, dependency is a product of learned helplessness. Learned helplessness occurs when the people lose their economic independence and become dependent on welfare programs. Through these programs they experience *loss of roles*, *loss of mastery* and *hopelessness*. These in turn translate into *destructive social behaviour*, including neglect of responsibility, drug abuse, family violence, self-abuse, homicide, incest and suicide.

Loss of Roles

Yolŋu, like other indigenous people around the world, have fallen from their original glory as independent, self-sufficient people to an unglamorous existence as virtual beggars. The 'loss of roles' experienced by such communities is typified in the role-loss experienced by the men. As Dr Richard Murray of the Western Australian Kimberley Medical Service has said: 'In colonised societies it's the men who lose their roles, it's the men who are emasculated by the colonising society. It's the men who have no useful role in life.'[124]

It is a strange phenomenon. In Aboriginal communities right around Australia, one thing is very evident: where the people have lost control, the men are dead or dying. Many communities are run mainly by women. If you ask where the men are, they will inevitably say, 'They drank themselves to death.'

Others have noticed this. Paul Wilson, for example, says that when Aboriginal families move from northern Queensland to Brisbane:

> . . . women effectively become the leaders and decision-makers of the [family] unit, even if men are present. In contrast to the past, when men were the undisputed leaders of the community, males in town are often unable to take command. Unemployment, itinerant labour patterns, imprisonment and regulations relating to social security payments for support mothers, often force them away from their homes, effectively placing women in charge.[125]

I believe that damage to the well-being of a community, which is certainly reflected in social indicators such as high morbidity and mortality rates, substance abuse, suicide, and domestic violence, is initially seen in the health and well-being of its men.

What happens is this: the dominant culture takes over the roles that the men traditionally fulfilled. In Arnhem Land, the economic resources and political functions—the province of the men—have been stripped away. This has left them feeling they have nothing to live or work for. They feel there would be little change in their community if they weren't even there: 'Not even my family would miss me if I was to die.' They believe that 'no-one would even notice', and they say to themselves, 'I'm a failure.'[126]

Their children also come to believe their fathers are nothing. Young petrol sniffers in the early 1980s said to me, 'We're ashamed of our fathers. They have nothing for us, not like you Balanda. You've got everything to give to your children.' These children had not long returned from a school excursion to Singapore, organised by dominant culture schoolteachers.

Women can lose their roles too. When children start to value Balanda teachers or social workers more than their mothers, the mothers feel divested of power and rejected. Dominant culture people can give the children 'better food' through a feeding program, or organise school outings, sports events, holidays, clothes or other goods which Yolŋu mothers have difficulty supplying.

Providing other institutions like child-care centres—which are now being built in Arnhem Land—will only lead to a further loss of role for Yolŋu women. This development will continue the destruction that Yolŋu women first experienced when the dominant culture removed 'birthing' from them. Many supporters of these centres point out that Yolŋu women will be in control of them, but how can this happen when they have to be licensed under Balanda law? How many Yolŋu women have the required dominant culture qualifications to be in charge of a child-care centre? Inevitably a dominant culture person, trained to the necessary accredited level, will run these institutions, and Yolŋu children will be required to assimilate dominant culture values at an earlier, even more vulnerable age.

Even if Yolŋu were in control, child-care centres are an idea from outside Yolŋu society and therefore will inadvertently affect traditional roles. And they will increase the level of dependency once again. No-one pushing these programs has told Yolŋu that they might have to pay about $40 per day to have their children looked after, as happens in the Balanda world. In fact, centre promoters are developing all sorts of subsidy schemes, and it appears that individuals will not have to pay anything until they have established their children in the centre. So again, the people think the service is free.

I believe that when these highly-subsidised centres open, the people will become dependent on them and the destruction of the knowledge base that Yolŋu women have had around womanhood and mothering will be complete. Yolŋu children will be even more knowledge-deprived. For the mothers themselves it will complete the cycle of dependency. They will believe it is the government's job to look after their babies while they go off and find another 'role' in life, as many of their men have done.

Loss of Mastery

Traditionally Yolŋu understood their environment in a complete and intimate way. They were highly skilled artisans, hunters, producers and traders and also had many other skills. Then in the mission days they turned from their traditional enterprises and directed their high levels of mastery to learning Balanda trades. They became builders, plumbers, painters, electricians, boat captains, deck hands, fishermen, stockmen, house-keepers, clerks, administrators and so on. Many were able to hold their heads high as they competed equally with Balanda in their chosen trades.

Now, however, the roles of Yolŋu in the ebb and flow of daily life are gone. Loss of meaningful employment and traditional living skills has left the people with no sense of mastery. They believe they have no skills of any value in the strange Balanda world. They have nothing to be proud of.

This loss of mastery is typified in the following story.

A Yolŋu man had been promoted from his home community to Darwin in an attempt to 'Aboriginalise' an organisation. He was not brought into this office to learn the ropes; in fact, he was placed at the *head* of this office with minimal specific training. No attempts were made to help him in his new position—such as providing special training to Balanda support staff—so he had all sorts of problems coping with the job. It became so bad that he began staying away from work, causing great frustration among the staff. This led them to 'name, blame and lecture' him.

One day, after the naming and blaming had reached a high level and the Yolŋu man was feeling very devalued, he and some of the Balanda staff went fishing. He had his fishing spear with him and moved to the front of the dinghy, where he stood riding the considerable swell. Then he started spearing fish. After he had speared his third large fish right behind the gills, one of the Balanda looked at him in awe. 'It's incredible how you can stand there in a rocking boat and hit those fish right behind the head every time,' he said.

The Yolŋu man turned to the staff member and said, 'Can you tell the other people in the office what you just said? Then maybe they can see that I'm good at something!'

In his new position, this man had no sense of mastery over the environment he was expected to operate in. Tragically, he died of a heart attack three months after this incident, in his early forties.

Even Yolŋu who have not left their home communities have experienced this loss of mastery over their environment. This is because dominant culture influence in these communities has changed the environmental mix to the point where the people are now estranged.

Some Balanda say that Yolŋu were always lazy, but the opposite is true. Traditionally on their estates Yolŋu worked very long hours. It took exceptional skill and strength to survive. Even when breaks were taken during the day, people would busy themselves with running repairs to tools and equipment, or converting raw materials into useable products. Having spent many years with the people on their homeland estates in the 1970s and early 1980s, I know how hard they can work. It is also clear from the people's ancient language that laziness was not part of their world-view. There are words in Yolŋu Matha that honour hard-working, skilled people and others that condemn laziness. It was easy in days past, for example, to be *ŋurr'yun* (proud of your own skill and highly satisfied in a job well done).

These people, once refined masters of their environment, are now heavily dependent on paternalistic shows of mastery by Balanda. The dominant culture sends in contractors and *even the army* to build the homes the people once built themselves. The result: the people feel good *at* nothing and good *for* nothing.

Hopelessness

All people need something to live for. Without a sense of purpose, people lapse into deep hopelessness and depression. This can happen to individuals in a mono-cultural group, but the impact is much worse on a group of people who are dominated by another cultural group. When the people in a minority group, like Yolŋu, believe they have lost out to the dominant culture, they are likely to see themselves as less privileged and even less human.

When life reaches these levels, destructive social behaviour such as drug abuse starts to occur. The drugs that people turn to are usually those that are available, although there is a degree of cultural acceptability involved in people's choices. While a number of drugs are being abused in Arnhem Land, for simplicity I will talk here about alcohol.

As 'Roy's Story' demonstrates, when Aboriginal men feel they have become nothing, they look for another role in life. Many find it in substance abuse. They become 'something' with the others involved in that abuse. As the alcohol takes over, they start to experience extreme mood swings and high levels of depression. Their emotions suffer a form of 'weightlessness' after every drinking bout, leaving them emotionally weak and very vulnerable.

After a drunken spree, the drinkers return to their families, out of money, half-sober and emotionally weak. They remember little about how much they have spent on grog or how much trouble they have caused. But the family does remember, and is probably carrying a great deal of anger and shame at the drunken actions and waste of money. So they act strangely to the now sober drinker. The drinker senses this anger and distance but can't work out why the family is acting this way. The family, on the other hand, is unable to raise the issue, for two main reasons:

- The drinker was the one who violated the social norms, and his family—like any other group of human beings—expects him to apologise for the abuse (which they *know* they have experienced).

- The drinker, on the other hand, does *not* remember the abuse he committed while drunk. In fact, except for the horrible sickness and emotional weakness, he probably has good, pleasant memories of 'flying high'. The family becomes more and more angry with him, believing he must know the hurt, shame and anger he is creating. But the drinker only feels great about his drinking because it takes away all his pain.

The distance between the drinker and his family increases with every drinking session. He feels the deep separation from his loved ones but can't understand it. At the same time he is sick both physically and emotionally, and can't understand why his family will not help him get the one thing that makes him feel better: more grog.

This separation experienced by the drinker results in him seeing his family as 'the problem' because he feels unloved. He starts to project what he is feeling inside about himself onto his loved ones, regarding them as useless, dumb, unintelligent, lazy, unloving, uncaring and so on.

From Drug Abuse to Violence

The volatile mix of alcohol, hopelessness and despair inevitably ends in violence. This violence is not played out against the dominant culture, the ultimate cause of the drinker's problem, but against his own family, friends and even himself. It takes many forms, from domestic violence, assaults, homicides and incest to self-abuse, suicide and assaults and homicides outside the family. These forms of violence are evident among dominated, dependent indigenous groups the world over:

> The peasant is a dependent. He can't say what he wants. Before he discovers his dependence, he suffers. He lets off steam at home, where he shouts at his children, beats them and despairs. He complains about his wife and thinks everything is dreadful. He doesn't let off steam with the boss because he thinks the boss is a superior being. Lots of times, the peasant gives vent to his sorrows by drinking.[127]

Violence now exists at alarming levels in many Aboriginal communities throughout Australia. For example, the levels of violence recorded on Cape York

Peninsula have been horrific.[128] Paul Wilson also writes about Aboriginal communities in northern Queensland: '. . . the rate for homicide on the Aboriginal reserves and communities studied [in the early 1980s] is 8-40 times greater than for other regions within the State.' He goes on to say these rates are 39.6 times higher than those experienced in the crime capitals of America. Rates of unreported assaults are probably ten to fifteen times the Australian state or national figures.[129]

This violence is now present across most of Arnhem Land. Some communities where alcohol is freely available display very high levels of verbal abuse, domestic violence, assaults, homicides, self-mutilation and suicides. The Gove area around the mining town of Nhulunbuy, where there are six alcohol outlets, is one of these areas. Yolŋu families are suffering profoundly, both from direct acts of violence and from the aftermath of family and personal breakdown. It is very obvious that alcohol, coming on top of the loss of control, is the trigger for this deadly spiral because the same level of abuse is not evident in those communities where alcohol is prohibited or not freely available.

Alcohol on top of loss of control also seems to be the main element in the violence in the Aboriginal communities of northern Queensland.

> Most of the fighting on the reserves was clearly related to drink, including cases in which criminal charges did not arise. . . . alcohol, perhaps more than any other factor, heightens tribal and family disagreements and jealousies and promotes considerable tensions within Aboriginal communities.[130]

Although the levels of violence in Arnhem Land are generally not yet as high as those in Queensland, the underlying levels of hopelessness do exist in almost all Yolŋu communities. The potential for escalation is clear.[131]

I must stress that this violence is not due to the nature of the Aboriginal people or their communities. I lived for eleven years in north-central Arnhem Land among kind, gentle people who looked after each other. There were occasional individuals who were aggressive, as in any community. It was only when alcohol came into the communities in the middle to late 1970s that we saw the first real acts of violence. So this is not a traditional condition. As Murrandoo Yanner, an Aboriginal leader from northern Queensland, states: 'Alcoholism is what turns a warrior into a woman basher and a father into a paedophile.'[132]

The Real Violence

The two stories recorded earlier in this chapter showed communities losing control of their lives as they were institutionalised in one way or another. Ultimately this is the end result of colonisation. The colonisers came out of a violent history of repression and counter-repression in Europe. The colonised had lived for thousands of years in comparative isolation, without invasion, secure in their ancient law. But as the colonisers saw it, Aboriginal people did not own the land and resources they used, and in the ensuing struggle Aboriginal people all over Australia lost out. With their birthright denied, they became beggars in their own land, dependent on welfare and other government programs for survival—programs that have produced a prison of dependency.

Prominent Aboriginal leader Noel Pearson has stated, 'Welfare is a resource that is laced with poison'.[133] Dependency is poison to the people's dignity, destroying their very soul and in the end, life itself. It is the direct cost of non-recognition by the dominant culture of Yolŋu as human beings with human needs, rather than children of some 'lost' culture.

The question we need to ask is: 'What is real violence?' Is violence only violence when someone is physically hurt? Or is there a deeper, more destructive violence that destroys a people's soul?

To me, institutionalised violence has been and remains the worst form of violence. It is subtle and almost hidden, wrapped up in the ethnocentric paternalism of the dominant culture. Welfare and the dependency it creates is the worst form of violence. It has created a living hell.

11
CHAPTER

'Stop the World — I Want to Get Off!'

The Stress of Living between Two Cultures

. . . unless man quickly learns to control the rate of change in his personal affairs as well as in society at large, we are doomed to a massive adaptational breakdown.

Alvin Toffler[134]

A common reality in Arnhem Land Aboriginal communities today is the extremely high levels of stress experienced by Yolŋu. They are dropping out of active involvement in the development of their own communities through social, emotional and intellectual withdrawal.

While poor communication is arguably the major contributor to this acute and endless stress, other compounding factors provide additional stressors. These additional stressors are not always easy to nail down. I hope the topics I raise here will shed light on them.

The human sciences over the last forty years have added much to our understanding of stress factors. A great deal has been written about conditions ranging from 'culture shock' and 'future shock' to 'multigenerational legacies of trauma' and Post-Traumatic Stress Disorder. I believe these phenomena wreak havoc in the daily lives of Yolŋu. But they hardly rate a mention in the dominant Australian culture as factors in the crisis.

Much of the literature about these phenomena around the world has been written from a dominant culture point of view and often about mono-cultural situations. Nevertheless, I believe that an examination of these known stress factors may help to explain what is happening in Arnhem Land. It is interesting to note that there is an emerging body of literature dealing with cross-cultural aspects of these conditions.

Culture Shock

> The culture shock phenomenon accounts for much of the bewilderment, frustration, and disorientation that plague Americans in their dealings with other societies. It causes a breakdown in communication, a misreading of reality, an inability to cope.[135]

'Culture shock' is a two-edged sword that cuts a wide swathe through Yolŋu society. First, they have to cope with dominant culture personnel who come to their communities, get stressed out by culture shock, use 'cranky English' and then leave without really contributing anything. Secondly, Yolŋu themselves are affected directly by culture shock as they have to live and work in 'non-Yolŋu-friendly' environments.

Culture shock was first described by the anthropologist Lalvero Oberg in 1954. Since then the term has become well-known. It is used to explain the anxiety produced when a person moves from his or her own culture to another. Visitors going overseas on a holiday can experience it. New immigrants or students coming to Australia suffer from it. Soldiers on peacekeeping missions have to deal with it.

> Culture shock is the loss of emotional balance, disorientation, or confusion that a person feels when moving from a familiar environment to an unfamiliar one. While it is a common experience, the degree to which it occurs will vary from one person to another. Individual personality, previous cross-cultural experiences, and language proficiency all affect a person's ability to interact socially in the new culture. The basic cause of culture shock is the abrupt loss of all that is familiar, leading to a sense of isolation.[136]

Culture shock is caused when we enter another cultural domain and find that many of the things that occur are different from what we are used to.

> When an individual enters a strange culture, all or most of these familiar cues are removed. *He or she is like a fish out of water.* No matter how broad-minded or full of goodwill he may be, a series of props has been knocked from under him. This is followed by a feeling of frustration and anxiety. People react to the frustration in much the same way. First they reject the environment which causes the discomfort: 'the ways of the host country are bad because they make us feel bad'. (My emphasis)[137]

Dr Carmen Guanipa of the Department of Counselling and Psychology at San Diego State University states the symptoms of culture shock as follows:

- Sadness, loneliness, melancholy
- Preoccupation with health
- Aches, pains and allergies
- Insomnia, desire to sleep too much or too little
- Changes in temperament, depression, feeling vulnerable, feeling powerless
- Anger, irritability, resentment, unwillingness to interact with others
- Identifying with the old culture or idealising the old country
- Loss of identity
- Trying too hard to absorb everything in the new culture or country

• Unable to solve simple problems
• Lack of confidence
• Feelings of inadequacy or insecurity
• Developing stereotypes about the new culture
• Developing obsessions such as over-cleanliness
• Longing for family
• Feelings of being lost, overlooked, exploited or abused.[138]

Oberg points out symptoms that include;

> . . . a feeling of helplessness and a desire for dependence on long-term residents of one's own nationality; irritation over delays and other minor frustrations out of proportion to their causes; delay and outright refusal to learn the language of the host country; excessive fear of being cheated, robbed or injured; great concern over minor pains and eruptions of the skin; and finally, that terrible longing to be back home, to be in familiar surroundings, to visit one's relatives, and, in general, to talk to people who really 'make sense'.[139]

Dominant Culture Personnel and Culture Shock

Almost all dominant culture personnel who come to Arnhem Land suffer these symptoms in one way or another, but most do not know what they are suffering from. This makes them leave in an almost constant stream, depleting the dominant culture corporate knowledge about the region, the Yolŋu people and the various professional domains. Medical personnel come and go on very short contracts. Many teachers stay less than a year, with the average dominant culture teacher staying in the East Arnhem region for 1.8 years.[140] This is a serious, perennial condition affecting all aspects of community and regional development.

Although culture shock is common in cross-cultural situations, it is scarcely acknowledged in the Australian context, especially in relation to Aboriginal communities. Because of this, little or no training is given to help dominant culture personnel deal with it or be less destructive to the Yolŋu population. And culture shock is *very* destructive, undermining the ability of dominant culture personnel to satisfactorily perform their professional tasks.

People suffering culture shock get depressed and angry, or feel demoralised and hopeless because they cannot accomplish what they are used to accomplishing. Many start to blame themselves because nothing in this new cultural setting makes sense to them. Another common response is to blame the host community and its strange culture. These dominant culture personnel spend much of their spare time with others from the dominant culture, criticising the people. Others 'lecture' the people, telling them what they should be doing.

The non-recognition of culture shock costs governments a fortune because community resource personnel come for such a short while and then leave in an emotionally, and sometimes physically, shattered state.

When I was working as a community development officer at Ramingining twenty years ago, one of the main jobs of that office was to conduct counselling sessions between dominant culture personnel and Yolŋu. Conflict would occur in the workplace, at the store, in the clinic, at the school or between contractors and members of the community. Only now, in writing this book, have I seen the important role that the community development team played.

Hundreds of hours were spent in counselling sessions, listening to one side of the story, mapping it out on the wooden floor of the office with a piece of chalk, then listening to the other side. Both English and Yolŋu Matha were used. When we had a good 'conflict map' on the floor, both parties could see where the mistake in understanding had occurred. Time and again we found that before doing this, both Yolŋu and Balanda had no idea why the conflict occurred. Both parties felt like 'a fish out of water'.

I have no doubt that if these sessions had not occurred, many Yolŋu would have stayed away from their jobs, from the clinic or wherever and would have become bitter and confused, as many are today.

Yolŋu and Culture Shock

As already indicated, Yolŋu experience culture shock in two ways:

They suffer the effects of 'fall out' from the culture shock suffered by dominant culture personnel.

They also suffer culture shock directly themselves. Despite being in familiar geographical surroundings, they continually find themselves in alien situations such as dominant culture-controlled hospitals, schools, courts of law or work places. These places are 'non-Yolŋu-friendly' environments.

• 'Fall out' from Culture Shock that dominant culture Personnel are suffering

One morning in October 1998 I received a phone call from a Yolŋu man on a community. I had not spoken to him for many years. Now in his sixties, he is one of the few Yolŋu in his generation who has survived to be in reasonably good health.

He asked if I knew of some way he could be involved in training Balanda and others who came to Yolŋu communities as support personnel, teachers, health sisters and so on. He had lots of ideas and we talked through some of the options. 'I want to try and do something before I die, that might change the situation,' he said.

I asked him what he saw as the main problem with outside personnel. He responded: 'It seems that the staff are *ŋoy-maḏakarritjmirr* (cranky from the depths of their being/soul). I am not sure what makes Balanda so cranky all the time; maybe it is your English language. Is it, *Wämut*?'

He went on: 'Staff are supposed to come to our communities to help Yolŋu learn to run our own communities. But when Yolŋu go to work in the office, the workshop, or on one of the work teams, they get this cranky English hitting them. They don't feel happy and don't want to go back to that work place any more.

'This is a big problem, *Wämut*. Our young people are not learning like we did.

Soon outsiders will be running everything while Yolŋu sit and do nothing but think bad thoughts about Balanda and themselves. The Balanda frighten our people away from work and then complain about them not coming. Can't they see they are the ones stopping Yolŋu?'

'Cranky' communication from stressed-out dominant culture personnel is like a physical assault on the people. It creates fear and confusion, making Yolŋu feel tired, disillusioned, angry and withdrawn. This is not the fault of dominant culture personnel; they are just people who have entered a strange culture where most of the familiar cultural cues are missing. They don't understand what is going on inside themselves, let alone the effects they might be having on others.

This tension can spill over into conflict between Yolŋu and their Balanda 'staff' people. Yolŋu are supposed to be learning from these Balanda so they can take over their jobs, but when conflict persists, Yolŋu want to be somewhere else. So they do not learn to take over the job. The stressed-out Balanda staff member then goes into blaming mode because Yolŋu have not turned up to work. For their part, Yolŋu feel they must be at fault in some way, because they see dominant culture personnel getting on well together and wonder why it is different with Yolŋu. Some Yolŋu will also blame Balanda—'Balanda just do not understand things' or 'Balanda should leave'—but generally Yolŋu simply withdraw, feeling there is no way they can get the Balanda involved to understand them. This adds immensely to Yolŋu feelings of inferiority, 'being different', hopelessness and loss of control.

• 'Non-Yolŋu-friendly' environments.

Some will ask, 'How can Yolŋu suffer from culture shock? They are living in their own culture and their own communities.' This is correct. But they still experience culture shock in areas within their community that are dominated by Balanda ways. In these areas English is the communicating medium and dominant culture personnel control the environment.

In these settings, all or most of the cultural cues familiar to Yolŋu are missing, just as they are for Balanda in a Yolŋu setting. Often Yolŋu do not recognise what is actually happening to them at this point; they just feel very strange and extremely stressed. This unfamiliar feeling is actually culture shock.

The Serious Effects of Culture Shock

'Culture shock' needs to be taken seriously because it is a direct, deadly factor in why Yolŋu warriors lie down and die. The following story tells us why.

In 1993 I was called to the Royal Darwin Hospital where a Yolŋu man about twenty-four years old had been admitted with kidney failure. The doctors had fitted him with a number of catheters so he could be hooked up to a dialysis machine, but the places where the catheters had been fitted had become infected, requiring them to be shifted again.

A team of three doctors and two sisters was carrying out the procedure when the young man attacked them, knocking one of the doctors across the room. A younger doctor, who had been brought up in Darwin, suggested they needed to get an interpreter so the young man would understand why the procedure was necessary. The senior doctor scoffed at the suggestion: 'He understands. He's just trying to make it difficult for us.' So the patient was sedated and the new catheter fitted without further difficulty.

But the young doctor was not satisfied. She contacted our office and asked if someone could come and talk to the patient. A Yolŋu colleague and I went along. At the young doctor's request we met away from the ward, because the other doctors had been so opposed to the idea of a translator. Those present were the young doctor, the male nurse from the dialysis unit, my Yolŋu colleague and myself. And of course the patient—Barry.

We began by talking to Barry about his rights. If he wanted to, we explained, he could sign himself out of the hospital and go home. We also made it clear that if he did this and became ill again, the local clinic would not be able to do much to help him because it did not have the appropriate facilities.

Next we talked about his condition. *We told him the way it was.* The doctor explained that Barry's kidneys had almost totally stopped working. Because of this, his lungs were filling with fluid, making it impossible for him to breathe properly. Without dialysis he would drown in his own fluid within three days. We translated all this for Barry and made it clear that he might have to be on dialysis for the rest of his life.

The next subject was his present treatment and the need to shift the catheters because of infection. After that we explained the importance of eating a special diet while on dialysis and that he would have to have a fistula fitted in his arm. We assured him that when his condition had stabilised, he would be able to leave the hospital and move out to the dialysis unit in Nightcliff. It was a lot of information, but this was no problem to Barry because the conversation was all in Yolŋu Matha.

When we had finished, Barry asked me to accompany him back to his room in the hospital to get his cigarettes. We walked in silence, took the lift to the ward, got the cigarettes and moved back to the lifts to go outside. In the lift he broke down and began to cry. 'I didn't know how sick I was,' he said. 'I thought it was a little thing and the doctors would just give me something and send me home again.'

'Have you been sick or taken something in the past that might have destroyed your kidneys?' I asked.

'Nothing I can think of, except I've drunk grog and kava.'

'How much grog?'

'Not much. I've only been drunk once.'

I assured him that that amount would not have affected his kidneys. 'How much kava?' I asked.

'Lots. Day and night without stopping.'

'How long have you done that for?'

'For about three Christmases [three years].'

'Well, the doctors don't know if kava hurts people's kidneys, but if you drank day and night for three years, then it could have been the kava that destroyed your kidneys.'

We rejoined the others and waited to see if Barry had any more questions. He said, 'No, I understand it all, and I want to help the doctors and nursing staff.'

I asked him if he could tell us why he had hit the doctor. Barry thought then responded, 'Because I hadn't understood anything the hospital staff had told me before. I was wondering why the doctors were being so cruel to me, sticking those metal objects into my veins and then shifting them all the time. I didn't complain at first because I thought the doctors should know what they were doing. But when they tried to put this metal needle thing into a vein in my neck, I got really scared. So I lashed out to save my life!'

It is common knowledge for Yolŋu that the veins in the neck are very important and if they are cut you die very quickly. No wonder Barry was terrified!

It must be remembered that Barry was effectively alone in that room, with no one he could communicate with intellectually. The people around him were saying things that made almost no sense to him. He had to work out from his limited knowledge what the doctors were doing to him.

Most Australians would find this experience hard to identify with. But imagine it this way. You are travelling in a foreign country when you suddenly get very sick. You are admitted to hospital finding it almost impossible to breathe. You are alone, with no one who can speak your language. You don't know what your condition really is. A team of medical personnel gather round your bed, saying things about you and to you that make no sense. Now they start to perform on you a drastic medical procedure that you do not understand. Suddenly their actions remind you of stories you have heard about foreign hospital staff stealing people's organs and selling them on the black market. How would you feel?

Anyone in this kind of situation will suffer massive culture shock. It was like that for Barry. He had heard many stories about Balanda doctors being sorcerers and killers who practised their dastardly deeds on vulnerable Yolŋu, and all the evidence he could get from the actual situation seemed to confirm that the stories were right!

As human beings, when we meet these types of situations, we usually react according to a 'cultural script' written inside us. Barry was acting from his 'cultural script'. He comes from a culture where everyone has a much greater understanding of the difficulty of communicating across languages. From his cultural script, he would have expected the doctors to make many more attempts to explain what was happening. He would have found everything occurring far too fast, not just that morning but throughout his time in hospital.

The speed of the communication, the use of English and the fact that the doctors undertook medical procedures without his real consent would have slammed him into culture shock. Retreating to his cultural script he found the rationale for the medical team's actions: they were sorcerers and murderers about to kill him.

The senior doctor was also suffering a degree of culture shock and went straight into naming and blaming mode: 'He understands. He's just trying to make it difficult for us.' This kind of response does not happen because doctors are inherently bad but because they too are human, with their own 'cultural script'. Dominant culture doctors are used to English-only communication and accustomed to particular responses when seemingly simple English is used. However, when they use these simple English phrases in a cross-cultural/cross-language situation and the same responses don't come, it can leave them confused and feeling the Yolŋu person is the problem. Out of this culture shock the doctor goes into reaction mode, acting out of his cultural script rather than making a reasoned response.

Culture shock is a known reality. Universities, the armed forces and modern international companies face it on a daily basis when they have people from different cultural/language groups mixing and working together. It *must* become a recognised factor in Australia where Yolŋu, and others like them, have to meet and work with the dominant Australian culture.

Future Shock

Alvin Toffler, in his book *Future Shock*, uses this term to explain the scenario that was facing the Western world as it raced up to the end of the twentieth century.

> Future shock is a time phenomenon, a product of the greatly accelerated rate of change in society. It arises from the superimposition of a new culture on an old one. It is culture shock in one's own society . . . [141]

It also seems that, without knowing it, Toffler explained very accurately what would happen to people like Barry when two different cultures collide.

> Different people react to future shock in different ways. Its symptoms also vary according to the stage and intensity of the disease. These symptoms range all the way from anxiety, hostility to helpful authority, and seemingly senseless violence, to physical illness, depression and apathy. Its victims often manifest erratic swings in interest and life style, followed by an effort to 'crawl into their shells' through social, intellectual and emotional withdrawal. They feel continually 'bugged' or harassed, and want desperately to reduce the number of decisions they must make.[142]

I remember in 1978 talking with a group of Yolŋu leaders about whether the world was flat or round. In their lifetime, much that was once held to be true had been brushed aside. According to the ancient stories, the sun and moon turned back into fish and swam back under great oceans to rise again. Now these old men were ready to look at new information and question things they believed in, spending many hundreds of hours doing so. Twenty years later, the people still have many, many questions about the Balanda world.

Yolŋu are suffering under massive cultural and social changes that they are unable to comprehend. This suffering manifests itself in the shocked reactions they display.

> Take an individual out of his own culture and set him down suddenly in an environment sharply different from his own, with a different set of cues to react to—different conception of time, space, work, love, religion, sex and

everything else—then cut him off from any hope of retreat to a more familiar social landscape, and the dislocation he suffers is doubly severe. Moreover, if this new culture is itself in constant turmoil, and if—worse yet—its values are incessantly changing, the sense of disorientation will be still further intensified. Given few clues as to what kind of behaviour is rational under the radically new circumstances, the victim may well *become a hazard to himself and others.* (My emphasis)[143]

Symptoms of Toffler's future shock were evident in Barry's story: 'anxiety, hostility to helpful authority, and seemingly senseless violence'. I would suggest that, if the young doctor had not contacted us, Barry would have gone on to display other symptoms, such as 'depression and apathy'. In fact, many Yolŋu patients in hospital display high levels of all Toffler's factors, including 'erratic swings in interest and lifestyle' and attempts to 'crawl into their shells through social, intellectual and emotional withdrawal'.

Yolŋu have a common saying: 'When you go to hospital you die twice—once from the sickness and again from fear of the hospital'.[144]

But future shock also affects Yolŋu living in their own communities.

On a 1996 visit to Ramingining I met an old friend. This old man came up to me and I met him joyfully as I had not seen him for over ten years. I told him how glad I was to meet him again and asked how he was.

His answer shocked me. '*Wämut*, I don't want to live any more in this lawless land. Our *Maḏayin* is not recognised by Balanda and now we live in a lawless situation. *Wämut*, I have lived all my life according to our law, spending much of my time teaching the law to our young people. But these young people do not want the way of law. They say they want to live in a lawless way like the Balanda. I no longer want to live in a place where my right to my land is always questioned by Balanda and where my sacred law is seen as rubbish. I am tired. I just want to die so I don't have to look at the mess this world is in now.'

I stood there stunned. When I lived at Ramingining he was one of my neighbours; he used to look after my garden for me when I was on holidays. But more importantly, I knew him to be a lawman (*ṉapuŋga ŋayi*—a middle-man/judge/arbitrator), and inside the traditional parliaments he was revered and listened to. Out in the community, however, he was seen as a little man, almost a joke, because the dominant culture system did not recognise him or the law he represented. Now his young people were starting to see him in the same way.

'Please don't talk that way,' I said to him. 'I've come back to Arnhem Land to help you get the Balanda to recognise your law and to educate your young people so they can see the importance of law.'

He sadly shook his head. 'No, it's too late. I am tired. Balanda come and change, change, change. They change everything. Even the things we learn from them at one time they come and change again. Life makes no sense any more.'

My old friend died two weeks after that discussion from an unknown condition, yet the day I spoke with him he was walking well and I thought he would get over his depression. He didn't.

Despite having a modern house, receiving a pension and owning a four-wheel drive that he bought with his own savings, this old man could not find happiness. Life made no sense to him because the thing he valued most was not recognised. It was as if he had been taken (in Toffler's words) 'out of his own culture and set down suddenly in an environment sharply different from his own'. Everything was different—the 'conception of time, space, work, love, religion, sex and everything else'. His whole way of life based on the *Madayin* was forced aside by a (to him) lawless, disgusting culture. Even though he still lived in Arnhem Land he was 'cut-off from any hope of retreat to a more familiar social landscape'. Further, the new culture he was now forced to live under seemed itself to be in 'constant turmoil', with its values 'incessantly changing'. This had left my old friend with a complete 'sense of disorientation'.

The cultural change that affected this man is now affecting all his countrymen. In some cases, whole Yolŋu communities living close to large Balanda populations are starting to display many of the symptoms of future shock.

Toffler's comments regarding Western society might have been overstated when he said, 'Unless man quickly learns to control the rate of change in his personal affairs as well as in society at large, we are doomed to a massive adaptational breakdown'.[145] This in general has not happened. But for groups like Yolŋu, 'future shock' is a daily reality, and the adaptational breakdown of their society is massive and rapid.

Was It Always This Way?

Many dominant culture personnel say, 'Maybe Yolŋu have always been this way'. I can state categorically they have not. A few Yolŋu in my early days in Arnhem Land showed these symptoms, but this was the result of the violent and repressive history they had experienced in their dealings with Balanda. The overall depressed apathy that now exists on communities is new.

In the more affected communities, close to the large mining town of Nhulunbuy, social, intellectual and emotional withdrawal is chronic. This is typified by the comments of a community leader who lives in one of these areas. When I asked him one day where he had been because I hadn't seen him for two months, he replied, '*Wämut*, don't tell anyone, but I am hiding at —— so no-one can find me.' He then listed all his problems, and all the Balanda who were looking for him. Not only did he have to sort out the normal stresses of daily life; he was also trying to sort out difficulties in his own family and clan caused by alcohol, lack of meaningful employment and so on. And he was grappling with Balanda law—the Local Government Act, the Northern Territory Land Rights Act and more—all of which he had to try to understand from Balanda who spoke English. 'I am just tired of all these problems,' he said. 'How can I live with this load?'

This wonderful old clan leader may well be the next fatality caused by a neo-colonial system that does not understand. Future shock was named in the late 1960s, and yet today we are still trying to 'find the answers'. The phenomena of culture shock and future shock enable us to see that the symptoms displayed by many Yolŋu are normal human responses to *abnormal* human situations.

Let's go back to Barry's story and see how it can be different.

The next day I visited the hospital to see how things were going. The young doctor who had phoned me came into Barry's room and told us there was an immediate problem that needed to be dealt with. When they put the catheter into the vein in Barry's neck under sedation, they put it in too far and it was resting on one of his heart valves, hindering its operation. They needed to undo the stitches and pull the catheter back a little off the valve.

The doctor asked me to explain this to Barry. I enquired if the hospital had an x-ray showing the catheter on the valve. The doctor said they did, because when they noticed Barry's heart was racing they took an x-ray to see what was wrong. I suggested to the doctor that she show Barry the x-ray.

We went out to the nurses' station where the x-rays where kept and the doctor put them up for Barry to see. Part-way through this process, a senior doctor came by and reprimanded the younger doctor for her 'stupidity in showing the patient the x-ray'. Barry, not recognising the 'English' interjection from the senior doctor, said to the junior doctor in English, 'I can see it, it's too close.' Then turning to me he said in Yolŋu Matha, 'That is dangerous, *Wämut*. I can see the metal object in the heart. We need to pull it back.'

I said to the young doctor, 'He's ready for you to pull the catheter back', then added for the senior doctor's sake, 'It's good to show Yolŋu their x-rays because they have a better knowledge of the body's anatomy—that is, the shape, size and position of body organs—than most Balanda do. An x-ray is helpful in communicating with Yolŋu. Seeing is believing.'[146]

We went back to Barry's room and the doctor removed the stitches, withdrew the catheter about twenty millimetres and re-stitched it into place, all without a local anaesthetic. Barry just sat there, hardly grimacing, even though it must have been excruciatingly painful.

As we can see from this story, Barry was keenly interested in his own health, although at first some of the medical people thought he was probably extremely disinterested, even hostile. Barry shifted from being a danger, not only to the medical system but also to himself, to a position where he complied almost completely and became responsible for his own health. This was only possible when he received information about his condition and the medical interventions in a form that made sense to him. I was told by a number of sources that Barry was almost a model patient from then on, complying with diet and other requirements while on his dialysis program.[147]

Multigenerational Legacies of Trauma

Culture shock and future shock together are enough to render life almost impossible for Yolŋu in a Balanda world, but there is another debilitating phenomenon that compounds them. Psychologists call it the 'multigenerational legacy of trauma'.

A growing body of research[148] and much anecdotal evidence suggests that long-term victimisation and trauma can lead to heightened levels of complex stress.

This is usually termed 'Post-Traumatic Stress Disorder', or PTSD. Despite this research, many dominant culture people fail to acknowledge the destructive relationship between the dominant culture and Yolŋu, preferring to blame the people's problems on some inherent weakness in them or their culture. This makes it very difficult for Yolŋu. When they try to talk about the wars and trauma they have experienced at the hands of Balanda, their stories of deep hurt and grief are usually met with comments such as 'We have to forget the past and get on with the future' or 'Do we always have to talk about the past? Can't we just live for tomorrow?' Strangely, many dominant culture people get agitated hearing about these past events, even though the dominant culture immortalises its own past defeats and tragedies with words like 'Lest we forget'. Research shows that unless people can grieve and speak about the hurts of the past, it is very difficult to live for the future.

This is a major subject and I feel very unqualified to deal with it. Yet I will raise it because, if the legacy of multigenerational trauma is indeed a factor in the Yolŋu crisis of living, we must come to grips with it.

Just Get On With Things

When Australian and American soldiers returned from Vietnam in the late 1960s and early 1970s, they were often told to forget the past and get on with their lives. It is now widely accepted that many of these Vietnam veterans experienced deep traumatic events that affected them so profoundly they could *not* just 'get on with their lives'. They needed help to deal with their past trauma, and the fact they did not get it caused many of them great hardship.

Large numbers of people in years gone by have experienced this type of trauma in circumstances such as war, torture, rape, the Holocaust, the atomic bombing of Japan, natural disasters, and community disasters such as factory explosions, aeroplane crashes, vehicle accidents and riots.[149] It is this type of trauma that has the capacity to create PTSD in its victims.

When Vietnam veterans suffering the psychological impact of trauma were diagnosed with PTSD, the opportunity occurred for appropriate intervention in their troubled lives. Many were also suffering from high levels of alcohol and drug abuse,[150] dysfunctional family life and domestic violence,[151] and self-abuse and suicide.[152] The clinical recognition of the veterans' condition allowed them and their families to rise above the negative stigma that had been applied to them by others. The identification of PTSD, writes researcher Matthew Friedman, filled an important gap in psychiatric theory and practice:

> From an historical perspective, the significant change ushered in by the PTSD concept was the stipulation that the etiological agent was outside the individual him or herself—i.e., the traumatic event—rather than an inherent individual weakness—i.e., a traumatic neurosis. *The key to understanding the scientific basis and clinical expression of PTSD is the concept of 'trauma'*. (My emphasis)[153]

The question needs to be asked: Is what Yolŋu have experienced trauma in its true clinical form? To help us at this point I would like to relate another story that first brought this whole subject to my attention in the early 1970s.

You Can't Say No To Balanda

In 1974, after a year in Arnhem Land, I was at Naŋgalala, about twelve miles from Ramingining, working as a mechanic. Naŋgalala was an unloading site, on the west bank of the Glyde River, for the development of Ramingining and it had turned into a small community in itself. I had started learning the language of the local landowners from the two remaining old men of that group. These men kept telling me stories about the land at Naŋgalala, and especially how the mission had built most of its buildings right on top of the *buḻ'manydji dhukarr* (track of the shark).

The shark, they explained, had come from the east and swum up the Glyde River, coming ashore and travelling overland to a billabong in another clan's estates, then coming back to their estate, where it now rested. Each time a septic tank had been dug or a bore put down at Naŋgalala, one member of their clan had died. Their stories were very graphic, and to convince me of their authenticity they showed me the marks of the shark—stones in the shape of a shark's fins at different places along the Shark Track. One of these markers was right outside where the community store had been built. Another was outside one of the staff houses.

After the old men's instruction, which covered many weeks, I started to mention the Shark Track story to other members of the small Naŋgalala mission staff. To my surprise, my story, exciting and very valuable as it seemed to me, was passed off as superstitious, pagan rubbish. To my even greater surprise, almost all the staff had been told the same stories by the old men in an attempt to convince mission authorities of the importance of their land. But I am afraid it was not making much difference. The need for staff housing or a better water and power supply had usually taken precedence over the people's concerns. This seemed strange to me as I thought we were at Naŋgalala for the good of the people.

A month or so later, the two old men and I were working in the workshop when the mission superintendent pulled up outside in his Land Rover with a Balanda visitor. The superintendent said he would like the two old men to go with him and the stranger to site two new bores. Apparently the man was from the Department of Water Resources in Darwin. The superintendent pointed out that it was the new town site of Ramingining, not Naŋgalala, that needed the bores, but the Department had got it wrong and done all the calculations for Naŋgalala. He continued, 'Seeing the preparatory work has been done for Naŋgalala, we might as well site the bores here, if the people agree to it, in case they're needed in the future.'

The superintendent asked me to go along to help make sure the old men understood what was happening. We got to the bore site, about 400 yards from the workshop, and climbed down from the Land Rover. With a white peg and hammer in his hand, the stranger said, 'Well, this is one site' and prepared to drive the peg in. The site was right on top of the Shark Track. The superintendent turned to the old men and asked, 'Would it be okay to put a bore here in case we need it later on?' The old men hesitated a moment and then said, '*Yo, manymak* (yes, good).'

I was taken aback. I expected them to reject it for sure; they were so adamant that members of their clan would die if this site was disturbed. I tried to explain to them in my very rough Yolŋu Matha what the superintendent was talking about. But they responded, '*Yaka. Manymak wäwa* (No. It's okay, brother).'

I didn't know what to think. We headed off to the next site, which was also right on top of the Track. The same procedure was followed with the same result.

We returned to the workshop, my faith in the people greatly shaken. I concluded that maybe they really were 'primitive' after all and did not know what they thought and had just been telling me 'black fella stories'.

Over the next couple of weeks I lost all interest in language learning. The old men must have picked up that I was upset and confused about what had occurred because about two weeks after the event something occurred that was to change my life.

I was with the older of the two brothers, and we were many miles from Naŋgalala down towards the barge landing near Milingimbi. We were on our way back to Naŋgalala when the old man asked me to drive over to a very large shell midden.[154] The midden was about one kilometre off the road and about eight to ten metres high, thirty metres wide and forty to sixty metres long. Large date palms were growing on top of it. The old man got out of the Land Rover and started climbing the midden, beckoning me to follow him. We found a good place to sit and he started to unfold a story. (The following conversation took place in Yolŋu Matha with a small amount of English. The old man also used sign language and mime.)

'After the big Balanda war [World War II] was over', he began, 'all the Yolŋu clans of this area came together and met here for a number of days to talk about the power of the Balanda. We wanted to find out where the Balanda got their power.'

As the old man told me of this meeting, he kept on saying to me over and over again, '*Dhuwali ganydjarr, wanhaŋur nhuma Balanday ŋuli märram* (Where do you Balanda get all this power/authority)?'

'We all sat here,' he continued as he raised himself from the ground. He walked around in a circle naming the clans in the positions where everyone had sat, and then returned to sit in front of me again. 'We all had this one big question: Where do Balanda get all this power and authority?'

'What power and authority?' I asked, confused.

'In the early days of the mission,' he explained, 'It used to take ten men to carry a pine log from the bush to the sea or the river. Now you Balanda put some liquid into a steel thing and one person can pull four or five logs to the river.'

'What's this steel thing,' I asked.

'*Botjin one*,' he answered. It took me about ten minutes to work out that '*Botjin one*' was the old Fordson tractor we had been working on in the workshop. So with fuel in, the Fordson tractor could do the work of forty or fifty men. 'Where,' he asked again, 'did you Balanda get this *ganydjarr* (power/authority)?'

I was still trying to soak up the full meaning of that story when he continued with another one. 'Before, I would spend two to three days making a spear. I would have to cut it and straighten it over the fire'—he started miming the actions he would go through—'then cut and fit a head to the spear. When all that was complete, I would have to creep through the grass'—he raised himself from the ground and went into a crouching position, then stalked though the pretend grass—'getting very close to the geese'—he brought his arm back and released the imaginary spear—'and spearing one goose.' He held up one finger in the air and sat down again. 'But today all I have to do is go to the store, throw down some paper [money], get a packet of shotgun cartridges, creep through the grass'—he raised himself again into the crouched hunting position, aimed and shot—'ten geese.' He held up ten fingers. 'Where do you Balanda get this *ganydjarr* from?' he asked again.

I was struck dumb by these stories. Why was he telling me these things? He continued, 'We talked about the Balanda *ganydjarr* for two days. In the end we decided that it was no good trying to fight the Balanda any more. All the clans decided that they *would not say no to Balanda any more* because they were all-powerful and were *mayali'miriw* (without meaning, and so could not be reasoned with).'

The old man rose and returned to the Land Rover. I sat for a moment looking around at where the clans had sat. Surely these people did not feel *that* threatened by Balanda? I definitely did not feel I had any special type of power. Why *did* the old man tell me these stories?

I returned to the Land Rover and we started back to Nangalala. A few kilometres up the road the pieces started to come together. I asked my old friend, 'Did you tell me this story because of the bore business at Nangalala.

'*Yo* (yes).'

'So if the Balanda dig the bores, some of your clan will die because of the Shark Track?'

'Yes,' he replied. 'When they dig one bore, one of us will die, maybe me or my brother or one of my sisters. Then when they dig the other one, one of us will die for that too.'

'Well, we have to stop them,' I almost shouted at him.

'No,' he said. 'You can't stop the Balanda, they always win, doesn't matter what you do.'

I could not understand his position. To me, you stand up and fight. When we got back to the workshop, we sat down with the old man's brother and went through the whole situation again. I told them I would go to the superintendent and get the bores stopped. They told me it would only cause more trouble. I did go to the superintendent and finished up having a big argument with him. To him what I was telling him was all 'pagan rubbish'. 'Anyhow,' he said, 'you were there when the old men gave their okay to the bores.' I did get him to agree to write a letter to Water Resources and have the bores taken off the drilling list. When I saw the letter had been written, I let the issue rest, although the whole episode left me with many questions.

Two years later I went on holidays. When I returned, to my surprise I found the bores had been drilled, then capped so they would not be 'a danger' to anyone. I went straight to see the old men to see if they were all right. They were alive, but one of their sisters and a close relative had died—they believed as a direct result of drilling the bores. Another clan, which had an alliance with the Naŋgalala people through the Shark Track, had come and built their camp very close to one of the bores, near the side of the track, to try to stop any more disturbances.

Psychological Scarring

This experience gave me a glimpse of the people's suffering, but it wasn't until years later, when these same old men, along with others, started taking me to massacre sites, that a window was opened for me into the depth of their trauma at the hands of Balanda. It was when I stood beneath the trees out of which the pastoralists and their gang had shot men, women and children . . . when I stood in the village where everyone had been brutally murdered . . . when I visited the pine forest where the big battle occurred . . . that the reality of these events hit home, making me cringe in horror at the cruelty and violence of those early years. Wherever we travelled, Yolŋu could tell graphic stories of slaughter. Yet to them these were not distant historical events; they were like yesterday—and the evidence was *the continuing deaths* of loved ones from modern development projects like the drilling of new bores.

The history of those years has left a great depth of fear within the people, from the oldest to the youngest. I remember on a number of occasions seeing women, young and old, running back to the different homeland villages that I visited. They were trembling in fear. All these incidents happened because they had seen unknown Balanda carrying guns, in a boat or travelling in a vehicle somewhere. When I spoke to these women, they could hardly talk coherently and kept looking over their shoulders in the direction where they had last seen the unknown Balanda.

A further story may help us to appreciate the depth of emotional scarring that has occurred among the Yolŋu population.

In the Dry season of 1982, I was with a group of middle-aged Yolŋu men on our way back to Ramingining from one of the homelands when we came upon some wild cattle. We decided to stop and shoot one for fresh meat. The animals did not run from us so we were able to get within shooting range without leaving our four-wheel drive utility.

One of the men in the front on the passenger's side—I will call him Joe—was a very good friend of mine. Joe had a rifle and was able to take good aim. I was in the back of the utility, waiting with the other men for the rifle to go off. I could see the gun being aimed, so I watched the cattle and waited. And waited. And waited. I was starting to wonder what was wrong when the cattle spooked and headed for the bush. Joe did not even attempt to shoot. He just cleared the chamber and drew the rifle back inside the cab.

I looked at the other men and asked what was wrong. They were as puzzled as I was. Joe yelled out to us from the cabin, 'Let's go and get some geese'. This really confused me, so I asked if I could sit in the front of the vehicle.

As I climbed in next to Joe and the vehicle started towards home, I asked him why he had not fired at the bullock.

'I just couldn't,' he said.

'What do you mean?'

'Well, it's like the past can't let us go. When I took aim at that *buliki'* (bullock), it's like all the stories of the past came racing back to my mind. I know that many of our people died just for killing *buliki'* on their own land. When I was aiming at that *buliki'*, all that past came back and made me shake in my guts.'

'Yes, but you have land rights and these cattle clearly belong to your people now.'

'I know all that, but it's just in here, shaking my guts,' he said, holding his shaking hand to his stomach.

Joe then said something to the driver in a dialect I did not understand very well. The driver detoured off the main track. We travelled for about three minutes and pulled up. We all got out of the vehicle on top of a cleared area. The men started telling me the story I recounted in chapter 1 of the Yolŋu who were shot carrying the rolls of barbed wire. They added that the war after that time was so bad that no-one was able to come back and bury these people properly. When they did return, the dingoes had left only scattered bones.

They finished telling me this story and we headed for Ramingining again. But we stopped every few kilometres while the men recounted story after story of death at the hands of the pastoralists. No wonder Joe's hands froze on the rifle. The trauma he and other Yolŋu have experienced has had a deep and lasting effect.

Steel of Character?

When I first came across this phenomenon of trauma in the early 1970s, I wondered if in some way Yolŋu men did not have the strength of character, or 'steel', to stand up for themselves or their community. For a while I thought that was the only plausible answer. But as I lived with them, I saw much evidence to convince me that these men were powerful, fearless warriors and extremely intelligent. Another story, this time of their courage.

This story occurred a year or so after the bore-drilling incident. Some Yolŋu men were out hunting. They had wounded a buffalo early in the day but had run out of bullets. So they had coaxed the wounded bull in the direction of the community at Naŋgalala by getting it to chase them, in the hope that someone in the village would have some more bullets to finish the job. This method had been used successfully before.

As the furious bull came rushing towards the community, one of the young hunters ran ahead to warn everyone. When they heard the news, many people climbed up on anything they could find to get out of the way. As the buffalo came closer, we watched it swinging its huge horns at any piece of grass or small shrub, then pawing the ground, letting us know it was well and truly ready for a fight if anybody was mad enough to try. The hunters' hopes that someone would have some bullets were dashed as nobody could find any; I even went inside for a .303 rifle, but I had no bullets either. The situation looked a little grim.

Just as the bull was about to enter the village, the two old brothers from the story about the bores, having put their children and womenfolk onto the roof of their homes, came running across the village, each with a spear in his hand. The bull never hesitated but charged straight at the old men. The two brothers split up to give each other room to move. The bull went for one of them. I held my breath as he stood there, then at the last second jumped sideways out of the reach of the treacherous, slashing horns. As the bull went by, the old man turned and tried to place the spear in the flank, behind the front leg. This manoeuvre was repeated over and over until the two men had successfully placed their spears.

The bullets that had been fired at the bull earlier in the day had just angered it, but now it was bleeding internally. It must have sensed it had met its match. After charging the old men a few more times it turned, making a beeline for the swamp to the south of the village. It reached deep water before it ran out of breath. That night it was the crocodiles that feasted, not the people!

I defy anybody to stand with only a spear and look a wounded, charging buffalo in the eye. These old men had no problem with it; in fact, they revelled in the adrenalin rush of the contest. But when it came to standing up to Balanda, they faded as though something inside them snapped. It seemed the raging, snorting anger of a buffalo was comprehensible, but the aggressive, lawless, meaningless actions of Balanda were just too much.

Transmission of Trauma to Children

The stories above could be multiplied many times, and the conclusion is clear: although in many instances the events occurred long ago, their traumatic effect has been passed from generation to generation. As children were told of the disgusting deeds perpetrated by the dominant culture, the Balanda and other Aboriginal people who took part were portrayed as monsters and the Yolŋu warriors as heroes. The monster image of the Balanda has been internalised at each generational level as *mokuy-mala* (white devil spirits), *bäpi-mala* (snakes) and many other negative images. The fear of Balanda is used to control young Yolŋu children to this day. This is a historical reality, just as Pol Pot has gone down in Cambodian history as a monster.

But it is not just this 'passing on' of history that has the affect of making the people victims. This victimisation is reinforced to every generation by their own experiences of dealing with the dominant culture.

In March 1999 I was told about an old Yolŋu man who had just died. He was travelling into Nhulunbuy when he discovered a section of road that had been upgraded and sealed, over an important piece of land of which he was a prime caretaker. The incident affected him so greatly that he returned to his home community, sat down and died two weeks later. The whole community was shocked and extremely angry with the government department responsible for not seeking permission to do the work. The old man's children—some of them under fifteen years old—now relive the trauma of the past, knowing in their minds that it was the actions of the dominant culture that killed their father. They will now have to grow up without a father.

The young man who told me this story—also in a son relationship to the deceased man—was extremely agitated and tense over the two days I was with him. He kept telling me that he was having great difficulty sleeping and was extremely angry with the Balanda and with himself because he was not able to help his tribal father by somehow stopping the Balanda destroying the important site.

Some will say there is no evidence of intergenerational transmission of trauma, but there is. In an important 1998 book, *International Handbook of Multigenerational Legacies of Trauma*, many papers are presented showing multigenerational legacies of trauma in various groups of people. For example, Vietnam veterans who were sons of fathers who had also served in combat displayed higher levels of PTSD symptoms.[155] The editor of the book, Yael Danieli, states:

> Within the field of traumatic stress, intergenerational transmission of trauma is a relatively recent focus . . . More recently, concern has been voiced about the transmission of pathological intergenerational process to the third and succeeding generations.[156]

The latest research is showing that suicide rates among the children of Australian veterans are three times the expected rate and death by accident is twice the expected rate.[157] Of course, there could be other factors affecting these children. But if it has anything to do with the traumatic experiences of their fathers at war, then it might help us to see why Yolŋu are also suffering from very high levels of self-abuse, accidental death and suicide.

Captives of the Dominant Culture

Another researcher, J. L. Herman, explains that prolonged trauma as well as sudden trauma can lead to PTSD:

> The current diagnostic formulation of PTSD derives primarily from observations of survivors of relatively circumscribed traumatic events: combat, disaster, and rape. It has long been suggested that this formulation fails to capture the protean sequelae [variable medical consequences of other events] of prolonged, repeated trauma. In contrast to the circumscribed traumatic event, prolonged, repeated trauma can only occur only where the victim is in a state of captivity, unable to flee, and under the control of the perpetrator. Examples of such conditions include prisons, concentration camps and slave labour camps. Such conditions also exist in some religious cults, in brothels and other institutions of organized sexual exploitation, and in some families.[158]

Herman goes on to explain that captivity leads to coercive control:

Captivity, which brings the victim into prolonged contact with the perpetrator, creates a special type of relationship, one of coercive control. This is equally true whether the victim is rendered captive primarily by physical force (as in the case of prisoners and hostages,) *or by a combination of physical, economic, social, and psychological means* (as in the case of religious cult members, battered women, and abused children.) (My emphasis)[159]

Chapter 10, 'Living Hell', shows the depths of despair that Yolŋu have reached in their relationship with the dominant culture. They are 'captives', almost totally dependent on the dominant culture for all their needs. The dominant culture now creates and controls the world that has collapsed in on Yolŋu. The dominant culture has become the perpetrator, coercively controlling Yolŋu.

In each generation, Yolŋu lose more and more of their true identity as they become what the perpetrator wants them to be. This is very similar to a woman in a violent, oppressive relationship. The woman is only needed by the perpetrator for her labour and sex; Yolŋu are only needed by the dominant culture for their land, resources and 'culture' for tourism. And for Yolŋu the relationship must be conducted on dominant culture terms, just as for the woman in the oppressive situation the perpetrator sets the rules.

This is not something that was planned; it is simply the nature of the relationship between dominant cultures and indigenous peoples all over the world. For Yolŋu, as for the woman, such a relationship means repeated victimisation and trauma. Marie-Anik Gagne states in her paper on the James Bay Cree:

> ...colonialism is the seed of trauma because it leads to dependency, then to cultural genocide, racism, and alcoholism. These in turn lead to sexual abuse, family violence, child abuse, and accidental death/suicides. . . . Manson et al. (1990, 1996) and O'Nell (1989) have in general found a disproportionately high percentage of First Nation citizens in the USA who suffer from anxiety disorders, exposure to traumatic events, and PTSD.[160]

I am not aware of any similar studies in Australia, but I am positive that if the studies were conducted—in a culturally appropriate way and in the language of the people—the same high levels would be found here.

Why do I worry about this? Because blaming Yolŋu for the crisis they now face is akin to blaming a battered woman, an abused child or a victim of war for the predicament they find themselves in, when the situation is almost totally beyond their control.

Community Violence

This situation is made worse for Yolŋu because the trauma comes at the hands of another community of people, not individual perpetrators. Moreover, it is seen to be deliberate. The US National Center for PTSD says about such 'community violence':

> Natural disasters are uncontrollable and unpreventable, but community violence is the product of people's actions. Even though most survivors of community violence are innocent victims, they may feel guilty, responsible, self-blaming, ashamed, powerless, or inadequate because they wish they could have prevented the violence even though it was beyond their control.[161]

Yolŋu too feel guilty, responsible, self-blaming, ashamed, powerless and inadequate because they wish they could have prevented the violence against their loved ones and their society, even though it was beyond their control.

Many Yolŋu believe—and from their perspective it is easy to see why—that the dominant culture is purposefully setting out to steal all their lands, waters and resources and to destroy them and their society. Because this is seen in most cases to be intentional, the actions of the dominant culture are even more painful and hurt even more deeply. The National Center for PTSD article continues: 'The damage caused by natural disasters is accidental. Community violence involves terrible harm done on purpose, which can lead survivors to feel an extreme sense of betrayal and distrust towards other people.' This has serious consequences for Yolŋu.[162]

Re-Traumatisation and the Agents of Trauma

Much of the stress and trauma in Arnhem Land is the result of past trauma *replayed* and therefore *re-traumatising* the people, in the continuing devastating relationship between Yolŋu and the dominant culture. It is imperative that all who come in contact with Yolŋu realise this, otherwise they too can become agents of this re-traumatisation. Every person who comes into contact with Yolŋu, or who has influence over programs or the lives of Yolŋu in any way, can help to revisit this trauma on the people. No-one is exempt from this possibility.

Even Aboriginal people, especially those who speak English as their first language, can become agents of the dominant culture and therefore agents of re-traumatisation. Often what happens is this: when the dominant culture tries to answer a problem from the dominant culture perspective, inevitably a short-hand solution is decided upon. Normally this involves getting a few Yolŋu or other Aboriginal people who speak English to meet together and design the answers for 'their people'. This can have disastrous consequences, as Freire says:

> But almost always, during the initial stage of the struggle, the oppressed, instead of striving for liberation, tend themselves to become oppressors, or 'sub-oppressors'. The very structure of their thought has been conditioned by the contradictions of the concrete, existential situation by which they were shaped. Their ideal is to be men; but for them, to be a 'man' is to be an oppressor. This is their model of humanity.[163]

Yolŋu generally appreciate Aboriginal people from other areas, both urban and traditional. They have a strong sense of identity in a common struggle against the dominant Australian culture. However, these people also need to be careful that this trust is not betrayed. No one can assume, by virtue of their ethnic origin, that they automatically understand or are somehow magically aligned to another group of people. Nor is anyone exempt from the normal failings of human nature.

Some Yolŋu themselves, hand-picked by the dominant culture rather than chosen by their own people, can become oppressors. Where the dominant culture works through a few chosen Yolŋu or other Aboriginal people instead of working with the whole community, the seeds of cronyism easily germinate. These chosen leaders, irrespective of their original intentions, can easily become corrupted because their position is supported and nurtured by the dominant culture, and therefore by its nature is in opposition to the people's traditional leadership. This leads these dominant culture agents, whether they are Balanda, Yolŋu or other Aboriginal people, to unconsciously build their *own leadership base*—a base which, by the very fact of its existence, is opposed to traditional leadership. So they become agents of trauma for Yolŋu.[164]

Stop the World I Want to Get Off

> There are numerous studies showing that individuals who are exposed to a traumatic event have an increased likelihood of poor self-reported health, morbidity (as indicated by physical examination or laboratory tests), utilisation of medical services, and mortality.[165]

Throughout Arnhem Land there is a common call from both dominant culture personnel and Yolŋu: 'Stop the world I want to get off!' And getting off they are, as is evidenced by the high attrition rates of dominant culture personnel and the ever increasing number of Yolŋu who intellectually and emotionally withdraw from active participation in their communities.

Dominant culture personnel are able to flee the war zone and retreat to the comfort of their own culture and society. However, Yolŋu refugees are left with no option of escape.

'Culture shock', 'future shock', the 'multigenerational legacy of trauma' and 'PTSD' are all recognised phenomena, yet they hardly rate a mention in the discussion of Aboriginal health. They need to be considered very seriously. I believe that here in Arnhem Land we are dealing with severely traumatised people and this is a major contributing cause of their health crisis. Must Yolŋu continue to bear the high cost of being different?

PART FOUR

WARRIORS THEY WERE AND
WARRIORS THEY CAN BE AGAIN

Much of what we have already discussed may leave many feeling that there is little hope for groups of people like Yolŋu. However I do not feel this way.

The facts speak for themselves. Yolŋu survived for many thousands of years in this land with a complex and complete social order to suit their environment. Yes, that environmental mix has changed, but because they were great warriors in a past age they have all the potential necessary to be great warriors again.

The external factors that brought this change to Yolŋu and their lands can be identified. When they are, policies and programs can be developed to counter them. These policies and programs can equip the people, allowing them to be masters again of their own environment.

In Part 4 there are three main themes.

Chapter 12 talks about the cultural processes used by different cultural groups to acquire new knowledge. In this chapter I will compare the Yolŋu cultural process of acquiring new knowledge against how Western doctors acquire the same. Some very interesting similarities exist. But strangely enough while dominant culture generally accepts the Western doctors' process as valid, the Yolŋu processes of acquiring new knowledge is hardly even considered.

Chapter 13 is an analysis of the 'real problem' pulling together historical records, research and other evidence from Arnhem Land and around the world. Its conclusions move us away from the usually held position as to the cause of this crisis that Yolŋu are facing.

Chapter 14 looks at dealing with the primary causes of the crisis instead of the symptoms. Some examples of successful programs to equip the people in their changed environment are also cited.

Yolŋu *were* great warriors and they *can be* great warriors again if some basic things change, so that Yolŋu are truly included in controlling and building their own development.

12
CHAPTER

Owners of Information

The Traditional Learning Process

...educators need to approach learning not merely as the acquisition of knowledge but as the production of cultural practices that offer students a sense of identity, place, and hope.

Giroux[166]

When I had written this chapter, I was not sure where to place it in the context of this book. Yet it is very important and I am sure its contents will shed light on many other things I have already shared. It will highlight further reasons why attempts at Western-style education have failed Yolŋu so badly.

When T. T. Webb came to Milingimbi in 1926, he got to know the people well and started learning Yolŋu Matha and the ways of traditional life. He became convinced that Yolŋu Matha and the people's 'ceremonial life' held the key to their development. He looked to Yolŋu *language* and *law* for the way forward. He said, '...we must secure not merely the consent of his will, but the approval of his intelligence.'[167]

All cultural groups have a defined cultural process for acquiring new knowledge.[168] When, for example, medical doctors from the dominant culture acquire new information, the canons of medical research must be respected or the new information will be rejected. For cultural groups like Yolŋu, it is just as important that we follow the correct cultural process.

Let's spend a little time thinking about how cultural groups acquire new knowledge. What are the cultural processes to assess and verify new knowledge as true and correct knowledge? It is necessary to understand this so that when new knowledge is taught to Yolŋu, it will not be rejected out of hand. If dominant culture people are clear on this, they can help Yolŋu bridge the wide knowledge gap and become effective and fulfilled members of Australian society in the twenty-first century.

Acquiring New Information—Not What, but How

This subject is not something we think about a lot. Within our own particular cultural group we follow the correct procedures almost automatically. But it becomes a problem when one culture—the dominant culture in this case—tries to teach new knowledge to people from a cultural group which as a whole has not yet accepted this particular knowledge as true and correct within its cultural knowledge base.

The older and more established the cultural group, the stronger the traditional process for acquiring new knowledge will be. If we ignore this defined cultural process, our attempts to add new knowledge to the people's pre-existing cultural knowledge base will fail. No matter how sophisticated the methodology or program, it will be totally ineffective because the cultural group will resist it, even if individuals appear to accept it.

Western professional cultural groups like doctors or engineers will not appropriate or accept new information unless it is introduced in the established ways that meets the demands of a time-tested procedure. If a particular educational process is activated to introduce the new knowledge, and it measures up to the demands of that process, then the new knowledge is appropriated. But if the new knowledge is forced on the group through a method that is not acknowledged by them as valid, the new information will most likely be rejected out of hand. For new information to be accepted by any group, the *process* is more important than the *content*.

The 'Right' Process in Balanda Society

I suggest the following are the main principles for all cultural groups in acquiring new knowledge. (There may be many minor elements not mentioned here.) I will list the steps and use a dominant culture example for clarity.

1. The information must come from a credible source. It is important that the person or agency introducing the new knowledge is seen by the cultural group to be credible in relation to the new knowledge. The person must be seen as 'qualified' according to particular cultural criteria. For example, a janitor, a wardsman or probably even a medical sister is not a suitably qualified person to teach or introduce new medical information to doctors. The information has to come from credible research done by qualified personnel.

2. The information must be delivered in a culturally correct way. New information needs to be introduced to the target group through the culturally valid path. For the medical profession, new information would usually be published in medical journals. If it isn't, doctors will not take it seriously.

3. The information must build on culturally accepted truths and knowledge. To be credible, new knowledge must build on other knowledge that has already been accepted by the group. New knowledge that cannot be corroborated in this way will be assessed and then rejected as intellectually incomplete. For doctors, new knowledge has to build on already established medical knowledge that has survived the tests of time and experience.

4. The information must be able to survive intellectual debate. The new knowledge must make intellectual sense to the hearer. Doctors would probably wait to see if new knowledge published in a medical journal survives critiques from the medical community before taking it seriously. But the new knowledge also needs to make intellectual sense to them personally before they will lend it their support.

5. The information must receive peer group affirmation. Only when new information receives peer group affirmation will it be accepted by the cultural group. This happens when many individuals become intellectually convinced that the new knowledge is correct, and these individuals make up a clear majority in the group. Then peer pressure requires those still not convinced to comply. When this happens, the cultural group respects and values the new knowledge, and will go on to maintain, update and re-teach it. This happens because the cultural group now sees this new knowledge as *true* knowledge.

The 'Right' Process in Aboriginal Society

Aboriginal societies also have sophisticated processes for accepting new information. But before examining these, we first need to remember that *within* Aboriginal society there are different cultural groups. The biggest difference is between those Aboriginal people who speak English as their first language and those who speak English as a second, third, fourth, fifth or sixth language. Yolŋu fall into the latter category. They are traditional in nature, still speak their clan languages as first language, live by their ancient law and think with a world-view that is different from some other Aboriginal groups and very different from the dominant culture.

Yolŋu have clearly established cultural processes for appropriating new knowledge. As mentioned earlier in this book, these processes are usually associated with the people's traditional universities and formal educational structures. Non-formal education procedures are also used to train people in many skills. The process I explain here is similar for both the formal and non-formal settings.

1. The information must come from a credible source—the owners of the knowledge. For Yolŋu to accept new knowledge, the information must come from a credible source. Yolŋu believe that the education experience for learning new knowledge must be organised by the 'owners' of that knowledge—that is, those who have the authority to hold or know about that particular thing. In traditional Yolŋu society, information and knowledge are 'owned' by particular groups of people, such as clans. Anyone who comes by that knowledge without being invited by the owners is seen to be breaking the law and harsh penalties apply. This is similar to 'corporate knowledge' and 'intellectual property rights' in Balanda society.

In oral societies, in order to keep information accurate it is made very valuable. So information is rendered sacred and in this way is kept scarce. It is given only to people who are seen as capable of appreciating it in its wholeness. Information is shared only by invitation from the owners and is usually paid for.

There are other divisions in knowledge ownership, such as gender. Women own and maintain the information about reproduction and blood. Men keep and maintain information about political and economic law and rights.

The 'cardinal rule' that any new knowledge must come from those who are seen as its 'owners' has major implications for health education. Who are the people Yolŋu see as the 'owners' of knowledge when it comes to disease and sickness?

When I talk to Yolŋu leaders about this, they say there are two types of *rerri* (sickness): Yolŋu *rerri* and Balanda *rerri*. Yolŋu *rerri* are those sicknesses that the people experienced before contact with Balanda: diarrhoea, light colds, itching, headache, sores, minor boils, minor ear-aches, some sore eyes, muscle aches and so on. The people have medicines for these: herbal medicines from a large range of plants and other things, like breast milk and white fire ash, as sterile cleaning agents. Their bandages were paper bark from the melaleuca tree, rich in tea tree oil—a natural antiseptic—traditionally secured with bush string.

Diseases like leprosy and yaws are recognised as coming from Macassan contact. All other sicknesses and diseases are seen as coming from Balanda.

Even some Yolŋu sicknesses are far worse now than they were before Balanda contact. As one old man said, 'Things like sore ears, the children have them all the time now. Before Balanda came only a few children had small ear-aches that lasted only a few days.' It is the same, he said, with sores and boils: 'People have big boils all the time, where before they would only get a small boil now and then. The children have sores all the time now, but before they only had small sores that healed up quickly. Even some of the Yolŋu *rerri* are now a bit like Balanda sicknesses,' he continued. 'They are much worse than they were before Balanda came. If Balanda understand these diseases and they have knowledge of why some of our old sicknesses are worse than before, then Balanda should teach us about them.'

The rest of the sicknesses and diseases are clearly seen as 'Balanda *rerri*'. These include pneumonia, all the STDs, flu, measles, mumps and so on, plus all the lifestyle diseases like diabetes, heart attack, hypertension, cancer, renal disease and stroke.

According to the proper process for appropriating knowledge, Balanda *rerri* come from Balanda and that makes Balanda the 'owners' of that knowledge. If this is how Yolŋu see things—and I know it is—then it is up to Balanda to teach the whole Yolŋu cultural group about these Balanda diseases. It is no good teaching this information to a few Yolŋu people and hoping they can teach their community. They cannot. People will not listen to them because they are not seen as the owners of the knowledge.

2. The information must be delivered in the 'culturally correct' way. The correct way for new information to enter the Yolŋu cultural group is with the approval of their respected political leaders (*ḏalkarra/djirrikay*) or 'elders'. These leaders are the ones selected by their own clans to protect their rights, much like politicians are elected in contemporary Australian society to protect the rights of Australian citizens. They also hold the knowledge about life and how to live; therefore the education process must be approved and controlled by these leaders before going to the rest of the citizens within their clan. Traditional education is usually taught through the clan structure where the owners of the information educate the clan.

There are two educational misconceptions that dominant Australian culture has about traditional Aboriginal society. I understand these misconceptions because I held them dearly myself until the people taught me I was wrong. They are:

(1) teach the children first and they will teach the adults, and

(2) teach some elders and they will convince others.

Misconception 1: Teach the children first and they will teach the adults.

Most dominant culture Australians, I believe, would agree that the best way to educate Aboriginal people is through their children. 'Start the children in school as early as possible and then they will be able to teach their people,' we say. In fact, this process is flawed and very destructive. For a start, it does not take into account the cardinal rule about the ownership of knowledge. But there are other problems with it as well.

Consider a parallel example. Suppose Japan had won the war and Japanese people were now the dominant cultural group in Australia. It is quite probable the Japanese authorities would use the same methods to teach the European community as dominant Australian culture uses to teach indigenous communities—that is, through the children. They would consider it good policy to indoctrinate the European Australian community by educating its children 'while they were young'. Of course, they would do this in the Japanese language, so the children could influence their parents about the Japanese way of living and thinking.

If this happened, how would the European Australian community respond? I believe there would be two main responses. First, I am sure the European community would be repulsed by this methodology, resisting it at every opportunity. Secondly, any knowledge given to the children that, from the adult European community's point of view, was strange and new would be rejected—totally.

This would leave the children caught in the middle. When they came home from school and asked their parents if something worked like this or that, their parents would say, 'I don't know. I thought that's what you went to school for!' Or if it were some knowledge that conflicted with the parents' pre-existing cultural knowledge base, the parents might respond: 'You don't want to believe that rubbish. They're just telling you that so you'll be confused. We know how that works. It's like such and such.' Imagine the confusing effect this would have on the child, on the child's faith in their parents, and on the educational process.

It is impossible for children in any society to influence their elders to the point of changing their cultural behaviour. The only influences that do occur in this type of education are all negative:

• it leads to an immense generation gap between children and parents;

• the children lose faith in their parents and elders, seeing them as unsophis-ticated and irrelevant;

• the children suffer a deep identity crisis when they reach the age of transition from childhood to adulthood, leading to unsociable behaviour such as substance abuse and vandalism.

• the children go on to become dysfunctional adults, suffering from a severe identity crisis, participating in continual substance abuse, violence and delinquent parenting behaviour, self-abuse and suicide.

All this happens because the knowledge the children are receiving at school does not fit with the cultural knowledge base of the parents and elders of their cultural group. This leads to tremendous intellectual conflict.

Now transfer this scenario to Yolŋu. Say the children learn about bacteria at school using a microscope, then go home and tell their parents they saw little things in water that can cause sickness. If the parents have never seen bacteria, or the whole world of bacteria and their relationship to sickness is not part of the parents' cultural knowledge base, the children's explanation would sound very strange. The word 'bacteria' itself would be gobbledygook and give the parents no picture whatsoever. The conversation might go something like this:

Parent: 'Don't tell me funny things like that. We know the Balanda have got secret knowledge about these things and if they really wanted us to know the truth, they would come and talk to our important people instead of tricking you children.'

Children: 'But we saw them.'

Parent: 'Yes, but the Balanda have got lots of tricks. Do you see them coming here and trying to tell us that funny story? No, because they know they can't trick old people like us. But they can trick you easily because you're only children with no experience of life.'

Or what if someone tries to tell the children that smoking is bad for their health? If this is taught to the children before it is taught to the adults in the culturally correct way, the information will be strongly rejected. The old people will say, 'Tobacco was here before Balanda. It's part of our ancient law that was given to us by the Great Creator Spirit. We sing songs about it and about its effects on us. These songs are very, very old. They call tobacco a holy substance. Who are these Balanda to tell you young people bad things about tobacco? Have they come to us old people and tested their knowledge about these things with us, the great debaters? Do they know the song cycles for tobacco? No, we know they don't and we know they won't come and test their knowledge. Why don't they mind their own business instead of trying to destroy our culture?'[169]

Trying to teach Yolŋu through their children is simply the worst form of neo-colonial imperialism. It will only harden the people's resistance to the dominant culture schooling system.

There are other effects suffered by the students themselves. I remember in the mid-1970s when a number of young people were sent to college and then returned to their community. I worked with many of them over hundreds of hours. One of their major complaints was that the old people did not understand them. This was not just a minor generation gap; some of these young men were unable even to talk with their own fathers. Many young people returning from college went straight onto the grog in Darwin, believing and saying, 'To be drunk is to be in heaven'. They were very confused.

I remember one young woman standing around her parents' home with a bag on her shoulder all the time, as though she was about to go away somewhere, anywhere. Her Western education had divided her from her people. She ended up a road accident victim in Darwin, run down by a car while she was drunk.

The elitist education system promoted by the dominant culture has much to answer for. We cannot continue to educate just a few of the people, hoping this will change things. We simply end up setting the people against each other, creating crisis in community.[170] The crisis occurs when newly Western-educated Yolŋu return to their communities and see their own people at a lower standard than they assess themselves to be. Many either become so disillusioned that they leave their communities and become drunks in Darwin or elsewhere; or they survive—there are a few who do—and set themselves up as community leaders in opposition to the traditional clan leaders.

Misconception 2: Teach some elders and they will convince their people.

I also held to this principle until it took the old man I was working with to an early grave. Let me explain.

About four months before he died, the old man, who was a clan leader, called me back to Ramingining to see him. I had been down south for a year due to my own ill health. The old man, my Yolŋu uncle in relationship terms, had taught me much about traditional law, and in return I had taught him much about Balanda economics and law. When I had to leave Ramingining, I left feeling he would be able to carry on teaching this new information to his people.

At the time of my departure, my adopted uncle was the chairman of the Ramingining council. Under his leadership the council controlled and did most of the work on their own community. He had an excellent understanding of contemporary legal requirements. For example, he was the first Yolŋu person at Ramingining to take out a hire purchase agreement for a motor vehicle and to understand what it meant. So when he called me to his sick bed, I was shocked to hear what he had to say.

After we exchanged the normal greetings my uncle said to me: 'Nephew, you must return to Arnhem Land when you are better and teach all Yolŋu the ways of your people.'

I was stunned. 'But you already know the foundational laws of the Balanda,' I protested. 'Weren't you able to teach them?'

'When I go to my people to tell them about Balanda ways, they listen to me while I am there with them because they find it hard to be disrespectful in front of me. But when I turn my back and leave them, they say things like, "How does he know about Balanda ways? Has he been to a Balanda university or to Canberra? No, he hasn't. If the Balanda have these laws and ways that he's talking about, why don't they come here and teach all of us?" In the end,' he concluded, 'they say, "He's just trying to make himself a big person so he can lord it over us".'

I had believed that if I just taught *him*, a respected clan elder, he would be able to teach his own people knowledge about the Balanda world. But I was wrong. This man died within the year with a heavy heart because his people would not listen to him.

New knowledge needs to be taught to the *whole* cultural group through the correct procedure. For doctors this is through a medical journal; for Yolŋu it must be through their traditional political leaders. But the process cannot stop there or it will fail. The new information must be taught by the dominant culture educator to the whole group, through the process the leaders suggest and approve. In other words, the education is done *with* and *through* the elders, *by* the dominant culture educator.

> . . . so-called 'leadership training courses' . . . are based on the naïve assumption that one can promote the community by training its leaders—as if it were the parts that promote the whole and not the whole which, in being promoted, promotes the parts. . . As soon as they complete the course and return to the community with resources they did not formerly possess, they either use these resources to control the submerged and dominated consciousness of their comrades, or they become strangers in their own communities and their former leadership position is threatened. In order not to lose their leadership status, they will probably tend to continue manipulating the community, but in a more efficient manner.[171]

The only education that will work for Yolŋu (when new knowledge is being delivered) is education of the whole community. This will end up costing less than the present system and will meet Yolŋu cultural requirements so that new knowledge can be assimilated.

3. The information must build on culturally accepted knowledge and truths.
In Yolŋu society, as in all cultural groups, new knowledge is rejected out of hand if it is not built on existing, culturally accepted knowledge. Within their cultural knowledge base, Yolŋu have a huge amount of knowledge about the world around them. For any subject Yolŋu ask themselves, '*Nhä dhudi dhäwu yuwalktja?* (What is the true, bottom or foundational story for this particular subject?)' This 'bottom story' is the objective truth about a subject. Any new knowledge must not conflict with good solid evidence and culturally accepted truths.

In October 1997 I became involved with a Yolŋu family because one of their relatives had suffered renal failure. The family wanted to know what caused the kidney failure and when it might have happened. 'We really love this person and we want to know who or what has caused her kidneys to fail,' they said. They listened to the information they were given and connected it with the knowledge they already had about the family member. They wanted an explanation of the *full* medical facts, in Yolŋu Matha, and cross-examined all the medical people involved. It was only when the family could see in their 'mind's eye' what had happened to the kidneys that they were satisfied.

All cultural groups treat information that cannot be corroborated from within their cultural knowledge base as suspect. Therefore new knowledge must build on existing, culturally accepted truths and knowledge.

4. The information must be able to survive intellectual debate. Yolŋu are very much like the ancient Greek philosophers. When they come across new knowledge, they discuss it over and over to see if it stacks up. New knowledge must survive the rigours of intellectual debate from within the cultural group. It will only do that if it is true and builds on their accepted cultural knowledge base.

This means new knowledge taken to traditional Aboriginal people has to be intellectually thorough or it will be rejected. I have found that when new knowledge meets this requirement, the intellectual debate within the cultural group starts to teach others within the group who were not part of the original educational process. I have come across 'introduced' knowledge that I taught in one community that has been carried hundreds of kilometres to other communities.

The dominant culture keeps coming up with all sorts of programs that do little more than insult the people's intelligence. The earliest of these I remember was 'Hookworm Charlie'. Charlie was a cartoon character who got hookworm. I remember asking a group of Yolŋu who had just watched 'Hookworm Charlie' for the third time what they had learned about hookworm and how to avoid getting them.

'It was funny!' they said in Yolŋu Matha.

'But what did you learn out of the film?'

'It was funny!' they repeated.

The film made a joke of a serious matter.

The dominant culture, because it names the people as simple, looks for simple things in its educational endeavours for them. But Yolŋu are highly intellectual people. Serious matters must be portrayed seriously, meeting people's intellectual requirements. The cartoon character, flannel-graph, flipchart and poster mentality that prevails in Aboriginal education belittles Yolŋu educational requirements and insults the people intellectually. No wonder it doesn't work.

I am not challenging these educational media; sometimes they can be used very effectively. But I am challenging the common mentality behind their use. Most of the educational material presented in this way is very simple, sometimes medically incorrect and does not meet the people's intellectual needs. The same mentality exists in video production.

From my experience, Yolŋu in general expect many more answers to the questions in their minds than most dominant culture people do. This could be because Yolŋu are dealing with knowledge from another cultural group, so it needs a bit more investigation to establish a well-supported fact in their minds. The same thing occurs when dominant culture people try to understand knowledge from the Yolŋu cultural knowledge base; many Yolŋu think Balanda ask the 'same old silly questions' about their culture all the time.

5. The information must receive peer group affirmation. For new knowledge to be accepted, maintained, updated and re-taught by a cultural group, peer affirmation of this new knowledge *must* occur. In traditional Yolŋu society, *more than two-thirds* of the adult community needs to be convinced about new knowledge so that peer affirmation can occur.

As already noted, it is not good enough for only the elders to receive the new knowledge, and the same applies to any other individual group within the larger cultural group, including health workers, schoolteachers and other Yolŋu professionals. All the clan must be involved, because the elders or others cannot be seen as being out of step with the rest of their clan or community. Elders and Western-educated Yolŋu must be seen as *ŋayaŋu waŋgany* (having a oneness of mind, body and soul with their people).

When new knowledge is delivered to the whole group, the group will all participate in active debate over:

• the credibility of the educator to know and teach this strange new knowledge;

• whether it was delivered in the culturally correct way;

• whether it was built on culturally accepted knowledge and truths;

• whether it survived the intellectual debate.

Only when a cultural group has worked through all these things and the new knowledge has survived, will it receive peer group affirmation.

I am not saying, of course, that anyone actually goes around with a clipboard and ticks off these things—that would be nonsense. This process simply happens as part of everyday living. Although it is a natural human process it is, however, very strong, and individuals within the group will defend it with vigour. Many messengers (including unsuspecting Yolŋu) have been rejected when bringing a 'correct' and even important message, because it has been delivered in the wrong way.

When the majority of a group sees some new knowledge as true and valuable, then it will be maintained, updated and re-taught. This maintenance, updating and re-teaching will be done from within the cultural group, not needing outside educators. This is no different from the way doctors maintain, update and re-teach new knowledge that they have accepted as valuable. It does not need the original researcher to maintain, update and re-teach it.

There are those who will point out that these principles are the same for all cultures, including contemporary dominant Australian culture, and this is true. The reason I need to write about them here is that when we come to providing education to Yolŋu, these fundamental educational truths are forgotten, shortcuts are taken and the education fails. But if new knowledge is taught by the 'owners of knowledge' through the culturally correct path, with content built on pre-existing truths, and if it is able to survive intellectual debate and receive peer group affirmation, then it will be maintained and re-taught, allowing Yolŋu to equip themselves and regain control of their lives in a modern context.

13
CHAPTER

Treating the Symptoms or the Cause?

An Analysis of the Problem

Perhaps it would be useful for public health specialists to start talking about a new category of disease . . . Such diseases could be called the 'diseases of development' and would consist of those pathological conditions which are based on the usually unanticipated consequences of the implementation of development schemes

Hughes & Hunter[172]

*W*arriors they were and warriors they can be again. Such is the underlying greatness of Yolŋu. Currently the revitalisation of their potential has been put on hold or at worst is being snuffed out. But Yolŋu can be a strong and vibrant people again.

This can only happen, however, if the dominant culture of this land will be responsible and creative enough to meet the challenge. The people cannot move on their own because they are not the only actors in this drama. The dominant culture must move first. Then, with the systems and knowledge needed, Yolŋu will be empowered to respond to the challenges facing them.

The state of health of Yolŋu at this time is chronically poor. The East Arnhem Region health statistics for 1985-91 (the latest published at time of writing) show a death rate 5.39 times the national average.[173] Unpublished figures supplied by the Territory Health Services suggest that this rate is decreasing, but this may in part be due to improved collection methods for obtaining population statistics. In May 1997 the THS published *A Draft Northern Territory Aboriginal Public Health Action Strategy*, which shows comparisons of death rates for the whole of the Northern Territory between Aboriginal and non-Aboriginal residents between 1993 and 1995 as follows:[174]

Heart & Circulatory condition	2.7	to	1
Respiratory disease	4.7	to	1
Diabetes mellitus	5.7	to	1
Kidney failure	8.0	to	1

These figures do not show regional differences, but if we were to factor in the regional variation shown by Plant et al (1995) then the death rate ratios for some of these diseases for East Arnhem Region would, I believe, be higher. The extent of the problem can be seen when we read in *The Chronicle* of THS's Chronic Diseases Network: 'the occurrence of end-stage renal disease [in some Northern Territory Aboriginal communities is] up to 50 times higher than the national average'.[175]

However we look at the statistics, the Yolŋu in Arnhem Land have a major problem in terms of health.

A Look at the Past

People often ask me, 'Have Yolŋu always been sick like this?' The question comes because dominant culture people tend to think that life must be better now than it was a decade or two ago.

It is hard to come up with comparative figures for health—none were kept in the past. But there are some well-recorded observations available:

> In 1957 Dr Hargrave examined 713 [Aboriginal] people out of 800-900 and found one with hypertension and one obese. In 1992 Dr Hoy found 30% overweight, 25% with early renal disease and 25% with advanced renal disease among adults.[176]

Jess Smith, who was the health sister at Milingimbi from 1954-71 and 1973-80, does not remember a large number of deaths from epidemics in that period. She says:

> I was told that a measles epidemic occurred in 1949 and deaths had occurred then. Again in 1969 many people came down with measles but no deaths. I can only remember one outbreak of scabies in about 1968 when the whole camp was treated. Hookworm was a continual problem throughout my time in Arnhem Land.

> There was some tuberculosis in earlier years and leprosy in small numbers right throughout my time. In about 1970 Milingimbi had an outbreak of 'Milingimbi Syndrome' with about 70-80 people coming down with severe headache, backache, fever and blood in the urine. The cause was never identified. None of the present day chronic diseases were present.[177]

Other writings, such as the *Records of the American-Australian Scientific Expedition to Arnhem Land* conducted in 1948,[178] indicate similar findings. A large number of Yolŋu from three communities were studied at that time. Nowhere in these records is there any reference to the general, chronic health problems that now exist. Graphs showing height for age for males in the 3-20 year age group placed Yolŋu on a comparable standard to white Australians.[179] Mean weights for male and female Yolŋu in the 3-15 year age group were down as against white Australians.[180] Testing during this expedition was extensive: 'Records were kept of any evidence of disease such as yaws, leprosy, tinea, scabies and tuberculosis'.[181] Many of the diseases common among Yolŋu today were not even recorded.

However, Yolŋu did have problems with sickness and disease in the past. Some of the old writings record a little of this. T. T. Webb wrote in 1951:

> The Aboriginal will survive an almost unbelievable amount of physical injury, because his hard and difficult life has evolved within him extraordinary powers of recovery. Yet at the same time they will die off like flies before such ailments as influenza, measles, and the like. That is because these things are new to them, and there has not been built up within them any measure of resistance or immunity to such things.[182]

Maisie McKenzie records an example:

> In May 1917 the [Goulburn] Island was hit by a malaria epidemic which raged through Arnhem Land from west to east. Lawrence [a missionary] became so ill that he had to be taken to Darwin, and after that every man, woman, and child contracted the disease in varying degrees of severity.[183]

Other records from 1948 relating to health show that Yolŋu did suffer immensely when diseases were introduced for which they had no immunity. This was common to indigenous people all over the world when they were first colonised by Europeans. There are few references to epidemics in Arnhem Land mainly because they were simply not recorded. The 1948 American-Australian Expedition witnessed only one epidemic:

> At all four settlements visited, there was at least one epidemic of coryza [inflammation of the mucous membranes of the nose], during the expedition's visit. The entire population succumbed in each instance with complete recovery within five days. At Yirrkala most cases progressed to an acute bronchitis, but no cases were severely affected and all recovered.[184]

It appears that the people suffered badly from these introduced diseases up until the mid-1940s when they must have developed a level of immunity. From anecdotal evidence, the mortality rates appear to have dropped dramatically at this time. By the mid-1950s Yolŋu experienced a real population growth; it was said that Milingimbi had one of the highest population growth rates in the world, although I have no figures to support this. Well-documented records do exist at Milingimbi, but I have not accessed them in recent years.

The other evidence we have of the past fitness of Yolŋu is the photographic records. These all show a very fit and healthy looking group of people compared with today's standards.

When the 1948 Expedition visited Arnhem Land, most people were still living in their traditional housing, considered by Balanda to be of a 'Third World' standard. Yet scabies infestations were almost non-existent.[185] Today, with modern housing, scabies are rife and people are dying from the complications of the disease (renal failure and rheumatic heart disease). Specialists have said to me privately, 'In the next few years Yolŋu will be dying from scabies alone'.

In the early 1970s I knew Yolŋu to be a physically strong race of people. In the mid-1970s one nursing sister and two health workers were able to look after the needs of a community of, say, 800 people. This is in vivid contrast to today. There are much fewer older people now, and the remaining adults are sickly with many illnesses and diseases. People in their thirties suffer from high blood pressure, heart attacks, strokes, cancer, renal failure, obesity and gout. These days it takes three nursing sisters and many Yolŋu health workers to look after the same number of people.

The burden of sickness and disease seems to me to have quadrupled in the twenty-six year period I have been associated with Arnhem Land. Doctors have told me, 'It's not a matter of treating the patient for all their complaints; it's only possible to treat their major health issue.' Patients seem to have so many health problems it is just not possible to deal with them all in the time available.

Looking for the Primary Cause

We have covered a lot of ground in this book. Many of the factors contributing to the Yolŋu crisis in living, and especially their deplorable state of health, have been explored. But are there any clearly identifiable *primary* and *secondary* causes? If there are, they need to be analysed and grouped so the *primary* causes can be identified and proper programs developed to eliminate them at their origin.

This question reminds me of a story from my early community development training days. It goes something like this.

The Babies on the River

A long time ago a community development officer went to work with a group of people who lived in an isolated rainforest. Their village was in a large clearing beside a beautiful river. The development worker had come, hoping he could help the villagers towards modernisation.

As he sat learning the people's language and getting to know them, the people came to him with a problem. That morning one of the villagers had pulled a cradle from the river with a baby in it. They asked the development worker if he knew where the baby might have come from. He said he did not know; he was a stranger to the area and did not know the source of the river.

'You must know where the baby came from,' he said to the people.

'No,' the villagers replied. 'We don't know the country up the river from us. According to our ancient ways and law, we are forbidden to enter other people's country, so many of us have never been out of our village area. As well, we are frightened of those foreign places because we can't speak their language or understand their foreign ways. You are an outsider who comes from that foreign world, so we thought you might have an answer for us.'

But the worker did not have an answer. In the end the villagers decided to keep the baby and look after it as one of their own.

Life went back to normal for a while and then another baby was found on the river. Again the people came to the development worker and asked him what should they do. 'Seeing you and I don't know where the baby is from, we'd better just look after the baby,' he said.

A week or so passed and again a baby came down the river. Then another week, another baby. Each time the people came to the development worker to ask for his advice, he could think of nothing to say except, 'Look after the babies'.

Soon the villagers were pulling a baby out of the river every day. Eventually the worker said to them, 'Now there are so many babies we must build an orphanage for them.'

'An orphanage?' the people said. 'We don't know what an "orphanage" is.'

The development worker explained that in the foreign world outside the village, an orphanage was used by the city people to solve this type of problem. At this the villagers became excited. If an 'orphanage' worked for the city people then surely it would work for them. They asked the worker how they should build it and started work the very next day.

The orphanage was built right in the middle of the village, and when it was finished the people and the worker looked at it with pride. After a couple of weeks, however, none of the babies had been taken there. The people were still looking after them in their homes. So the worker told them to bring the babies and put them in the orphanage.

'But who will look after them?' the people asked.

'People will have to come and work in the orphanage,' the worker explained.

'But how can we do that when we have our own families to look after?' they wondered.

Both the worker and the villagers walked back to their homes disappointed. The worker had thought the people understood what an orphanage was about, but obviously they did not. The people, on the other hand, did not know anything about an orphanage, or if in fact it was really the answer they wanted. When they had asked the worker for advice, they thought he would give them a sophisticated, city people's answer that would solve their problem, not one that would create more work.

So for a long time the orphanage just sat there in the middle of the village. The babies continued to come down the river. Each time another one arrived, the worker lamented the fact that the orphanage was not being used and that all the energy and resources he and the villagers had put into it had gone to waste. In the end he decided to run the orphanage himself, and at the same time teach the people how to run it.

A number of years passed and at last the orphanage was full of babies. The development worker still did most of the work because the people found the whole idea of keeping babies in a place by themselves, rather than with families, very cruel. But they continued to help the worker in different ways because they felt sorry for him. They also provided all the food and resources for the orphanage. This took up much of their time and made them extremely poor, with sometimes not enough to eat themselves.

One night the worker sat talking to a visitor who had come from the big city to see how the development work was going. He spoke about how over the past two years the people had become poorer and poorer because of the strain that all the babies put on the village. He was very sad.

The visitor listened carefully to the worker's hopes and dreams for the development of the village. It was obvious to him that the arrival of the 'river-babies' had stopped the worker's modernisation plan. He also wondered where these babies were coming from. 'Why don't you go up the river and find out?' he asked. 'If you can discover the *reason* behind the problem, maybe you can really help the people *solve* the problem and then get back to real development.'

The worker was excited about this. But then he said, 'I can't go because I'm so busy in the orphanage. It would collapse if I were not there even for a day.' So the visitor said, 'I'll look after the orphanage while you're away.'

The next morning the worker and the visitor were up very early. First the worker showed the visitor what to do in the orphanage. Then the worker packed for his trip up the river to find the real solution to the problem. As he left the village in a canoe, heading up the river, a thought occurred to him. He should have done this when the problem first appeared. Then maybe the villagers and he would not have had to suffer so much.

It might be hard for us to understand why the development worker did not go up the river much sooner. It seems the obvious thing to do. But before we get too critical of him, we need to see that dominant Australian culture is just like the worker. The dominant culture has been very good at creating all sorts of programs to care for the 'river-babies' on behalf of the people, but almost no resources have been spent on discovering and dealing with the primary causes— why the 'river-babies' are coming down the river in the first place.

Until this is done, the 'river-babies' will continue to come and resources will continue to be wasted on programs that do not work for the people but actually make their problem worse.

Posing the 'Million Dollar' Question

About the middle of 1997, a community nursing sister who had been in Arnhem Land for many years asked me, 'Richard, what is wrong? The people now have good water supplies, good sewerage systems and good housing. But they're still sick and dying. What else do we have to do? What's missing? Have we done something wrong?'

This sister was at a complete loss when it came to improving the people's health. Like many others, she had believed that if the people's living conditions improved, their health would improve. Now she had been in the community long enough to see that this was not so.

While environmental changes are important in the overall health strategy, there *is* another underlying cause that has a greater effect on health and well-being. So what is it?

I find this question difficult to respond to concisely because the answer demands that those asking the question *see things in a new way*. People from the dominant culture in particular need to have a *critical* understanding of what is happening to Yolŋu and then to take the first steps to *make a difference*.

The 'million dollar' questions for Arnhem Land are: What are the 'river-babies', the *secondary symptoms*, and what are the factors that lead to the 'babies' being put on the river, the *primary causes*? When we have these answers we will understand the real causes behind the chronic health conditions that Yolŋu now face.

After years of reflection and interaction with Yolŋu, I do not for one minute believe that their primary problem lies in:

• some inherent weakness in the people themselves;

• their physical conditions, such as lack of housing or sewerage;

• the fact that a low level of English literacy exists.

In many places the people are living in what could be classed as deplorable physical conditions, yet there is more Western-type housing in Arnhem Land now than has ever existed for the same population base. Good community infrastructure in most cases is in place. Is the problem that the housing and infrastructure are not being maintained, or that the housing stock is diminishing as quickly as it is established? Both these things are true, but why is it so? Overcrowding and lack of housing stock is one of the symptoms, not a primary cause.

Others suggest the cause is low levels of English literacy. Are they saying that only those who can read English are capable of 'knowing'? This is not supported by researchers like Bernado, the recipient of the 1996 UNESCO International Award for Literacy Research, where he states:

> The absence of any clear direct effects of literacy on any of the cognitive functions studied poses major problems for the development view that literacy leads to global changes in thought, particularly changes towards more abstract and formal thinking.[186]

High levels of English literacy would give the people more access to contemporary knowledge, but unless the other issues raised in this book are dealt with, the people could end up with a *lesser* capacity to know and think than they had traditionally.

These kinds of suggestions, I am afraid, do not come from serious analysis. And with poor analysis we start treating the symptoms rather than the primary causes. If the symptoms remain the focus of everyone's efforts, 'the problem' will never be solved. As Dr Peter Evans asserts, 'Something else, something much deeper, causes their lives to ebb away, causes so many to die so young and not a few to take their lives. Other factors launch them upon a journey towards early death.'[187]

In a study of 3,617 American men and women by Lantz et al, we see that factors other than unhealthy behaviours can cause high mortality rates:

> These factors include:
> 1. A lack of social relationships and social supports;
> 2. Personality dispositions, such as the loss of a sense of mastery, optimism, control and self-esteem or heightened levels of anger and hostility;
> 3. Chronic and acute stress in daily life and work, including the stress of racism, class distinction and other phenomena related to the social distribution of power and resources.[188]

Many of these factors, as we have seen, are present in the Yolŋu context. Other evidence strengthens the argument. Westin et al describe the medical consequences over a four-year period for dismissed factory workers following the closure of a sardine factory in Bergen on the west coast of Norway.[189] The unemployment following the closure had a devastating effect on people. Three times as many ended up on disability pensions than in the control group of the study, which was in a factory that continued to operate.

It is usually assumed that people receive disability pensions because of a work-related accident or such. But in this situation, people were no longer able to work and provide for their families because they had lost *meaningful employment*. A follow-up study showed that this level of disability continued for five to ten years after the closure of the factory.[190]

For people involved in factory closures, loss of meaningful employment can lead to loss of work-skills mastery, loss of optimism, loss of control and self-esteem, and heightened levels of anger. These are serious causes of poor health. And Yolŋu face them all.

The Trip up the River

Readers who have travelled the length of this book have already met the primary factors behind the people's problems. All these can be summed up in one phrase: The people have suffered *an almost total loss of control* over their lives and living environment.

Words from my early community development training echo in my head: 'It's all a matter of control—*whose*?' When control of the lives of a whole group of people lies in someone else's hands—in the case of Yolŋu, in the hands of the dominant culture—hopelessness will inevitably result. With such hopelessness the people lose the very will to live.

It is ironic that the policies of recent eras—self-determination, self-management and currently self-reliance and self-sufficiency—have failed to put control in the people's hands. Well-stated policies will never in themselves give control to the people. Whether they work or not will always depend on how they are applied, and it is in their application that these policies have failed.

Many Yolŋu do not even know what the terms self-determination, self-management, self-reliance and self-sufficiency mean, and they have no linguistic tools (like dictionaries) to find out. Right from day one Yolŋu expectations and dominant culture expectations of these policies were completely different. Many Yolŋu thought these terms related to some form of independence, but they quickly became disillusioned as the impact of modern dominant culture development continued like a steamroller and the people became its victims. The end result of this victimisation was near-total dependence on the dominant culture to answer all their needs and wants. Any group of people who are affected this way will inevitably suffer from poor physical condition, ill-maintained housing and community infrastructures, malnutrition, destructive social behaviour, vandalism, lack of desire for education, substance abuse, neglected individuals, violence, suicide, and high levels of morbidity and mortality.

These are the 'river-babies', the symptoms that are visible when either the health professionals or others from the dominant culture visit the community or when they, in Darwin or Canberra, read or talk about the Arnhem Land communities. The outsiders are usually good at setting up structures and programs in an attempt to deal with these symptoms. But these structures and programs:

• are outside answers and therefore culturally inappropriate and alienating;

• demand a large amount of outside support and many resources, which are then not available to address the primary causes;

• do not address the primary causes and therefore do not solve the problem.

For over twenty years I have worked with Yolŋu, lived with Yolŋu, attended their places of learning, and been with them in their traditional councils of law. I have participated in scores of personal health interventions, talked with Yolŋu after the death of relatives, and been with them in endless workplace situations. I have assisted people returning to their traditional homeland estates, worked with them as they built their own airstrips, and helped them set up schools and communication systems. From all this I know that when the people have *heard* all the relevant information in a language they understand, *initiated* a response or intervention that fits their cultural ways, and then *physically brought into being* what they have decided upon, 'the problem' seems to fade and almost disappear.

When the people have control over their lives, they know they are as human as dominant culture people. This allows them to be proud and to be actively involved in their destiny. Control is the essence of good health.

Others in the Same Boat

Others have also seen that good health can have more to do with a person's sense of control over their life than with the good things others give them or do for them. Professor S Leonard Syme, for example, reports the results of a twenty-year research project. His own health interventions were failing, so he went looking for answers. His findings show that 60% of some diseases seem to relate more to the client's level of control over their lives than to socio-economic factors.[191]

Syme's work was in an American setting, yet he also refers to research by Michael Marmot covering British Civil Servants. He cites: 'British Civil Servants at the very bottom of the Civil Service hierarchy have heart disease rates four times higher than those at the top.' This supports other research findings. However, there is something more surprising:

> [British Civil Servants] one step down from the top of the hierarchy, Civil Servants who are professionals and executives, such as doctors and lawyers, have heart disease rates that are twice as high as those at the top; those at the very top being upper-class directors of agencies, all of whom have been educated at Oxford and Cambridge and whose career usually ends with a knighthood.

Syme continues:

> It is not surprising that those at the bottom have higher rates of disease than those at the top but it is surprising that doctors and lawyers one step from the top also have higher rates. Doctors and lawyers are not poor, they do not have bad houses or bad medical care, they do not have poor education or poor nutrition. It is not just those at the bottom.

Feeling good about yourself and in control of your life is clearly linked to good health. If British Civil Servants, who operate within their own language, political, economic and social systems, suffer from loss of control and consequential bad health, how much more difficult will it be for minority cultural groups like Yolŋu?

The Symptoms and the Primary Causes

Yolŋu then have almost totally lost control of their lives and living environment as the dominant culture has moulded them to fit its own reality. Some are coping very well against all the odds, but the majority are collapsing from the unrelenting strain. The 'river-babies' or *secondary* symptoms are:

• poor physical conditions

• hopelessness

• apathy

• overcrowded living conditions

• housing and community infrastructure not maintained

• disinterest in education and training

• malnutrition

• destructive social behaviour

• vandalism

• lawlessness

• chronic substance abuse

• neglected individuals

• violence

• suicide

• unemployment

• possibly post-traumatic stress disorder

• high levels of morbidity and mortality

These secondary conditions are the direct result of the *primary* cause: the people's almost total LOSS OF CONTROL.

This loss of control can be attributed to a number of factors. The best way for us to see all these factors is to list them out, starting at the point of contact with Western society. These factors are:

1. Yolŋu clans' and nations' loss of sovereignty;

2. The dominant culture 'naming' Yolŋu culture with demeaning names;

3. The dominant culture's non-recognition of traditional law and Yolŋu legal codes;

4. The dominant culture's non-recognition of Yolŋu proprietary property rights;

5. The dominant culture's non-recognition of thirteen years of war, and Yolŋu victories over pastoralists;

6. Introduction of many Western diseases to Yolŋu in one lifetime;

7. Unacknowledged traditional economic system, national and international trade;

8. The dominant culture's destruction of trepang, pearling and crocodile skin industry and trade;

9. Unacknowledged massacres and slaughter early this century;

10. Many Yolŋu forced off their estates to live on missions and settlements;

11. Institutionalisation during welfare era;

12. Traditional health systems and knowledge not acknowledged;

13. Total economic collapse in Arnhem Land;

14. Yolŋu economics replaced with Balanda rations and modern welfare;

15. Rampant, debilitating dependency and learned helplessness;

16. Yolŋu confused about dominant culture world, in particular economics and wealth generation;

17. Yolŋu confused about dominant culture authority, legal and political systems;

18. Yolŋu confused about disease causation and modern medicines;

19. Yolŋu confused about dominant culture technical development;

20. Yolŋu confused about dominant culture agriculture, horticulture and aquaculture;

21. Decision-making removed from Arnhem Land to Darwin and Canberra;

22. Yolŋu lost the fight to stop mining on their lands;

23. Balanda mining towns developed;

24. Influx of large numbers of dominant culture people in 1970s and '80s;

25. Destruction of traditional knowledge and values through Western influences;

26. Continual communication failure, unfamiliar language and world-view;

27. The dominant culture not appreciating the massive communication failure;

28. Alcohol and other drugs become freely available;

29. Intervention programs are developed out of the dominant culture 'naming';

30. Dominant culture professionals not trained for the Arnhem Land situation;

31. Constant turnover of inexperienced dominant culture staff and the resulting loss of dominant culture corporate history of Arnhem Land;

32. Historical trauma, culture shock, future shock not acknowledged;

33. No language centres to chart the languages and develop dictionaries and other language tools;

34. Only a few interpreters or communication facilitators exist;

35. No active, comprehensive mass media service in Yolŋu Matha;

36. Meaningless contemporary education and training;

37. Use of foreign health, education, administration and legal systems (which Yolŋu do not understand) to run infrastructure and enterprises on Yolŋu communities;

38. Almost a total loss of meaningful employment to outsiders;

39. Loss of mastery over being good at something like a job or an artistic or life-skill;

40. Loss of mastery over living environment;

41. Yolŋu economic thinking and activity now centred on welfare;

42. Loss of fulfilling roles within community and families;

43. Nothing to live and be educated for.

The result of all this is that all the factors that researchers Lantz et al and Syme (above) identify as the factors leading to high mortality rates, are clearly manifested in the lives of Yolŋu today:

• A lack of social relationships and social supports;

• Personality dispositions such as the loss of a sense of mastery, optimism, control and self-esteem and heightened levels of anger and hostility;

• Chronic and acute stress in daily life and work, including the stresses of racism, class distinction and other phenomena related to the social distribution of power and resources.

• A complete loss of control over their own lives and the living environment around them.

This situation is not confined to Yolŋu in north-east Arnhem Land. The same conditions are seen in west Arnhem Land. The 1997 *Kakadu Region Social Impact Study*[192] stated;

> Social problems are seen as a manifestation of a *lack of real control*, and the absence of *any sense of control*, among local people. The smothering of Aboriginal values and priorities by overlying non-Aboriginal structures *generates a sense of inadequacy and powerlessness*. (My emphasis)

The same report quotes one of the people:

> Yes, Aboriginal people do feel powerless. Balanda are on top with laws and powers. Bininj [Aboriginal people of West Arnhem Land] are underneath or hiding because of legal power.

When the dominant culture continues to treat issues like inadequate housing, water, sewerage, health services and nutrition, or high-risk behaviour patterns such as smoking or alcohol abuse, as the primary causes of the problem, they are looking at the wrong end of the cycle. These symptoms at times need to be dealt with, but to concentrate most resources on them is to keep building 'orphanages' without trying to find the source of the babies. If 'loss of control' is the main issue, then programs must be developed to return control to the people. When this happens, then programs that are developed to tackle the symptoms can also be redesigned and implemented in ways that do not take more control from the people.

'Victims of Progress'—A World-wide Reality

In 1975 John Bodley, an American anthropologist, gathered evidence from all over the world regarding the suffering of indigenous people at the hands of forced 'Western development'. He wrote:

> This is perhaps the most outstanding and inescapable fact to emerge from the years of research that anthropologists have devoted to the study of culture change and modernization. In spite of the best intentions of those who have promoted change and improvement, all too often the real results have been poverty, longer working hours and much greater physical exertion, *poor health, social disorder, discontent, discrimination*, overpopulation, and environmental deterioration—*all this combined with the destruction of the traditional culture*. (My emphasis)[193]

The same problems seen among Yolŋu can be seen, for example, among the Sioux Indians of South Dakota, who are twice as likely to die of diabetes, three times as likely to die from tuberculosis and four times as likely to die from alcoholism than non-native North Americans.[194]

When I first read Bodley's *Victims of Progress* in the late 1970s, I did not realise I was reading a prediction of the social and health problems that we were to see in Arnhem Land within a decade or two. Some of his statements were prophetic:

Economic development seems to increase the disease rate of affected people in at least three ways. First, to the extent that development is successful, it makes the developed population suddenly become vulnerable to all the diseases enjoyed almost exclusively by 'advanced' peoples. Among these are *diabetes, obesity, hypertension, and a variety of circulatory problems.* (My emphasis)[195]

These are the diseases that now devastate the people of Arnhem Land.

Secondly, development disturbs traditional environmental balances and may dramatically increase certain bacterial and parasitic diseases.[196]

This seems to be what has happened with scabies, diarrhoea, boils, ear infections and so on.

Finally, when development goals prove unattainable, an assortment of poverty diseases may appear in association with the crowded conditions of urban slums and the general breakdown in traditional socio-economic systems.[197]

Crowded Western-style housing, poverty-related diseases, substance abuse that is almost killing out some clans or family groups and welfare dependence all make Yolŋu feel worse and worse about themselves. Domestic violence leaves them thinking Yolŋu are somehow worse than Balanda: 'Balanda can drink and not get into trouble, but we drink and go mad. What is wrong with us?' Now Yolŋu feel that because they are Yolŋu they are missing out on any opportunity to be equal. This makes for greater levels of anger and hopelessness.

As one Yolŋu leader said to me: 'Have we broken the ancient law and are suffering the sanctions, or has the Great Creator turned against us? Surely not, as we are the object of his creation. So why do we live in this constant state of war?'

Yolŋu warriors first fought to protect their loved ones, property and homelands from foreign invasion, then made the necessary changes and in the mission days became highly skilled tradesmen. However, the past wars and later time of cultural adaptation seem like a picnic compared with conditions in the modern 'enlightened' world. How can Yolŋu regain control and become masters of their own environment once more?

It is a complex yet simple story. People wish and need to be treated as human beings. To do this we need to stop treating the symptoms and start dealing with the real underlying causes.

14
CHAPTER

Rewriting the Future

The Way Ahead

. . . [good] health is to a great extent dependent on a good sense of coherence—a sense that life is comprehensible (makes sense and has some order and organisation), manageable (predictable and controllable by oneself or others that one trusts), and meaningful.

A. Antonovsky[198]

It is impossible to go back and simply 'fix' many of the events and errors that have created the crisis discussed in this book. We only look back so that the primary causes of the problem can be identified and appropriate responses developed. Yolŋu *can* regain control of their lives through changed dominant culture attitudes leading to appropriate policies and programs. Then Yolŋu warriors will be able to stand tall and live again, proud of their traditions and histories in a new and modern world.

As we have seen, policies like self-determination and self-management have not delivered to Yolŋu what was expected of them. Because of dominant culture naming of Yolŋu and lack of understanding of the *real* Yolŋu way, self-determination was never really possible. The crisis in Arnhem Land today is the *direct* result of the people's loss of control over their lives and living environment. This 'loss of control' is the *primary* cause of their crisis, and Yolŋu suffer all sorts of physical, psychological and social symptoms as secondary conditions.

The human potential Yolŋu possess must be tapped and released to the world before it is too late. The cardinal principle is *to motivate and equip the people to take control of their own lives and their contemporary living environment.*

For this to really happen we must *almost* reverse current trends. How can this happen? In a nutshell, we need to take the 'non-Yolŋu-friendly' environment that now exists and create a more 'Yolŋu-friendly' environment. Instead of Yolŋu having to do all the hard work in communicating, adapting and coping, dominant culture personnel, structures and policies need to change to create more 'Yolŋu-friendly' environments.

To do this we need to take the factors that have caused this loss of control—that is, the ones that we can do something about—flip them over and take appropriate action to empower Yolŋu in a real way. As soon as these changes are activated we will find the people assuming a higher degree of control over their lives, and some of the secondary conditions now evident in Arnhem Land will just disappear.

Five Steps to a More Yolŋu-friendly Environment

A true discussion of this subject would require a book in itself. Our undertaking in this chapter is more modest. From the list of forty-three factors in chapter 13 that lead to the loss of control, I have chosen the five areas that, if addressed, can have the greatest impact in terms of returning control to the people. They are:

• Take the people's language seriously;

• Train dominant culture personnel;

• Approach education and training in a different way;

• Replace existing programs with programs that truly empower the people;

• Deal with some basic legal issues.

Where these issues have been discussed in depth in earlier chapters, I will deal with them here only in summary form. I will also give some examples of how, when applied, these measures can truly make a difference.

Take the People's Language Seriously

The 1993 Council of European Communities' directive on the movement of doctors across European borders (93/16 [article 20]) states:

> Member states shall see to it, that, where appropriate, the persons concerned acquire, in their interest and in the interest of their patients, the linguistic knowledge necessary to the exercise of their profession in the host country.[199]

If I were asked to name the number one thing that could help create 'Yolŋu-friendly' environments, I would have to say: *Take the people's language seriously*. Of course, nothing is as simple as one single answer. But if the people's language were taken seriously by the dominant culture, a great many positive things would flow out of it.

Remember, the people think and maintain information in Yolŋu Matha, not English. Because the dominant culture does not appreciate this fact, Yolŋu are intellectually marginalised at almost every point of contact with the dominant culture. This means they cannot receive, with any real understanding, national or international news, health warnings and information, contemporary education and training, or general knowledge from outside their cultural world.

There are, of course, some very tired dominant culture arguments that stop the people's language being taken seriously. 'There are too many languages; which one do we choose?' is a common excuse. But Yolŋu know up to five or six languages, and there are common languages known over large areas. These are the languages that need to be learnt.

The consequences of continuing to ignore the people's language are very serious. At present, for example, the United Nations Covenant On Civil and Political Rights is broken every time a Yolŋu person is arrested and taken before a Northern Territory Court. It states:

> Article 14 (3) In the determination of any criminal charge against him, everyone shall be entitled to the following *minimum* guarantees, in full equality:
> (a) To be informed promptly and in detail *in a language which he understands* of the nature and cause of the charge against him; . . .
> (f) To have the free assistance of an interpreter if he cannot *understand or speak* the language used in court. (My emphasis)[200]

From my knowledge, I would say that ninety-nine per cent of Yolŋu are not able to understand a large amount of the English used in court, from the time a police officer reads out the charges to the end of the proceedings. Dominant culture people find it hard to imagine how disempowering it is to stand in a supposed 'court of law' accused of charges you cannot understand and to undergo a trial where the language used is totally foreign. You have no hope whatsoever of understanding ninety per cent of the communication—including communication with your defence counsel! If we fail to meet the communication requirements that are required *legally*, imagine how badly everyday communication fails.

The people's languages are valid. The House of Representatives Committee Hearings and the Royal Commissions are unanimous in supporting the need for indigenous Australians to have access to information, education, interpreting services and training in their own language.[201] Language must indeed be taken seriously.

How Do We Take the People's Language Seriously?

First, establish well-funded language research. This research would need to continue the 'charting' of Yolŋu Matha languages (see chapter 5), spawn important services such as interpreter and translation services, and develop an English/Yolŋu Matha dictionary and other language materials for educational and training purposes.

Secondly, set up a media outlet operating in the people's language. Such a service would allow Yolŋu to gain relevant, contemporary knowledge and news the same way other Australians do. This service could be used to run education programs in Yolŋu Matha covering areas such as health, law, commerce and economics. It could also produce current affairs programs and be used to teach 'secret English' terms, equipping Yolŋu in a better way for their verbal intercourse with the broader dominant culture.

Some may point out that there are already Broadcasting for Remote Aboriginal Communities Scheme (BRACS) units on many of the communities. However, this scheme does not work, for many of the same reasons other programs have failed. First, these units exist only on the major communities and broadcast on FM frequencies, which means they do not carry much further than a two or three kilometre radius. There are almost ninety homeland estates in Arnhem Land that get no radio service.

Secondly, each of the BRACS units operates on a budget for about half a person. This makes program development impossible. Most of the really effective unit operators are Yolŋu, but they have the same problems in accessing information from the dominant culture world as their contemporaries do. Tony Binalany Gunbalga, a long-time BRACS operator, pointed the problem out to me. 'A lot of Balanda come and tell me I should be translating the news into Yolŋu Matha. But I can't understand the English news in the first place, so how am I going to translate it? He continued, 'I need a Balanda like you, *Wämut*, who knows English and can also speak our language. Then we can work together so I can get a good understanding of the news items and put them to air.'

A new Yolŋu Matha media outlet could take the form of a radio station transmitting over the whole region, incorporating the BRACS units if they wanted to join. This service would need access to dominant culture professionals who speak English as a first language and Yolŋu Matha as a second language. They would work with a range of Yolŋu, including the BRACS operators and others, to create programs.

Thirdly, Yolŋu Matha must be taught to dominant culture personnel who enter Arnhem Land. This teaching should be done even though most dominant culture personnel will not learn the language in a thorough or complete way. Just in trying to learn the language they will discover many things about communicating in the cross-language situation:

• They will learn how complicated it is to learn and speak another language.

• They will learn all about communication methods such as the need to slow down and speak distinctly, giving the Yolŋu person a better chance to hear the English being used.

• They will learn some Yolŋu Matha words that can be used while speaking English, making it much easier for Yolŋu to hear and process the English.

• They will learn how to read and pronounce Yolŋu Matha so that at least Yolŋu names can be spelt and pronounced correctly. The correct use of names is a big issue. When clinics and hospitals have confused people's names in the past, it has had disastrous consequences, even ending in death for some Yolŋu.

Some dominant culture people will learn language to a deep level. These people can go on to become the pool of dominant culture personnel who do the effective training and education that Yolŋu desperately require.

There is another reason why dominant culture personnel should at least start to learn Yolŋu Matha. The learning process changes the balance between Yolŋu and dominant culture personnel in that the English speakers must ask Yolŋu for help. In everyday life this does not happen very often, but when it does it changes the whole relationship. This can have a very positive psychological effect on Yolŋu. When a dominant culture person sincerely asks a Yolŋu person about a particular word, the Yolŋu person is empowered straight away. The Yolŋu person becomes the teacher, the dominant culture person becomes the student. Most Yolŋu are being taught or told things by dominant culture people most of the time. But when Yolŋu are asked a question about Yolŋu Matha—in which they are the experts—it is the English-speaking person who experiences how hard it is to learn across the cultural and language barrier.

Any person who is familiar with 'transactional analysis' will understand what I am talking about.[202] Most Yolŋu are in a typical 'child state' when they are communicating with dominant culture people, while most dominant culture people unconsciously assume the 'parent state'. But at the very moment a dominant culture person asks a Yolŋu person to help them learn a Yolŋu Matha word or phrase, the dominant culture person places themselves in the 'child state', asking for help. The Yolŋu person will automatically assume the 'parent state' as they start teaching. In a short time, the two parties will be interacting 'adult' to 'adult', as equals, which is the ideal state for human-to-human communication. This alone is enough reason for all dominant culture personnel to learn Yolŋu Matha.

Information is power, and in a free democratic society access to information is an essential right. For people like Yolŋu it is a matter of a 'fair go' and a chance to survive.

What Are 'Leaking Kidneys'?

In November 1997 a colleague and I sat with a group of Yolŋu health workers to talk about renal failure. Some health professionals had visited them two weeks earlier and conducted a number of sessions. Two of the health workers approached us requesting a teaching session with all the health workers. 'We want to talk about *dinytiny rerri* (kidney disease),' they said. 'We had a workshop here a couple of weeks ago and we're a bit confused.'

When we sat down with the health workers, it soon became clear they did not have a very good understanding of the process of renal failure at all, despite the recent input.

We asked them in Yolŋu Matha what they wanted to know about kidney disease. They said they were confused about the whole subject. Someone got out the book they had received at the workshop. One section talked about 'leaking kidneys', showing (as I recall) a black and white diagram of a kidney and drops of something coming from it.

We asked the group, 'From this book and the workshop, what do you think "leaking kidneys" mean?'

They were all silent. Then one senior health worker said, 'To me it means that the blood is leaking from the kidneys.' The others just said, '*Yuw!* (We don't know!).'

My colleague, who has a medical background, said, 'You can have blood leaking into the urine, but that's not what they are talking about here. The "leaking kidneys" here involves protein leaking from the kidneys into the urine.'

'What's this "protein" about?' asked one of the health workers.

We questioned whether anyone knew what protein was; did it give anyone any meaning or picture? No-one had any idea.

This left us with a problem. How were we to explain protein to the health workers? We drew on our educational methodology: use a word or phrase from the people's language that generates discussion and thinking around the subject we want them to learn about. These generative words or phrases are not just any old words, but key words or phrases that encapsulate the people's world-view and thinking about the subject. We thought for a moment, then suggested we talk about the two traditional Yolŋu food groups: *murnyaŋ'* and *gonyil* (see chapter 9).

We led the group in a discussion, getting them to tell us all the varieties of food they could think of that fitted into these categories. This way the people became our teachers. The whole group participated. We focused first on the *murnyaŋ* (carbohydrate) group and discussed how it gives energy to the body. This led to a discussion about sugar as fuel for the body, how sugar burns in a fire, how a vehicle needs fuel—petrol or diesel—to create the power to run the motor. It was a true two-way discussion between the health workers and us.

When this conversation petered out, we began discussing *gonyil* foods and how these build the body. We said, 'That "protein" we were talking about before in relation to kidney failure is a substance that comes from *gonyil* food.' We explained that it is protein that builds up the body and repairs muscle tissue. 'This protein normally stays in the blood as the blood passes through the kidneys, but finding protein in the urine is an early sign of kidney disease that *could* lead to kidney failure. "Leaking kidneys" refers to finding protein in the urine. It should not be there and is only present if the tiny blood vessels in the kidneys have allowed it to leave the blood and pass into the urine.'

'How does this happen?' the health workers asked.

We had brought with us coloured photos, books and resources to facilitate the discussion, so we showed them a diagram of different types of capillaries and especially the fenestrated ones in the kidneys. 'The protein leaks through these fenestrated capillaries when they become damaged,' we explained.

The health workers asked a lot of questions, which led us to talk about the degeneration of the kidneys and how creatinine levels rise in the blood. We used coloured medical drawings of the kidneys and the small nephron filters in them to facilitate this discussion. The health workers were very interested in the nephrons, and asked more questions about fluid wastes and how they get from the blood stream into the collecting renal tubes. This took us back to talk about the fenestrated capillaries. More questions were raised about the reasons why these small capillaries stop working and become permanently damaged. Eventually my colleague and I said we would have to return to give a deeper explanation at a later date. This was because we were still developing the explanation of the process in Yolŋu Matha and found ourselves out of our depth!

Finally, one of the health workers asked, 'Well, what are these creatinine readings we get back for the patients all the time?'

I asked the group if they knew the English term 'creatinine' and whether it conveyed any meaning to them. All of them pushed out their bottom lip, indicating they had no idea. I explained that creatinine *is like* 'urine in the blood', and that when the rubbish can't get out of the kidneys into the renal tubes, down to the bladder and out to the toilet, it stays in the blood. When there is a high level of rubbish in the blood, it poisons the body and can kill you. We discussed this at length.

The health workers were shocked at the permanent nature of renal failure and that it could become a terminal condition. Among themselves they discussed a case they knew in which a patient had been recently hospitalised. We took some butcher's paper and drew a scale of normal and abnormal creatinine levels, plotting the different levels of kidney damage to the failure stage.

At this point the health workers became highly concerned for some of their patients who they knew had high to very high creatinine levels but were not complying with the prescribed treatment. They asked my colleague and me to help them tell this story to these people. One of the health workers was appointed to work with us, and we spent the next few days on the community working through some of these cases.

The above discussion lasted about an hour. Because it took place in Yolŋu Matha, the second language for my colleague and me, we were at a disadvantage. But the health workers were in control in their first language. It was a 'Yolŋu-friendly' environment.

Without language being taken seriously, most of the dollars currently spent on Yolŋu health are almost completely wasted. Furthermore, the people suffer needlessly. Health workers and other Yolŋu want to and can learn even the most complicated medical information. It is the dominant culture that must change its thinking for this to happen.

Train Dominant Culture Personnel

Dominant Culture professionals, staff and others are coming to Arnhem Land in greater numbers than ever before. At the moment these people come with the national accreditation training levels required by the dominant culture to work in a dominant culture setting. But this training does not equip them to work in a cross-cultural/cross-language situation. If these people are going to do their work well, they need special training on at least three levels:

General orientation. All dominant culture people coming to Arnhem Land, even if 'only to live in a Balanda township', should have general orientation: cultural awareness, history of the area and some understanding of language dynamics. This will help create a more 'Yolŋu-friendly' environment and an on-going corporate culture which includes basic skills in communication across languages. Other important information, such as how to handle culture shock and how to be less 'destructive' to Yolŋu, could also be taught at this level.

Special training for educators and trainers. All dominant culture personnel involved in training or education should receive special cross-cultural and cross-language educational training. These people first need to be taught Yolŋu Matha to a good level of fluency. They need to learn how to discover the Yolŋu world-view and the importance of knowing the people's cultural knowledge base. These people should be trained in the same way as those going to another country.

Communication facilitators/educators. A special group of dominant culture personnel need to be trained to a very high level. These people would be used to do special education projects in areas such as health or economics. They could also facilitate communication sessions between the people and outside profes-sionals who do not know the language. Their training would cover the first two levels plus deeper training in language, community development and community education. This third group would be selected from people who have already completed levels one and two and who show an aptitude for language and good communication skills.

I know that when training programs such as these are talked about, many respond by saying, 'Why should dominant culture people be trained rather than Yolŋu?' or 'It's just too expensive!' Let's consider these two responses.

Why Should Dominant Culture People Be Trained?

I have heard this argument since the late 1970s. Its influence is very destructive because it unwittingly releases 'secret and cranky English' on Yolŋu. Untrained dominant culture people are a *major* part of the problem. However, appropriately trained dominant culture people are a very important part of the answer.

Dominant culture personnel without training are the epitome of the problem Yolŋu face in their loss of control. Because they are not trained to work with the people, their very presence marginalises and destroys the Yolŋu workforce, killing dreams of self-management and self-determination and allowing outside personnel and contractors to take over almost everything. If the current trend continues, Yolŋu will soon be a minority in their own homeland estates.

Many people say: 'Only Yolŋu should be trained. Then they can take over the jobs these dominant culture personnel are currently doing and run their own communities.' But the people who push this type of thinking are the same people who would tell someone to pull themselves up by their own bootlaces.

My question is: Who is going to train Yolŋu so they can be in a position to do these jobs? It is dominant culture knowledge that Yolŋu are having trouble learning, so they need dominant culture personnel to train them. But the dominant culture personnel who come as teachers, trainers and resource people cannot do their jobs *precisely because* they have no training to communicate, teach or instruct in a cross-cultural/cross-language setting.

Others say that Yolŋu should just go to an Aboriginal college and learn there how to run their communities. But again, unless these colleges have properly trained teachers, almost no learning will occur even though it is an 'Aboriginal college'. Cognition demands more than an ethnic desire to teach and help your own people; it demands competent educational methodologies.

Not just educators and trainers but all dominant culture personnel who come to Arnhem Land—council clerks, bookkeepers, mechanics, health sisters and more— need special orientation and training. Currently they walk straight into their jobs with no skills to work with Yolŋu co-workers. They cannot communicate with them except on a very shallow level. Dominant culture personnel, who may have legal responsibilities in their particular job, will try their best to assess where Yolŋu co-workers are up to, but with all the communication problems and the thinking that dominant culture naming creates in their minds, it is not long before they have unintentionally alienated their Yolŋu co-workers.

Many, many Yolŋu have spoken to me about this type of situation. New person after new person comes and changes things over and over again because they cannot communicate with Yolŋu workers to find out where things were up to.

On top of this, day-to-day business communications with the outside world are in English. This gives dominant culture personnel an immediate 2,000 km advantage over Yolŋu workers. Balanda personnel end up with *all* the information but few skills to pass it on to their Yolŋu co-workers. When the dominant culture personnel start running everything because Yolŋu do not know what is going on, the tit-for-tat naming starts between the two groups. The dominant culture personnel blame Yolŋu for not doing more, while Yolŋu blame the dominant culture personnel for keeping all the information to themselves and running everything.

To regain control, Yolŋu need adequately trained dominant culture personnel who can help create a 'Yolŋu-friendly' environment.

It's Just Too Expensive

The second objection to training dominant culture personnel is that it is just too expensive. I have great difficulty with this argument. How can training be too expensive when at the present time dominant culture personnel are paid to professional levels but are unable to operate effectively at that level in the Yolŋu context? Surely this is a waste of money by anyone's assessment. And what about the cost to Yolŋu?

From the story about 'leaking kidneys', we can see that if Yolŋu do not understand basic facts about kidney disease the cost to the government will be massive. Dialysis for *one* patient is estimated by Territory Health Services to cost the Northern Territory government $60,000 to $80,000 per year. And people remain on dialysis for the rest of their lives. In some areas of the Northern Territory there are dozens of Aboriginal people on dialysis, and the numbers are expected to increase massively in the next few years. Add to this the cost of new and improved facilities—new health clinics and dialysis machines in some remote Aboriginal communities—and the total bill runs into millions of dollars.

Then there is the cost of family dislocation and dysfunction caused by illness, imprisonment and generally not knowing how the dominant culture world works. This cost remains hidden, but I believe it too is millions upon millions of dollars.

Furthermore, the cost of recruiting and relocating doctors, sisters, teachers and community resource staff on short-term contracts is high. Many people leave mid-term because they suffer massive culture shock or become unbearably frustrated, at a cost to the Northern Territory and Australian governments of further millions of dollars every year. All this because no specialised training exists so that people can do their jobs effectively, find a degree of job satisfaction and therefore stay long term.

Dominant culture personnel, trained to appropriate levels to work effectively with Yolŋu, will make a huge difference in positive outcomes for Yolŋu and therefore overall cost effectiveness.

In general there is a vast array of new information needed for Yolŋu to survive and effectively take control of their lives. It is dominant culture knowledge that Yolŋu require and it must be taught appropriately by dominant culture personnel. Dominant culture personnel *must* be trained.

Approach Education and Training in a Different Way

For Yolŋu the battle to maintain their way of life is almost lost. The Balanda world now controls everything and the people are very confused. But the education that comes from the dominant culture does not recognise this and just pushes mainstream activities in the hope that somehow Yolŋu will learn.

For Yolŋu to learn, however, they need special education to first fill in the 'missing links' or 'gaps' in their 'conceptual universe' regarding the contemporary world. Only when their conceptual universe is adjusted and well-developed in relation to this 'new world' knowledge will they be ready for more 'normal' skill-based education programs.

Who Designs Yolŋu Education?

At present almost all the education and training programs for Yolŋu are built around mainstream curricula that fit dominant culture national accreditation (learning) needs, with content that matches the cultural knowledge base requirements of the dominant culture (or more frequently, the dominant culture naming of the people). So the programs do not meet the real learning needs of Yolŋu.

In August 1998 I was involved in a discussion with an educator, new to Arnhem Land, about this issue. He said, 'Yes, but when I develop a course according to the training curriculum, I have to have it so that both Balanda and Yolŋu can do the course. If I make it simple enough for Yolŋu to understand, it will be insipid for the Balanda and so simple that they learn nothing.'

But what is needed is not a simplified course where no-one learns anything. Both Balanda and Yolŋu need *relevant* courses that meet their different learning needs. This will require *separate* courses for each group. That is, for learning to occur the courses need to:

• start from where both groups of people are at;

• meet the different cultural knowledge base content requirements of the respective groups;

• be delivered in a language that each group of people thinks in and constructs knowledge in.

Just imagine Balanda going to a course constructed to meet Yolŋu learning needs and delivered in Yolŋu Matha. How interested would they be? Would they learn anything? Of course not! Yet everyday Yolŋu attend education sessions developed around dominant culture requirements and delivered in English.

As I write this, the young educator is still in Arnhem Land, but he has an impossible task. First, he has to develop courses according to the dominant culture national accreditation criteria so the institution he works for will be funded. Secondly, he has no idea what knowledge Yolŋu already have and what they do not know, so how can he understand what content is appropriate? Thirdly, how can he deliver his courses without the language of the people? At the moment he is stuck at the dominant culture 'naming'—keep it simple.

This educator will probably leave in about a year, maybe sooner. He will depart very frustrated, like hundreds before him. Someone will come and take his place and the same scenario will recur, as it has with his two predecessors within the last two years. These educators complain to their bosses in Darwin, who in turn see it all as 'just too hard'.

The Balanda education system has as yet no real understanding of cross-cultural/cross-language learning problems. So good educational money and the efforts of many good educators continue to be wasted. Meanwhile, Yolŋu become permanent casualties of a system that unwittingly promotes ignorance. 'Mindless schooling, meaningless work and disempowered communities are antithetical to good health.'[203]

Education Around Concepts Needs to Happen First

Most education for Yolŋu is aimed at skill-based training—learning to read and write, for example. But the simple reality is that while the people remain mystified about how the modern world works, education, including education in skills, seems pointless. They might learn to read and write a bit, but they do not really get excited about it because much of what they read makes no sense to them. On the other hand, when Yolŋu have a *basic* conceptional understanding of how the dominant culture works and are able to understand the world around them, they will *demand* skill-based education, including learning to read and write.

In some ways, dominant culture teenagers also display the same confusion when they say, 'What's the use of all this education'? These teenagers, however, can ask their parents or teachers questions to fill in the missing links in their understanding of the world. If their conceptual universe is developed as they dialogue with parents or teachers, they will get excited about learning skills to operate in the world around them. But if the missing links remain, they will continue to be confused and to see education as a waste of time.

A friend of mine quotes a simple but telling example of this. Her eight-year-old son was sitting with his grandfather one day when he asked, 'Grandad, in the old days was there any colour in the world?' The family had been watching some old black and white films and had also discussed how TV used to be black and white, so her son obviously thought that maybe the world used to be black and white. Of course, his grandfather was able to tell him that it was the TV and films that had changed, not the world itself. He could even talk about how the chemicals in film and the electronics in cameras had changed, allowing colour to be recorded.

My children also ask many things about how the world works: Where does money come from? Who picks the Prime Minister? What is his job? Why do I have to wash my hands before eating? How do I catch a cold? How did they build the first aeroplanes? Where are cars made? Can the man in the shop eat any food he wants to'? As they get older, the children's questions get deeper: Why does the council have signs near all the drains that read 'Playing in or near the drain is prohibited'? What does prohibited mean? When these last two questions were asked, we discussed the word 'prohibited' and its ramifications—how the council could be sued if someone was hurt playing in the drain and so on. The discussion around these 'missing links' allowed the children to develop their conceptual universe about the world.

Now, my children are fortunate. They have parents who understand the dominant culture world, so getting an explanation of the missing conceptional links about that world is not a problem. But Yolŋu children, teenagers and adults, who are asking many of these same questions, cannot get answers because their world is dominated by a strange cultural/language group. Their conceptional universe remains incomplete and confused.

Dominant culture people have little idea just how confused people like Yolŋu can become. For example, traditional Aboriginal people all over north Australia believe that somehow the Queen of England creates all the wealth in the world. Yolŋu have a joke that the Queen's toilet paper is made from $100 notes and her carpets from $100 and $50 notes. At the 1999 republic referendum, elders right across north and central Australia said, 'How can we cut off the Queen? Who will help us?' Many dominant culture people see such statements as quaint and naïve, but they are actually the result of dominant culture educators not applying good educational methodologies.

It is even harder for Yolŋu to fill these gaps because of the uncharted aspects of Yolŋu Matha and English and because this intangible conceptional knowledge can only be explained through *gurraŋay matha* (intellectual language).

This problem of conceptual confusion has a compounding effect. Many disillusioned Yolŋu parents, who themselves have had first-hand experience of dominant culture education, see no use in pushing their children to school to suffer the same levels of torment and confusion. They themselves are unemployed and cannot operate in the crazy Balanda world, so why should they encourage their children to go the same way?

Many people say to me, 'If all this is so, how can Asian students come to Australia and learn in our universities even though English is their second language?' We must remember that these students come from communities that are still involved in production and trade and still have their political and legal processes, which they understand, in everyday use. They are not confused, to the same degree, about how the contemporary world works and they also have good dictionaries, from English to their own language, to continue a self-discovery.

Education and training for Yolŋu must first meet their conceptional education needs. As stated above, when their conceptual universe concerning the contemporary world is well-developed, they will *demand* skill-based education as all other groups of people do.

Discovery Education

The content of education and training needs to be driven by the learning needs of the people. Freire comments:

> We must never merely discourse on the present situation, must never provide the people with programmes which have little or nothing to do with their own preoccupations, doubts, hopes, and fears—programmes which at times in fact increase the fears of the oppressed consciousness. It is not our role to speak to the people about our own view of the world, nor to attempt to impose that view on them, but rather to dialogue with the people about their view and ours. We must realize that their view of the world, manifested variously in their action, reflects their situation in the world. *Educational . . . action which is not critically aware of this situation runs the risk . . . of preaching in the desert. (My emphasis)*[204]

Now this is not an easy thing for the people to participate in. At times they are not aware of what it is they don't know about the dominant culture world. Yet it is absolutely necessary for the people to be involved, and I believe they can be, through the use of *problem-solving* or *discovery education*.

Problem-solving education is an educational methodology that allows the people to drive the educational content. Djiniyini Goŋarra calls it 'discovery' education because people 'discover' knowledge from what they are hearing and seeing. The dialogue basis of this methodology allows them to own new information rather than having it fed to them indiscriminately.

This methodology delivers concept-based education around 'problems' that the people want answers to. It provides knowledge around a particular subject the people are interested in because it is affecting them at that time.

> The starting point for organizing the programme content of the education . . . must be the present, existential, concrete situation, reflecting the aspirations of the people. Utilizing certain basic contradictions, we must pose this existential, concrete, present situation to the people as a problem which challenges them and requires a response—not just at the intellectual level, but at the level of action.[205]

The first step in the process, then, is that a subject is identified by the people themselves, centred on a 'problem' they have. It might be confusion about a family member's sickness, a question about hire purchase, a problem around a budget deficit or a desire to know how Balanda businesses operate—any problem where the 'rubber hits the road' for them as a cultural group. Various problems/subject areas can be grouped into categories—medical, economic, legal, and so on. There will probably be overlapping confusion and lack of knowledge between the individual subject areas.

Once the people have identified a problem, the educator begins initial investigations around that subject. After thorough research the educator builds up a comprehensive understanding of the people's questions and the nature of their confusion (for example, the differences between their perception of reality and the actual objective situation).[206] The educator also builds up a list of key Yolŋu Matha words and phrases which can be used later to generate discussion and thinking.

Educational props like newspaper cuttings, good pictures, video clips, reports, interviews or the availability of an 'expert' are sourced and collected. These resources allow the people to validate for themselves the content of the education session when it occurs.

The next step is the 'delivery' of the education. This is 'dialogue based' in the people's language. It involves working from where the people are 'at'. The educator does not operate prescriptively, just giving the people the 'good oil'. No! The previously investigated generative words and themes are used to create discussion, motivate, inform and contextualise the knowledge being considered by the people. Sometimes the educator may act 'dumb' to get the people to teach him some language, or may ask the people to explain a generative word. This is so the people switch on their thinking and own the process, seeing it as an investigation of the subject through which new knowledge will be discovered.

Sometimes if the group is working with an 'expert' as a resource person—say, a doctor or registered nurse—the educator might ask questions on behalf of the people. The educator should know what questions the people have from his or her earlier investigation. In this way the education session continues in an investigation mode, and the educator is seen to be alongside the people seeking information from the doctor, rather than beside the doctor giving instructions. This helps the people see it is okay to ask questions, and they understand that the dominant culture educator does not know everything, making them feel better about their original confusion.

Of course, the educator translates the initial question to the doctor to allow the people to own it, and then translates the information from the doctor to the people—also keeping the doctor up to speed about what the people are saying. The subject is discussed backwards and forwards so that the new knowledge is constructed on top of the people's existing knowledge.

Many times during such a session the people will take the educator to a new level of understanding about the subject being discussed. This could include deeper insights into the people's world-view, new language terms and so on. The educator will encourage this dialogue so that both learn from each other.

When Yolŋu first experience this form of education from dominant culture personnel, they find it a bit strange. They are so used to sitting quietly and being talked at in English. Many need a lot of encouragement before they believe they also have something valid to offer to the educational experience.

As I have mentioned above, problem-solving education can be used around different types of problems. These do not have to be major issues. I say this because the following example is a story of a rather large community development program where I used problem-solving education within the program. This program successfully allowed Yolŋu to become responsible controllers of their own environment around one issue.

Our Young People Are Sniffing Petrol—Can Someone Help Us?

In 1981-82, while I was living at Ramingining, many of the elders came and asked me to help them solve a petrol sniffing problem. At the time there were forty-two teenagers involved.

I knew from my training as a community development worker that the people would have to solve the problem themselves if the solutions were going to be lasting. But I also knew they could not do it by themselves; they were already displaying signs of powerlessness by the fact that they asked me for help. As an outsider, I had to be careful how I worked with these people to make sure the strategies I used would empower them to solve their problem.

The initial investigation. The first stage of the project was to find out everything that had already been tried in other communities to deal with petrol sniffing. I was looking for what had worked and what had not, and trying to see why. Through this process we constructed a good history of petrol sniffing, from its introduction by Balanda servicemen who started sniffing petrol at Milingimbi during World War II, to all the programs that had been tried since then to deal with the problem: social work, banishment, recreational activities, fuel additives and substitutes.

To each of the different approaches we applied the test of whether they empowered Yolŋu or not. It soon became obvious that where these programs failed to empower the people, they also failed to solve the problem. In fact, in many cases they made the problem worse. Only the social work approach, carried out by Rev B. Clarke in the late 1960s, showed any signs of empowering the people. This approach entailed working with the people around family problems, using a translator to facilitate communication. Much of the petrol sniffing stopped at this time, but started again a few years after the program ceased.

The recreational programs seemed to be the most destructive of all because most of them were organised by dominant culture people, further alienating the sniffers from their own elders and parents. It even seemed that some of the young people who were non-sniffers before the programs started, became sniffers so they would not miss out on the program's benefits.

The elders who came with me to check the effectiveness of recreation programs went straight to talk to the elders of the affected community. They came back with a strong resolve never to let recreation programs be used at Ramingining. The reason: the programs had 'taken the children further away from their parents'. The other elders said: 'Now the recreation worker is seen as the one with all the good things for the children. The parents are too frightened to go and find out what is going on at the basketball courts and recreation hall because they're not sure the recreation officer wants them. The children certainly don't want them; they're too busy with the recreation officer.'

These recreation programs seemed to be based on the assumption that young people were sniffing because they were bored. I had never heard the sniffers at

Ramingining say that is why they sniffed, but I was hearing it from both Balanda and now Yolŋu on other communities that had long-term petrol sniffing problems.

Much later, in 1998, I heard the same excuse again. I was standing beside a government worker in one of the communities. This worker had not been in the community long. He commented, 'Gee the kids must get bored around this place. There's not much to do, is there? That's probably why they get into things like sniffing petrol.'

I assured him this is *not* why Yolŋu children sniff, but it is the big dominant culture excuse as to why they sniff. Even Yolŋu themselves use this excuse now. They have heard it for so long they believe it.

I continued, pointing out to the worker that he was standing in paradise. He only had to get a fish spear, walk less than 200 metres and he could spear fish. I mentioned the many other things that Yolŋu children could do. After a few minutes' discussion he agreed that boredom was probably not a problem. Yet this kind of paternalistic dominant culture reasoning has brought suffering to many disempowered traditional Aboriginal communities.

After the evaluation of existing programs was complete, the elders and I continued to talk through what they knew and did not know about petrol sniffing. The people, to my surprise, wanted to know the health information about sniffing. They were also puzzled why their young people were sniffing and asked me to talk to them. The elders said the young people would not talk to them, but they might talk to me because I was a Balanda.

The sniffers. I spent a number of weeks talking with the sniffers themselves, getting a good picture of what was going on in their lives. They were aged between twelve and sixteen, with some younger children joining them occasionally. All were boys, although two girls did participate sometimes.

The sniffing had started in earnest about two months after a group of children came back from a school excursion to Singapore. This trip had been organised and almost completely funded by the efforts of the head teacher and dollar-for-dollar grants by the Education Department. (Of course, the Education Department had been told that the children's parents had raised the money, but they hadn't.)

Contrary to everyone's intentions, the trip backfired. What was meant to be an exciting and enriching educational experience had actually given the children a completely false understanding of how the world works and turned them against their own families. The more I listened, the more I realised this 'educational' excursion had left them very confused and frustrated, hating the fact that they had been born Yolŋu and black.

While getting to know the sniffers, I also started looking for information on the effects of petrol sniffing, and I accessed health personnel who might be used later in the education program.

The process. The education process, which used the language of the people to ensure they participated to the highest possible level, began with discovering their cultural knowledge base about petrol sniffing. I realised I had two 'cultural groups'—the elders and parents, and the young sniffers. What I learnt from each group was further broken into categories:

• what they knew about petrol sniffing;

• what they didn't know about petrol sniffing;

• the knowledge they saw as *fact* that was actually contradictory to medical or other objective knowledge about the world.

Once I was sure of this information, especially where the contradictions could be established, then and only then was I ready to be involved in the education process.

While working with the general community, I also worked with a core group of Yolŋu leaders. This group I could trust with my life, and we shared many deep and personal things together in confidence. Because of this trust, I could talk at a deep level about community development and community education methodology. In fact, it was this group that taught me many of the Yolŋu-specific methodologies. As I discovered new things from the community, I would test them with this group to make sure I was hearing them properly. Then we would discuss the best way to carry out the education.

> Cultural sensitivity in health education programs can only be realised when we centralise the cultural experiences of the marginalised in the production of knowledge and cultural identity.[207]

Without the teaching that came to me from this group, I believe I would never have understood many of the issues raised in this book. They were the ones who defined my cultural sensitivity. At times they would display the same levels of dependence that the community displayed, in that they really wanted someone to come and solve the problem for them. At these times I tried to help them see the need for the people to find an answer themselves so they could have an element of control over their lives.

The contradictions. This team told me that people wanted to know the *dhudi dhäwu* (real, true foundational information) about petrol. After many discussions it became clear they wanted to know the full 'physical and mental deterioration' that occurred from petrol sniffing. This was good, because it fitted with the need to address the contradictions I had discovered in the people's cultural knowledge base. Some of these contradictions were:

• The adults did not see that it was the petrol making the sniffers sick. Because it was Balanda servicemen who first sniffed petrol, a Balanda substance, Yolŋu assumed it must be harmless. Further, because petrol was a new substance for Yolŋu, they had no knowledge of whether it was dangerous or not.

• When I asked the sniffers, 'Why aren't you frightened of getting sick and dying from petrol sniffing?' they said, 'We're not frightened because if we get sick we'll go to the hospital and the doctors will give us some medicine or an operation and make us better again.' Again, I could see the sniffers had no real knowledge about the physical effects of petrol sniffing, or of the limitations of the medical system.

So I brought in a doctor as a resource person. He worked first with the core group, but before he spoke to them, I briefed him fully on what was happening in the community and what sort of information he needed to tell the elders. It was essential for the doctor to be able to work from the people's cultural knowledge base, otherwise he would probably have confused them by working from his own cultural knowledge base.

Using me as the interpreter, the doctor taught the elders the 'cause and effects' of petrol sniffing. He told them how the sniffers' actual physical appearance changes as they progress through different levels of sniffing, what happens inside their body and why, right up to the point of death. He even told them what death from petrol sniffing would look like, in a very graphic way. This doctor had seen two men die from inhaling petrol fumes—Balanda painters who worked painting the inside of large petrol storage tanks. They died violent deaths, the effects of the lead poisoning contorting their bodies.

When the elders had heard the story and asked the doctor all their questions, they said, '*Wämut*, you and the doctor need to take this story to all the other elders and to all the parents and family members in the community.' So we did, going from family group to family group and from clan to clan.

When I was talking with the young people, some of them told me that the reason they sniffed was because Balanda were 'lucky'. 'They are *rommiriw* (lawless) and *raypirri'miriw* (lacking discipline of mind, body and soul).'

I asked them what they meant.

'You Balanda can sleep with any girlfriend you want to without anyone getting cranky at you,' they replied. 'You can have as many cars and houses as you want and it doesn't matter if you smash them up, you can just get another one. You Balanda have everything where Yolŋu have nothing. We are ashamed of our fathers; they have nothing for us, not like you Balanda.'

'We are frightened of the discipline and law of our old people,' they went on. 'We want to be *free* like Balanda.'

I asked them to clarify this statement.

'We want to be *rommiriw* (lawless) and *raypirri'miriw* (lacking discipline) just like Balanda.'

They had a very different understanding of freedom than I did, so I asked them where they got these ideas.

'From school.'

'Where from school?'

'From the teachers and the videos.'

'What things do the teachers say that tell you this?'

'They say Australia is "a free country" where you can "do whatever you want". They tell us we "should be able to marry anyone we want" and "if we don't want to go to a ceremony, the old people should not be able to force us" because this is a "free country".'

'And what do you see on the videos?'

'How Balanda live. You can smash up one car and just get another one. Or you can have different girlfriends any time you want.'[208]

The Singapore trip had also confused them greatly. Many of them thought that Balanda can just go to luxury motels, eat great food and make a mess that someone else will clean up—all for free. No one had explained the hard economic facts of life to them, probably because no one could. On returning home, the children felt ashamed because they had to sleep on the floor and eat unsophisticated food, 'not food like Balanda have'. They became ashamed of their fathers 'because they cannot provide good things like Balanda fathers can'. 'All they do is talk about their old law. What good has that done them—they still have nothing good [cars and groovy clothes] to give us.'

They were sniffing to forget who they were!

New discoveries for all. With these clear contradictions between what they understood and objective reality, we were slowly able to show them the truth about the medical situation: that in fact there was no medicine or operation that would *yuṯakum* (make new, rejuvenate) their brain damage. With the help of the doctor, we explained to them the whole process of dialysis if they were hospitalised in an emergency.

I also shared the sniffers' confusion about Balanda law and economics with my reference group of elders. Over many months we worked through aspects of Balanda law and how it related to Yolŋu law. Much of what I learnt about Yolŋu law throughout this period was totally new to me. A whole new world of codified ancient law opened up. As the elders taught me new concepts, I taught them the corresponding concepts in Balanda law. We were all struck by the profound similarity of each other's law.

As the months went on, I also worked with the sniffers when they were in trouble with Balanda law. This happened when they broke into someone's house or stole petrol. Whenever they had to go to court I would help them by explaining Balanda law to them. This allowed them to see that what they had learnt at school was wrong—that in fact Balanda *did* have law.

I also made sure the term 'free country' was explained carefully.

Then we discussed what 'ceremony' really meant to them. 'It's where the old people teach all the law and how to live properly,' they said. I showed them how Balanda young people are also forced to go to 'ceremony' (school) by law, and how many of them go on to higher levels of 'ceremony' (tertiary education), spending many years just learning, learning, learning. I pointed out that many would have very little money while they were still learning. Finally, I spoke about how Balanda got their houses and cars, sometimes spending all their lives paying them off.

Throughout all these discussions I used newspaper cuttings, asked other Balanda to tell the story of their mortgage or found some other way to allow the sniffers to objectively validate what I was saying.

After about eighteen months of this process, I asked the group of elders what they would do about the petrol sniffing if there were no Balanda in the community. They said they would bring back a particular ceremony. 'Why aren't you using this ceremony here now?' I asked.

'Because the missionaries stopped us from holding it.'

'Well, no-one here is going to stop you now!' I assured them.

Within three months of that meeting I heard sounds come from the bush, and all the women in the community responded with a strange noise made by the hand placed over the mouth. I asked one of the elders what it was. He said that it was *Gakawarr*, the ceremony we had discussed. In this ceremony the elders were able to teach their ancient law and the new knowledge they had learnt from the doctors and others I had brought in. The people's ancient ceremonial process, together with new modern information, was used in *their* university to instruct their young adults in a way that they understood.

This ceremony lasted for about three months. All the petrol sniffers were taken inside for instruction. When they had finished, many came to me and thanked me for supporting the elders, for having the ceremony re-opened and for all the other information. 'Before, we were confused about you Balanda and frightened of the elders,' they said. 'Now we can see the whole thing clearly.'

Petrol sniffing stopped at Ramingining after this, nearly seventeen years ago. It has never really been a problem there since, although petrol sniffing continues to be a major problem in many other Arnhem Land communities. In Ramingining the ceremonial process and the information continues to be taught by the people, with not one dollar cost to government and with the people in control of that part of their lives.

When the people discover real answers to their questions, their conceptional universe is satisfied about that particular subject and they will take action to bring the problem under control.

A successful methodology. This process at Ramingining taught me the power of problem-solving education. As a model it has been practised worldwide by a small number of people using the educational methodology espoused by the South American educator Paulo Freire. In Australia only a few people have practised it, even though many Australian educators have studied Freire's works and some have even taught his theories. Few, however, have understood it through the refining process of practice.

I believe this methodology has not yet reached its full potential in Australia because the aspect of language and its relationship to the learning process has not been truly understood by mainstream, monolingual Australian education-alists.

This methodology does not conflict with sound educational principles, but it does conflict with the dominant culture's educational practices where they are directed at another cultural group. It seems to me that it is the *cultural requirements and needs* of the dominant culture that are normally met in educational debate, structuring and practice, rather than the requirements of sound educational theory. And this is the reason why, in general, education for groups like Yolŋu is failing. It will continue to fail unless we approach education and training in a new, theoretically competent way.

Replace Existing Programs with Programs That Truly Empower the People

For Yolŋu to regain control of their lives, all present programs need assessing to see if they are part of the answer or *part of the problem*. Where programs do not return responsibility and control to Yolŋu and their communities they must be modified or replaced with programs that do. This change should be done in a *sensitive* and *constructive* way. If the forty-three factors leading to 'loss of control' listed in chapter 13 were used as a guide, this could be done. The following are three examples where this could happen.

First, information. We say that in modern society 'information is power', yet Yolŋu are clearly marginalised information-wise due to present policies and programs. Programs need to take the people's immense intellectual ability seriously.

Second, employment. Unless Yolŋu have meaningful employment, things will only get worse in terms of health. Yet housing programs aimed at improving the people's health continue to use contractors to build housing while the people sit and watch. In December 1999, for example, I heard again of a community that is to receive four houses in 2000. Two were to be built by outside contractors and the other two built by their own building team. But now they are being told that outside contractors will be given the four to build because they took too long to build their last two houses in 1999. And this is despite the fact that the Yolŋu team is a brand new team of trainees, formed by the community in an attempt to find meaningful employment for their young people so they will have something to live for. Those responsible for such programs have all their priorities wrong and do not see the holistic approach necessary to deal with human problems.

Third, communication. Where programs are seen to come out of the dominant culture's negative naming of Yolŋu, they need to be scrapped. Millions of dollars have been wasted, for example, on developing books, videos, CD-ROMs, flip charts, posters, puppet shows and the like that tell simple stories about highly complex issues. But Yolŋu demand highly intellectual information for complex issues, just as 'English-thinking' people do.

In each of these cases, evaluating programs from the perspective of whether they empower Yolŋu reveals major flaws that need to be corrected. Incidentally, when evaluating programs, the issues created by using English as the main communication tool need to be taken into account. Just as programs fail due to difficulties with language, so true evaluation can fail because of the communication factor. All programs need to be evaluated in an authentic way.

So what is the alternative? Here is an example of an education program that empowered people with *real* information, giving them *real* control over their lives.

The Galiwin'ku Melioidosis Education Program

In April 1996 I received a phone call from the Chief Executive Officer of ARDS, Djiniyini Gondarra. He was at Galiwin'ku attending a meeting of clan leaders of the community. There had been six deaths in the community in as many weeks. Two leaders had died of Melioidosis in four weeks and another man, critically ill in Darwin, was expected to die in the next few days. Djiniyini reported to me that the leaders said it was not right for middle-aged people to die like this. They told him the people were scared. Many were thinking of leaving the island to live in Darwin because they believed the deaths were being caused by a *galka* (sorcerer).[209]

'We need to be able to show the people that these deaths are caused by bacteria.' Djiniyini said. 'Can you do that?'

I had already investigated this subject and conducted some education sessions with individual Yolŋu and family groups, so the generative words, resources and language around the topic were developed enough. I agreed to bring the microscopes and show the people bacteria, then tell them about Melioidosis. Djiniyini asked about the characteristics, the life cycle and the method of entry to the body of Melioidosis. We went through the story on the phone and he hung up to go and tell it to the old men.

About half an hour later he rang back saying they had a real problem with the story about Melioidosis. 'If this Melioidosis lives in the ground here at Galiwin'ku and it has lived here for thousands of years, why hasn't it been killing us [Yolŋu] before? We know this country and it was never known to be "sickness country".'

I explained to Djiniyini that Melioidosis was only a problem now because the people's immune systems were depressed.

'What is immune system?' he asked.

I explained the immune system and he wanted to know if I could show the people. 'It's no good just talking about it,' he said, 'the people need to see it to believe it.'

Once again, I had already researched this subject and had acquired dark field equipment for the microscope so the people could see live blood. 'We have the gear for the microscope that could show the people their blood,' I said. 'They will be able to see their red and white blood cells.'

Djiniyini said he would talk to the leaders to see if they wanted me to come to Galiwin'ku and show them this whole story. An hour later he rang back. The leaders wanted me there the next day.

When I arrived in Galiwin'ku the following morning I was met by one of the leaders. He took me straight to the council office where the council chairman greeted me. 'Yes, we know why you are here,' he said. 'The men will help you set up in the council chambers. You can stay there all week and I will come in about one hour when I have finished some meetings.' But others beat him to it. While I was still setting up, all the leaders came and we had the first education session within fifteen minutes of my arriving in the community!

I spent four days at Galiwin'ku, showing the leaders and an 'at-risk' group—the main kava drinkers—the whole story of immune systems and Melioidosis.[210] In that first week, up to fifty people a day came through the council chambers. It took about an hour to take a group of five through the whole story. They were long days.

After this episode I was not able to return to Galiwin'ku for a couple of months, so I started training an ARDS female educator. She was an accountant based in Galiwin'ku and had extremely good language skills. She became acquainted with the education methodology and had already practised it in AIDS/HIV education, in which we were both involved.[211] We had both already spent many hours with a traditional Yolŋu educator developing many generative words and getting a good handle on the language terms around pathogens and the immune system.

Then in July 1996 the Menzies School of Health Research asked us to work with them in studying Melioidosis at Galiwin'ku. We said the community had already asked us to do Melioidosis education, so we would be happy to work in with their medical experts in a collaborative relationship.

We already had a good general understanding of Melioidosis, but before we started a larger formal education program we wanted to make sure we had a complete, medically correct understanding. In this case we restudied the life cycle of Melioidosis and all there was to know about it until we could see 'in our mind's eye' exactly how the Melioidosis bacteria lives in the soil, then moves from the soil to the body of the host. We understood how it reproduces and does battle in the host; how it can lie dormant in the body; how and why it can break out, multiplying in the blood stream and causing septicaemia. Only when we had this clear image in our minds were we ready to work with the people in Yolŋu Matha. (This is a general rule we use before we move to a point of translating or working in Yolŋu Matha on any subject.)

Next we developed a storyline that we showed to the Menzies experts for validation or correction. They verified that the story was medically correct. We contacted the clan leaders again to make sure they were behind the process all the way.

The education was carried out prior to the 1996/1997 Wet season. Over 700 adult women, some of them sitting through the process more than once, and 140 men went through the education process. At the invitation of the community health workers, we also spent time with individual Yolŋu who had positive serology readings. This had been picked up in a voluntary screening program organised by Menzies.

According to local clinic records, in the eighteen months prior to April 1996 the community of Galiwin'ku suffered thirteen cases of Melioidosis, five of which were fatal. But the results to September 1998 showed that not one case of

Melioidosis had been identified at Galiwin'ku since June 1996. In that time a physical contamination site was discovered and cleaned up. But something else had led to the absence of Melioidosis over those two years. Melioidosis continued to occur in other communities in the region throughout this period.

I believe one of the major reasons for the change was that the people had been enabled to understand thoroughly what Melioidosis is and how it occurs, and this knowledge empowered them to create their own effective action against it.

A Program That Empowered the People

The key to the Melioidosis story, like many other health stories, was the facts around the immune system. As we showed the people live blood, we homed in on the white blood cells, which we call in Yolŋu Matha 'body warriors'. These white blood cells look like white jellyfish as they seek out and kill foreign invaders. The people get very interested in them and we talk about how to keep these body warriors strong by eating good food.

This program was successful because it allowed the people to create their own health interventions—those that suited their lifestyle and culture. We didn't tell them what to do but discussed some of the options, letting them make their own decisions. This method allows true ownership of the action the people decide on.

In June 1997 the people of Galiwin'ku told me about many of their interventions. They included:

- If people get cuts on their feet they make sure they don't get mud in them.
- More people are wearing thongs and shoes in the Wet season.
- Other people are making sure that if they get a cut, they go to the clinic straight away.
- People are cleaning up around their homes so there is nothing to cut their feet on.
- Some homeowners are filling in puddles and making lawn areas to keep the children safe.
- People are keeping the children from playing in the mud, telling them, 'Get out of that mud. Don't you know there are things in that mud that can kill you?'
- Families are making sure that leaking taps are fixed so there is no mud under them. If a tap is still leaking, they make sure the children do not play under it.
- Some people are going hunting twice a week so they get fresh food to ensure their 'body warriors' are strong enough to beat any Melioidosis already in the body.

About two weeks after the education finished Yolŋu organised a clean-up of the Galiwin'ku township. No dominant culture personnel were involved in its organisation, although many were co-opted to help. The people said, 'We must clean up before the Wet season so there will be less chance of people cutting themselves and less food on the ground to feed these little things [bacteria].'

All these interventions are cost-negative to government and do not lead the people to become more dependent on the dominant culture.

The significance of this story is its graphic demonstration that people can learn. They *want* to learn. But for the dominant culture to be able to help Yolŋu repair or complete their conceptional universe:

• dominant culture experts must be trained so they can do this education;

• the education process must be theoretically sound. Yolŋu must be involved in its curricula and content development. It must work from their world-view and cultural knowledge base and be delivered in the language in which they think and construct knowledge;

• *all* the people as a cultural group need to be educated, empowering them all, not just an elite few.

When empowering programs are implemented the people will not just create the interventions necessary to avoid or minimise contact with these diseases. They will also adopt overall healthier lifestyles and become more responsible for their health. By adding modern knowledge to their cultural knowledge base they lay the foundation for easier appropriation of other new medical knowledge. And perhaps most significantly of all, they regain a degree of control over their lives, becoming masters of one more aspect of their contemporary living environment.

Deal with Some Basic Legal Issues

> All peoples have the right of self-determination. By virtue of that right, they freely determine their political status and freely pursue their economic, social and cultural development.[212]

In order to return *full* control to Yolŋu, certain justice issues need to be addressed. It is a common understanding all over the world that the two things required for effective development are a *security of tenure* and a *rule of law*. Without these two basic legal requirements, human societies anywhere will find it extremely difficult to maintain social order and almost impossible to move forward in development, particularly economic development.

However, the present legal situation in Arnhem Land, rather than creating legal stability, creates legal anarchy.

A Security of Tenure

Yes, Yolŋu do have 'land rights', established under Federal Government legislation.[213] But this is not a form of land tenure that Yolŋu can understand. These 'land rights' are not recognised at Yolŋu law; rather, they were created in a shape and form that suited Balanda law. For Yolŋu this continues to cause much confusion, hurt and division between clan and nation alliance groups.

Now the people have a 'land council', over which they have no direct control, making decisions about their land and resources. Imagine how many dominant culture businesses would thrive or even survive under such a system of land tenure.

The present 'land rights' legislation has in fact produced some of the same kinds of 'cronyism' that have been typical of Western influences on 'developing nations' in Asia and Africa over the last 100 years. True democracy—that is, Yolŋu participating in processes of decision-making and controlling abuses of power—is not possible with the present structures because they do not reflect the legal processes and institutions in the *Maḏayin*.

Don't get me wrong. Yolŋu in general are protective of the present 'lands rights' system. 'Land rights law is not our law but it is all we have,' they say. Yolŋu *do* want the protection and rights the present legislation affords them over their estates. But at the same time, they dream of the day when these rights will be recognised in the form of their traditional tenure and the rule of law established in the *Maḏayin*.

But when your birthright is denied and your right to participate in the democratic processes is disallowed because of language problems, what is there left to live for? Just as Yolŋu stopped seeding oysters for pearls because others came and stole their pearls, so they will show very little interest in economic development until they know they have a true security of tenure.

A Rule of Law

The communities of Arnhem Land are awash with confusion over issues of law and order. This confusion comes from the fact that 'Australian law' does not recognise 'Yolŋu law', the *Maḏayin*.

This non-recognition means the people are not able to operate and practise their law in an open way, nor are they able to apply its sanctions to lawbreakers. This allows the lawbreakers and rebels within their society to go unpunished. On many occasions, contemporary Australian law actually protects these lawbreakers and punishes the traditional law-keepers and peace officers. At the same time, the people are required to live according to Australian law—a system they neither understand nor assent to.

Having to live under two laws means that double jeopardy and injustice are common. It also means that the people are forced to practise lawlessness by having to decide which law or code they will follow at any particular time. To comply with one code often means breaking the other. Because of this confusion and 'forced law-breaking', Yolŋu communities are degenerating into anarchy.

In earlier days patrol officers, and later police officers, travelled all over Arnhem Land telling the people they had to give up their traditional law and would be imprisoned if they practised it. In fact, many traditional Yolŋu 'police' and 'officers of the law' spent time in Balanda jails for trying to maintain the *mägaya* (state of peace) that the *Maḏayin* law created. The suppression of the people's law has been, from their perspective, ruthless and senseless.

To make this situation even more confusing, police and other dominant culture people (school teachers, community staff, government workers) now keep telling Yolŋu they should sort out the 'law and order' issues according to their own law. This leaves the people caught in the middle. If they apply their law, they know from experience they could be dragged before dominant culture courts and end up in a Balanda jail. The mere thought of this for Yolŋu is terrifying.

This issue is really very simple to understand. If dominant culture people were tomorrow expected to live under the rule of the *Maḏayin*, cultural and social degeneration would be rapid. In a very short time Australian society would be in anarchy, because dominant culture citizens would not understand the institutions and laws they were supposed to now live under. It is the same in reverse for Yolŋu.

Recognising the people's traditional law, the *Maḏayin*, which includes their form of land and resource tenure, needs to be addressed in a true, 'fair-go' Aussie way. If the unique Yolŋu of Arnhem Land are to be great warriors again, difficult challenges like this *must* be faced.

Warriors Once More

Although many of the issues raised in this book are complex, in the end they come down to simple basics. Good health is not just a state of an absence of disease. It has a great deal to do with how people feel—like feeling there is something worth living and fighting for.

Many Yolŋu are desperate. They hope for something to change so that they can find some small joy in living again. Many have no idea of what has caused the deep darkness they must live through, and some grab at any idea given to them by the dominant culture as 'the answer'—only to be let down again. All want to stand tall, shoulder-to-shoulder with other Australian citizens, as true equals in developing this great nation.

Financially, the changes I have outlined should cost the nation no more than it is spending now. In fact, they should cost less in the future as the new programs empower Yolŋu, allowing them to create interventions that work around 'Yolŋu-friendly' environments where they are able to resume mastery over their own living environment.

However, Yolŋu must be empowered before they can take control of their own destiny. This will only happen if the dominant culture sees things in a totally new way. While some dominant culture people have joined Yolŋu in their struggle, others do not want to see change. All Australian citizens, governments, professionals and most importantly, policymakers, must accept the responsibility that comes from being part of the dominant culture. It is time to actively create 'Yolŋu-friendly' environments so that the Yolŋu of Arnhem Land are empowered.

Then they can become *djambatj mala*—great warriors—once more.

PRONUNCIATION

A GUIDE FOR YOLŊU MATHA WORDS

The transition of an oral language into a 'written' form (i.e. additional to its more usual 'spoken' forms) usually requires making a number of technical linguistic decisions. Fortunately for us these decisions were largely made for Yolŋu Matha as a result of the countless hours of linguistic research and analysis performed by schoolteacher/linguist Beulah Lowe and her Yolŋu associates while Beulah was stationed at Milingimbi Mission from 1953-77. A phonetic script was developed to facilitate ease of learning and was subsequently standardised in all the Yolŋu-speaking missions (now Yolŋu townships) of north-east Arnhem Land.

The key to successfully pronouncing many of the words that occur in Yolŋu Matha is to give particular 'attention' and 'emphasis' to correct pronunciation of the vowel sounds. Unlike English, stress in Yolŋu Matha is *always* on the *first* syllable.

Vowels

All Yolŋu languages and their associated dialects possess 3 vowels that each have a long and a short sound, namely:

Short :   a , i , u

Long :   ä , e , o

    a   as in   ado , cup , mother , under

              e.g.   mala   Balanda   galka

    ä   as in   father , star , garden , fast

              e.g.   mägaya   Bäpa   Wämut

    i   as in   hit , this

              e.g.   yirralka   manikay   Maḏayin

e   as in   fee , sea , heat

         e.g.   mel   rerri   nhe

u   as in   foot , put , could   (never as in 'but')

         e.g.   buku   gapu   buliki

o   as in   sore , law , for , awe , your   (never as in 'pot')

         e.g.   yol   mokuy   rom

Consonants

Many of the consonant sounds that occur in Yolŋu Matha have the same sound in English namely:

b	as in boy		d	as in dog
g	as in gun		k	as in bucket
l	as in luck		m	as in mill
n	as in never		p	as in rapid
r	as in red		t	as in take
w	as in way		y	as in you.

Some other consonant sounds are familiar sounding to us but look different when written, such as:

ŋ   as in   sing , lung , dong

         e.g.   riŋgitj   gaŋga   ŋir'

Some are very similar but not exactly the same as sounds formed in English.

ny, dj and tj are alveodental consonants and formed when the blade of the tongue is pushed forward towards the upper gum ridge and the tip of the tongue is behind the bottom teeth.

ny   similar to new ,   (<u>not</u> as in nest, nil, liner etc.)

         e.g.   manymak   waŋgany   nyäl

dj   similar to jingle , jump , jingo

         e.g.   djäma djugu' Djinaŋ

Pronunciation

| tj | similar to much , lunch |
| | e.g. djambatj Gumatj riŋgitj |

Other consonants are new sounds and have no equivalents in English.

dh , nh and th are interdental sounds pronounced with the tip of the tongue poking through between the top and bottom teeth.

dh	e.g. dhäwu dhuyu dhuw
nh	e.g. nhe nhuma nhä
th	e.g. matha bathi ŋathu

ḍ , ḷ , ṇ , ṭ are retroflexed sounds. The tip of the tongue curls up and then back onto the roof of the mouth.

ḍ	e.g. ḍiltji ḍalkarra Maḍayin
ḷ	e.g. ḷuka ḷirra ḷom
ṇ	e.g. waṇa Gäṇgaṇ ṇapuŋga
ṭ	e.g. yuṭa baṭa waṭu

rr is a flapped ' r ' . The tongue flaps once against the roof of the mouth (similar to the Scottish rolled R).

| rr | e.g. gumurr dhukarr märram |

Some Additional Rules

Stress is always on the first syllable.

Long vowels only occur in the first syllable of a word, never after.

Two consonants y and w are not voiced or sounded where they occur at the *end* of a *word*, but they *can* change the sound of the preceding vowel.

    y   e.g.   manikay   Nhulunbuy   waŋgany

    w   e.g.   rom-miriw   Bäpaw   bukuw

Where "n" is followed immediately by "g" they must be pronounced as two separate sounds (as opposed to the ŋ sound as in sing).

ng	e.g.	gungam	gun – gam
		Raminginiŋ	Ram – in – gin – iŋ
		Milingimbi	Mil – in – gim - bi

BIBLIOGRAPHY

BOOKS

Austin, Tony *'Waste Lands Act'—Simply Survival of the Fittest: Aboriginal Administration in South Australia's Northern Territory 1863-1910*, Historical Society of the Northern Territory, Darwin, 1992.

Bernardo, Allan B. I. *Literacy and the Mind: The Contexts and Cognitive Consequences of Literacy Practice,* UNESCO Institute for Education, Germany & Luzac Oriental, Wiltshire, England,1998.

Bodley, John H. *Victims of Progress*, Cummings Publishing Company Inc., Philippines, 1975.

Brewster, E. Thomas & Brewster, Elisabeth S. *Language Acquisition Made Practical*, Lingua House, Colorado, USA, 1976.

Cherry, Colin *On Human Communication: A review, a survey and a criticism*, The MIT Press, Massachusetts, 1971.

Christie, Michael J. *Aboriginal Perspectives on Experience and Learning: The Role of Language in Aboriginal Education*, Deakin University, Victoria, 1985.

Cole, Keith *The Aborigines of Arnhem Land*, Rigby, Adelaide, 1979.

Crystal, David *The Cambridge Encyclopaedia of Language*, Cambridge University Press, Cambridge, 1987.

Danieli, Yael (ed.) *International Handbook of Multigenerational Legacies of Trauma*, Plenum Press, New York, 1998.

Dermody, Kathleen *A Nation at Last: The Story of Federation*, AGPS Press, Canberra, 1997.

Devitt, J. & McMasters, A. *Living on Medicine: A Cultural Study of End-stage Renal Failure among Aboriginal People*, IAD Press, Alice Springs, 1998.

Dewar, Mickey *The 'Black War' in Arnhem Land: Missionaries and the Yolngu, 1908-1940,* Australian National University North Australia Research Unit, Darwin, 1992.

Dixon, R. M. W. *The Languages of Australia,* Cambridge University Press, Cambridge, 1980.

Egan, Ted *Justice All Their Own*, Melbourne University Press, Melbourne, 1996.

Eldon, Kathy & Mike *The Story of Medicine*, Wayland Publishers Ltd, East Sussex, England, 1977.

Elkin, A. P. *Aboriginal Men of High Degree: Initiation and Sorcery in the World's Oldest Tradition*, Inner Traditions International, Rochester VT, 1994.

Freire, Paulo *Pedagogy of Hope,* The Continuum Publishing Company, New York, 1995.

Freire, Paulo *Pedagogy of the Oppressed.* Penguin, Great Britain, 1972.

Gagne, M. *'The Role of Dependency and Colonialism in Generating Trauma in First Nations Citizens'*, in Danieli, 1998.

Giroux, Henry A. *Border Crossings: Cultural Workers and the Politics of Education*, Routledge, Chapman & Hall, New York, NY, 1992.

Hall, Robert A. *The Black Diggers—Aborigines and Torres Strait Islanders in the Second World War*, Allen & Unwin, Sydney, 1989.

Harris, John *One Blood*, Albatross Books, Sydney, 1990.

Harris, Thomas A. *I'm OK—You're OK*, Pan Books, Great Britain, 1973.

Hughes, Charles C. & Hunter, John M. *The Role of Technological Development in Promoting Disease in Africa*, in Farvar, M. Taghi & Milton, John P. *The Careless Technology: Ecology and International Development*, The Natural History Press, Garden City, New York, 1972.

Lamilami, Lazarus *Lamilami Speaks*, Ure Smith, Sydney, 1974.

Lowe, Beulah *Temporary Gupapuyŋu Dictionary*, printed by Methodist Overseas Mission at Milingimbi, NT, 1960-75.

Macknight, C. C. *The Voyage to Marege'—Macassan Trepangers in Northern Australia*, Melbourne University Press, Melbourne, 1976.

McKenzie, Maisie *Mission to Arnhem Land*, Rigby, Adelaide, 1976.

Mirritji, Jack *My People's Life*, Milingimbi Literature Centre, Milingimbi, 1976.

Mountford, Charles P. (ed.) *Records of the American-Australian Scientific Expedition to Arnhem Land*, Vol. 2, Melbourne University Press, Melbourne, 1956.

Perkins, Harvey L. (ed.) *Guidelines for Development*, Christian Conference of Asia, Singapore, 1980.

Plant, A. J., Condon, J. R. & Durling, G. *Northern Territory Health Outcomes; Morbidity and Mortality 1979-1991*, Northern Territory Department Health and Community Services, Darwin, 1995.

Powell, Alan *Far Country—A Short History of the Northern Territory*, Melbourne University Press, Melbourne, 1982.

Rolls, Eric *Sojourners*, University of Queensland Press, Brisbane, 1992.

Rosenheck, R. & Fontana, A. 'Warrior Fathers and Warrior Sons: Intergenerational Aspects of Trauma', in Danieli, 1998.

Searcy, Alfred *In Australian Tropics*, 1909. Reprinted by Hesperian Press, Perth, 1985.

Stanner, W. E. H. *White Man Got No Dreaming: Essays 1938-1973*, Australian National University Press, Canberra, 1979.

Thomson, Donald *Economic Structure and the Ceremonial Exchange Cycle in Arnhem Land*, Macmillan & Co Ltd, Melbourne, 1949.

Toffler, Alvin *Future Shock*, Pan Books, London and Sydney, 1970.

Webb, T. Theodore, *The Aborigines of East Arnhem Land,* Australia, Methodist Laymen's Missionary Movement, Victoria, Melbourne, 1934.

Wells, Edgar *Reward and Punishment in Arnhem Land*, Australian Institute of Aboriginal Studies, Canberra, 1982.

Wilson, Paul *Black Death White Hands*, Allen & Unwin, Sydney, 1982.

PERIODICALS

Airhihenbuwa, Collins O. 'Health Promotion and the Discourse on Culture: Implications for Empowerment', *Health Education Quarterly*, Vol. 21 (3), Fall 1994, pp. 345-353

Bailey, Sandra 'Renal Services Update', *The Chronicle*, Bulletin of the Chronic Diseases Network of the Northern Territory, Vol.1.12, June/July 1998.

Clark, M. Margaret 'Cultural Context of Medical Practice in Cross-cultural Medicine', *The Western Journal of Medicine*, December 1983, 139:6.

Evans, Peter J. 'How to really improve the lot of the poor", Opinion, *The Age*, July 21, 1998.

Hancock, Trevor 'The Mandala of Health: A Model of the Human Ecosystem', in *Family and Community Health*, 8 (3), pp. 1-10, Department of Public Health, Toronto, Canada, 1985.

Herman, J. L. 'Complex PTSD: A Syndrome in Survivors of Prolonged and Repeated Trauma', *Journal of Traumatic Stress*, 1992, Vol. 5, No. 2, pp. 377-393.

Koch, Tony 'Pearson hits welfare "poison" ', *The Courier-Mail*, April 30, 1999, p.1.

Lantz, Paula M. et al 'Socio-economic Factors, Health Behaviors and Mortality: Results from a Nationally Representative Prospective Study of US Adults', *JAMA*, Vol. 279, No. 21, pp. 1703-8, June 3, 1998.

Marsella, Anthony J., Friedman, Matthew J., & Spain, E. Huland 'A Selective Review of the Literature on Ethnocultural Aspects of PTSD', *PTSD Research Quarterly*, The National Center for Post-Traumatic Stress Disorder, Vol. 3, No. 2, Spring 1992.

Meisler, Andrew W. 'Trauma, PTSD, and Substance Abuse', *PTSD Research Quarterly*, The National Center for Post-Traumatic Stress Disorder, Vol. 7, No. 4, Fall 1996.

Madigan, Michael, Koch, Tony and Retschlag, Christine 'Beattie backs Pearson on "poison" attack', *The Courier-Mail*, May 1, 1999, p.1.

Miller, B. 'Learned Helplessness and Aboriginal Intra-Cultural Crime and Violence', *South Pacific Journal of Psychology*, 1992, 5.

Missionary Review, Methodist Overseas Mission Board, Sydney, 5 October, 1933.

Riggs, David S. 'Posttraumatic Stress Disorder and the Perpetration of Domestic Violence', *NC-PTSD Clinical Quarterly*, The National Centre for PTSD, Vol. 7, No. 2, Spring 1997, pp. 22-25.

Schnurr, Paula P. 'Trauma, PTSD and Physical Health', *PTSD Research Quarterly*, The National Centre for Post-Traumatic Stress Disorder, Vol. 7, No. 3, Summer 1996.

Segal, J., Hunter, E. J. & Segal, Z. 'Universal Consequences of Captivity: Stress Reactions Among Divergent Populations of Prisoners of War and Their Families', *International Journal of Social Science*, Vol. 28, No. 3, 1976, pp. 593-609.

Stewart, Cameron 'The Sioux's Last Stand', *The Australian Magazine*, July 11-12, 1998.

Spinney, Laura 'Tongue Tied', *New Scientist Magazine*, 24 July, 1999, pp. 38-41.

Syme, S. Leonard 'Individual versus Community—Interventions in Public Health Practice: Some Thoughts About a New Approach', in *Health Promotion Matters*, Vic Health, Issue 2, July 1997, pp. 2-9.

Webb, T. Theodore 'The Future of the Aboriginal', *Missionary Review*, Methodist Overseas Mission, Sydney, May 1951.

Westin, S., Norum, D. & Schlesselman, J. J. 'Medical Consequences of a Factory Closure: Illness and Disability—A Four-year Follow-up Study', *International Journal of Epidemiology*, Vol. 17, No. 1, 1988, pp.153-61.

Westin, S., Schlesselman, J. J., & Korper, M. 'Long Term Effects of a Factory Closure: Unemployment and Disability During Ten-years Follow-up', *Journal of Clinical Epidemiology*, Vol. 42, No. 5, 1989, pp.435-41.

THESES

McLellan, M. A. Study of the Wangurri Language, PhD thesis, Macquarie University, 1994.

Wilkinson, M. P. Djambarrpuyŋu—A Yolŋu variety of Northern Australia, PhD thesis, University of Sydney, 1991.

OTHER

'Aboriginal Youth Suicide', *Four Corners*, Australian Broadcasting Corporation, October 26, 1998.

'Aboriginal Public Health Action Strategy and Implementation Guide, 1997-2002', Public Health Strategy Unit, Territory Health Services, Northern Territory Government, Darwin, November 1997.

Amery, Howard, *They don't give us the full story: Attitudes to Hospitalisation Amongst Yolŋu People of North-East Arnhem Land – A Comparative Study*, Funded by Territory Health Services, Nhulunbuy, August 1999.

Australia, Parliament 1992. *A Matter of Survival: Inquiry into Aboriginal and Torres Strait Islander Language Maintenance*, House of Representatives Standing Committee on Aboriginal and Torres Strait Islander Affairs (36th Parliament).

Australia's Indigenous Languages, Senior Secondary Assessment Board of South Australia, Hyde Park Press, 1996.

Case Study on AIDS Education, unpublished booklet, Aboriginal Resource and Development Services Inc, 1995.

"English Language", Microsoft® Encarta. Copyright © 1994 Microsoft Corporation. Copyright © 1994 Funk & Wagnall's Corporation.

Free to Decide, Report of the Commission of Enquiry, United Church in North Australia, Arnhem Land, March-April 1974.

Kakadu Region Social Impact Study 1997, Report of the Aboriginal Project Committee, June 1997 Supervising Scientist, Canberra.

Learning Lessons: An independent review of Indigenous education in the Northern Territory, Northern Territory Department of Education, Darwin, 1999.

Lowndes, John Allan *Coroner's Report* , Case No : 9108664, Rel No: 106/91, Northern Territory Of Australia, 6 May 1992.

Menzies School of Health Research '*Treatment Program for Kidney Disease in an Aboriginal Community in the NT*', unpublished, Darwin NT, p. 1.

Mortality of Vietnam Veterans: The Veteran Cohort Study. Report of May 1997, Department of Veterans' Affairs, Canberra, 1997.

Official Journal of the European Communities 93/16/EEC. 1993, April 5.

'Ottawa Charter for Health Promotion', International Conference on Health Promotion, (jointly organised by WHO, Health and Welfare Canada, and Canadian Public Health Association), Ottawa, Canada, November 17-26, 1986.

'Report on the Provision of Health Services to Aboriginal Communities in the Northern Territory', Legislative Assembly of the Northern Territory, Public Accounts Committee, Report 28, 1996.

South Australian Parliamentary Papers 1895-1904, South Australian Government Archives, Adelaide, South Australia.

Territory Health Services. *A Draft Northern Territory Aboriginal Public Health Action Strategy 1997-2000*, Northern Territory Government, Darwin, May 1997.

United Nations International Covenant on Civil and Political Rights, General Assembly resolution 2200 A (XXI) 16 Dec 1966; Entry into force 23 March 1976 in accordance with article 49.

Watson, M. L. '*The communication problems of Tribal Aboriginal Women in the Maternity Ward*', unpublished dissertation, Darwin Institute of Technology, Graduate Diploma in Teaching English as a Second language, January 1987.

Webb, T. T. 'The Aborigines of East Arnhem Land', Ninth Methodist Laymen's Memorial Lecture, Wesley Church, Melbourne, March 26, 1934.

WEB SITES

Friedman, Matthew J. 'Post-Traumatic Stress Disorder: An Overview', The National Centre for PTSD: www.dartmouth.edu/dms/ptsd/Overview.html, 30 Sep 98.

Guanipa, Carmen, *Culture Shock*: www.edweb.sdsu.edu/people/CGuanipa/cultshok.htm, 27 Sep 99.

International Student Handbook 1995-6, College of Wooster, USA: www.wooster.edu/oisa/handbook/culture.html, 5 Oct 98.

National Center for PTSD, The Fact Sheets www.dartmouth.edu/dms/ptsd.html, 30 Sept 1998.

National Center For PTSD, The PTSD and Community Violence Fact Sheet: www.dartmouth.edu/dms/ptsd/FS_Community_Violence.html, 30 Sept 1998.

Oberg, Lalvero Editorial, Worldwide Classroom: www.worldwide.edu/planning_guide/Culture_Re-entry_Shock/Culture_Re-entry_Shock.html, 11 Jan 1999.

REFERENCES

1   Plant et al., 1995, p. 46.
2   Mountford, 1956, pp. 31, 33.
3   ibid., p. 43.
4   Hughes & Hunter, 1972, p.93.
5   Rolls, 1992, p. 12.
6   Macknight, 1976, p. 1.
7   Searcy, 1909, p.15.
8   ibid., pp.134-35.
9   ibid., p. 32.
10 ibid., p. 33.
11 Trepang are sea slugs from the holothurians family. Usually they are about 10 to 15 cm in length, although they can be found bigger. There are two varieties along the north and east coasts of Arnhem Land and they are either black or grey in colour.
12 Thomson, 1949, p. 86.
13 South Australian Parliamentary Papers, Annual Papers 1895-1904.
14 Thomson, 1949, pp. 86ff.
15 Information from personal communication with Yolŋu of many different clans.
16 Lowe, 1960-1975.
17 Rolls, 1992, p. 11.
18 Cole, 1979, p. 7.
19 Aboriginal people right across Australia called these strange animals *yarraman'*
    (Australia's Indigenous Languages, Senior Secondary Assessment Board of South Australia, 1996).
20 Harris, 1990, p. 147.
21 Cole, 1979, p. 80.
22 Austin, 1992, p. 3.
23 Cole, 1979, p. 3.
24 ibid., p. 3.
25 Left Hand Lee and others, personal communication, 1998.
26 ibid.
27 Cole, 1979, p. 80.
28 ibid., p. 80.
29 Macknight, 1976, p. 123.
30 Powell, 1982, p. 61.
31 McKenzie, 1976, p. 16.
32 ibid., p. 10.
33 Lamilami, 1974, p. 78.
34 ibid., p. 87.
35 ibid., pp. 77-92.
36 McKenzie, 1976, p. 23.
37 Djoma Gaykamaŋu, personal communication, 1982.
38 I met this man in 1978, when I was part of a reconciliation ceremony carried out at this massacre site. Along with about ten other Balanda, we re-enacted the massacre as the Yolŋu described it. At one point, we (the Balanda) fell to our knees asking forgiveness from this man. As his son brought us one at a time to shake his hand, we were all struck silent. The old man wept quietly and every muscle in his body quivered as he took our hands in forgiveness.
39 Webb, in Dewar, 1992, p.22.
40 Harris, 1990, p. 737.
41 The best written reference to this whole sad story is Egan, 1996.
42 *Missionary Review*, Methodist Overseas Mission Board, Sydney, 5 October, 1933, p. 6.

43   Harris, 1990, p. 742.
44   ibid., p. 748.
45   McKenzie, 1976, p. 79.
46   Personal communication with Yolŋu who witnessed the incident, including the person gaoled.
47   Hall, 1989, p. 168.
48   ibid., p. 168.
49   McKenzie, 1976, p. 180.
50   McKenzie, 1976, p. 228.
51   Powell, 1982, p. 185.
52   Wells, 1982, pp. 51ff.
53   From an open letter written by John Waṉamilil Malibirr
54   McKenzie, 1976, p. 190.
55   ibid., p. 193.
56   Powell, 1982, p. 224.
57   *Free to Decide*, 1974, p. 9.
58   ibid., p. 14.
59   ibid., p. 14.
60   ibid., p. 27.
61   ibid., p. 16.
62   ibid., p. 26.
63   ibid., p. 54.
64   ibid., p. 32.
65   Personal Communication, 1994.
66   Personal communication with many Yolŋu and Balanda who worked in the fishing industry during that time.
67   The Yolŋu building teams built all the housing under *buku-djugu'*, a traditional form of contract giving. This meant the teams worked to their own timetable. They worked hard and were only paid when the contract was completed as dictated by traditional law. It was not strange to see these teams working all weekend or even on Christmas Day. Because *buku-djugu'* has a very strong enforcement at traditional law, it was no problem for the building team at Ramingining to finish the houses on time and within budget.
68   *Free to Decide*, 1974, p. 34.
69   ibid., p. 32.
70   Kava is the root of a Pacific Island plant, *Piper Methysticum*. It is ground and mixed with water, and the resulting drink used ceremonially by the people of the Pacific. It has been drunk in Arnhem Land since the early 1980s. Despite attempts to introduce it with the attendant ceremonial rules of the Pacific, its use is not covered by traditional law. Consequently it has been overused, and abused, by some Yolŋu who often drink non-stop for days on end.
71   'Treatment Program for Kidney Disease in an Aboriginal Community in the NT', Menzies School of Health Research, Darwin NT, unpublished, p. 1.
72   Plant et al., 1995, p. 116.
73   Hancock, 1985, p. 5.
74   'Aboriginal Public Health Action Strategy and Implementation Guide, 1997-2002', Public Health Strategy Unit, Territory Health Services, Northern Territory Government, Darwin, November 1997, p. 17.
75   Freire, 1972, pp. 38-39.
76   Hancock, 1985, p. 5.
77   Thiong'O, Cited in Giroux, 1992, p.19.
78   Others have found this to be a major problem for other groups of Aboriginal people as well. For example, Devitt and McMasters (1998, p 139) write: 'Communication or, more precisely, the lack of communication, emerged from our study as a core issue for Aboriginal renal patients in Central Australia.'

79   Amery, 1999, p 21-23. '80% of Yolŋu expressed satisfaction with the level of care they received, only 27% expressed satisfaction with the level of explanation about diagnosis and treatment provided by doctors'. Many had real concerns as to 'the lack of sufficient information provided by medical staff'.

80   Clark, 1983, p. 807.

81   ibid., p. 807.

82   Devitt & McMasters, 1998, p. 139.

83   Australia, Parliament, *A Matter of Survival*, 1992, Executive Summary, paragraph 4.82.

84   Carlyle, in Cherry, 1971, p. 68.

85   Searcy, 1909, p. 36.

86   Crystal, 1987, p. 6.

87   Dixon, 1980, p. 4.

88   Wilkinson, 1991; McLellan, 1994.

89   Spinney, 1999, p. 38.

90   Christie, 1985, p. 65.

91   Microsoft® Encarta, 1994.

92   Brewster & Brewster, 1976, pp. 5-8.

93   McKenzie, 1976, pp. 181-82. In regard to the linguistic analysis of Yolŋu Matha, McKenzie describes the situation up to the 1950s:

'Language has been described as the shrine of a people's soul. In it are all the deep and intimate thoughts of a race.' So said [Methodist Overseas Mission] General Secretary John Burton in 1940. As far back as 1927 he had advocated learning the local tongue. T. T. Webb took up the cry in the 1930s and the new General Secretary, the Reverend Cecil Gribble, continued it in the 1940s.

It wasn't until the 1950s, however, that any really serious studies were made by the missionaries. Several of them were interested and many learned to speak local languages reasonably well, but all were too busy to do anything in the nature of grammar analysis or written work. This meant that they were missing out on the most basic ingredient of their work: the means of communication.

94   Australian Parliament, *A Matter of Survival*, 1992, Executive Summary, paragraph 4.82.

95   Ottawa Charter for Health Promotion, International Conference on Health Promotion, (jointly organised by WHO, Health and Welfare Canada, and Canadian Public Health Association) Ottawa, Ontario, Canada, November 17-26, 1986.

96   This last comment referred to the euthanasia debate in the Northern Territory in the late 1990s. Many Yolŋu believed that under liberalised voluntary euthanasia laws they would be put down like animals. This was mainly because they didn't understand the dominant culture's processes of law. And even if they did, they did not 'hear' the *voluntary* nature of the law, because their experience with dominant culture since before the turn of the last century speaks louder than any reassuring words.

97   Mirritji, 1976, p. 71.

98   Eldon & Eldon, 1977, p. 51.

99   *Learning Lessons*, 1999, Case Study 32, p. 117.

100 ibid., Executive Summary, p. 2.

101 Similarly, Paulo Freire writes from his Brazilian experience: 'Hence, in the name of respect for the culture of the peasants, for example, not to enable them to go beyond their beliefs regarding self-in-the-world and self-with–the–world betrays a profoundly elitist ideology. It is as if revealing the raison d'être, the why, of things, and to have a complete knowledge of things, were or ought to be the privilege of the elite'. Freire, 1995, p. 83.

102 Many dominant culture educational and medical personnel who have worked with Yolŋu may doubt this because they know from experience that culturally Yolŋu *do not* ask questions. But this is because the appropriate communication mores are not understood. Permission must be given to the Yolŋu person to ask questions. Even then, they may still not ask what they want to know because there must be strong trust that the 'teacher' will

not reveal to them restricted knowledge that will get them into trouble later. The people also must feel comfortable that their question is not going to get them preached at, and that they will be able to understand what is said to them so they don't look and feel stupid. With proper training, dominant culture personnel can be in a position where they are asked these questions by Yolŋu. This has been my experience.

103   'The overall results of the study reveal an unequivocal absence of such direct effects of literacy. In the first four cognitive tasks studied (conceptual understanding, conceptual organization, conceptual comparison, and deductive reasoning), there was consistently no systematic difference between the performances of the illiterate participants, the literate participants, and the schooled participants.' Bernardo,1998, p.123.

104   If she did value them, the fact she did not know these terms would not be a problem. She could learn these comparatively quickly from her old people and would remember them because they fit into the language structure she thinks and constructs knowledge in.

105   A note of caution: As explained in chapter 7, some Yolŋu are now learning what bacteria are. But they are still only a small group. Dominant culture people testing Yolŋu on this knowledge need to be sensitive to this when asking questions about it. The people do not need dominant culture people telling them that they don't know this or that, or that they are confused about the world around them. This will probably earn a severe rebuff from the people. Sensitive discussion starting from your own confusion is a better way to discover where the people are at.

106   A similar phenomenon has occurred in many developing nations where mothers leave their traditional work so they can get cash to buy milk formula to feed their babies. These women believe that milk formula is a special food and that their children will grow to be like the babies depicted on the formula container and advertising billboards.

107   I use the word 'false' here because it is a more correct interpretation of the Yolŋu Matha word used at this point. The word for 'imitation' would not work because the people have no concept of an 'imitation food'.

108   This is supported by recommendations 12, 13 and 14 in Australia Parliament, *A Matter of Survival*, the Report of the Inquiry into Aboriginal and Torres Strait Islander Language Maintenance by the House of Representatives Standing Committee on Aboriginal and Torres Strait Islander Affairs, 1992.

109   Freire, 1972, p. 65.

110   Elkin, 1994, p. 68.

111   *Mel-manapan luka* is a traditional term used to talk about healthy eating. I learned it from the old people at Ramingining in the early 1980s. It has a much wider meaning than just 'eat the eyes out of all different types of food'. To Yolŋu it speaks strongly of eating traditional fresh foods in all their variety.

112   Stanner, 1979, p. 24.

113   Dermody, 1997, pp. 1-5.

114   Note that I am not saying we should stop working through the councils, associations and other structures that now exist on communities. We must keep using these structures, otherwise we will simply cause more confusion. Rather, I am trying to explain why many of these current structures are not working. Then, instead of laying the blame at the people's feet, we can look for ways to empower them so they can create programs and structures that give better results.

115   When explaining a patient's chances of survival, it is important not to use percentages. It is better to say: 'If ten people had this sickness, this is how many would get better and how many would die.' Drawing stick figures on a piece of paper is useful.

116   Personal communication, 1993.

117   Perkins, 1980, p. 19.

118   Personal communication with many Yolŋu leaders.

119   This story is a full, meaning-based translation of the story that Tony told. He used a combination of English, Yolŋu Matha (which I translated for the officer) and mime action.

120 Ramingining had more work than people willing to do it in those days—something that had been pointed out to the government officers many times.

121 Lowndes, in his coroner's report dated June 2, 1992.

122 Miller, 1992, p. 41.

123 Although Roy used Kriol, or an 'Aboriginal English', in telling this story I have recorded it here in meaning-based modern English so that the full and deep richness of his thinking comes through to the reader.

124 'Aboriginal Youth Suicide', ABC *Four Corners*, October 26, 1998.

125 Wilson, 1982, p. 43.

126 Personal communications with Yolŋu men.

127 Freire, 1972, p. 40.

128 Miller, 1992, pp. 38-44.

129 Wilson, 1982, pp. 4-5.

130 ibid., pp. 56-57.

131 Paulo Freire saw the same sorts of violence among the people of South America in the 1960s when people were suffering under a system of control imposed by another cultural group. He wrote: 'Submerged in reality, the oppressed cannot perceive clearly the "order", which serves the interests of the oppressors whose image they have internalised. Chafing under the restrictions of this order, they manifest a type of horizontal violence, striking out at their comrades for the pettiest reasons.' (Freire, 1972, p. 38.)

132 Madigan et al, 'Beattie backs Pearson on "poison" attack', *The Courier-Mail*, May 1, 1999, p.1.

133 Koch, 'Pearson hits welfare "poison" ', *The Courier-Mail*, April 30, 1999, p.1.

134 Toffler, 1970, p. 11.

135 ibid., p. 19.

136 International Student Handbook 1995-96, College of Wooster web site, USA.

137 Oberg, Worldwide Classroom web site, January 11, 1999.

138 Guanipa, C web site, September 27, 1999, p. 1.

139 Oberg, op. cit.

140 *Learning lessons*, 1999, Table 15, p. 76.

141 Toffler, 1970, p. 20.

142 ibid., p. 297.

143 ibid., p. 20.

144 'The attitude of Aboriginal people towards hospitalisation and western medical practice can be summed up in one word, "fear".' Watson, 1987.

145 Toffler, 1970, p. 11.

146 When using x-rays, some older, senior male Yolŋu object to others seeing their skeletal shadow. Therefore the use of x-rays should be undertaken discreetly.

147 I did not see Barry until four years after that intervention, when I discovered that he had reverted to some non-compliant behaviour. This was because he was unable to get further information that made sense to him about the progression of his condition.

148 See Danieli, 1998.

149 Friedman et al, 1998.

150 Meisler, 1996; Friedman et al, 1998.

151 Riggs, 1997.

152 National Center for PTSD, Fact Sheet, 30 Sept 1998; Segal et al, 1976.

153 Friedman, September 30, 1998.

154 A shell midden is a pile of discarded shells. Shellfish were harvested and cooked on the coals of a fire. They were quite often eaten where they were cooked and the shells discarded in the one pile. Over many thousands of years the middens begin to approach the size of the one described here.

155 Rosenheck & Fontana, in Danieli, 1998, pp. 225-242

156 Danieli, 1998, p. 3.

157 *Mortality of Vietnam Veterans: The Veteran Cohort Study,* 1997.

158 Herman, 1992, pp. 377f.
159 ibid., pp. 377f.
160 Gagne, 1998, p. 358.
161 National Center For PTSD, PTSD and Community Violence, www.dartmouth.edu/dms/ptsd/FS_Community_Violence.html, 30 Sept 1998.
162 It is worth noting that the various factors described in this book compound the trauma experienced by Yolŋu. A similar observation was made by Marsella et al (1992, p. 2) regarding African-Americans: 'Several authors have discussed factors that might have placed blacks at higher risk for PTSD, such as: racism in the military and at home as well as limited economic opportunities (Allen, 1986); a 'tripartite adaptational dilemma' consisting of bicultural identity, institutional racism, and residual stress from trauma (Parsons, 1985); and the exacerbation of traumatic stress by racism and non-membership in the majority culture (Penk & Allen, 1991).'
163 Freire, 1972, p. 22.
164 Bernardo states, 'Others (see e.g. Parajuli, 1990; Rahnema,1998) have already argued that any effort attempting to make strong delineations between those who have access to literacy practices and those who do not has the effect of delegitimizing the knowledge and cognitive skills of the illiterate members of the population. This effect unfairly discrim-inates against a traditional mode of thinking and the people who practice this mode of thinking; the discrimination is against the people and the mode of thinking that was responsible for creating the community's culture thus far.'1998, p. 134.
165 Schnurr, 1996, p. 1.
166 Giroux, 1992, p. 170.
167 Webb, 1934, p. 34.
168 I am using the term 'cultural groups' in its widest possible sense to include professional groups within the dominant culture, like doctors or engineers, or a clan within a particular group of indigenous people, or a whole group of indigenous people like Yolŋu.
169 The *manikay* (instructional song cycle) for tobacco is sung at every *Yirritja* funeral, which would equate to about half the funerals held in north-east Arnhem Land.
170 Literacy programs must *include* and be supported by the whole community. Bernardo, states, 'Otherwise, the introduction of the new activity (*teaching literacy to a few*) will create a division between those who have access to literacy skills and those who do not. This situation can easily turn towards discord and marginalization, not to mention oppression.' 1998, p.134.
171 Freire, 1972, p. 112.
172 Hughes & Hunter, 1972, p. 93.
173 Plant et al, 1995, p. 46.
174 Territory Health Services, 1997, p. 5.
175 Bailey, 1998, p. 5.
176 'Report on the Provision of Health Services to Aboriginal Communities in the Northern Territory', 1996, p. 72.
177 Personal correspondence and communication, 1998.
178 Mountford, 1956.
179 ibid., p. 29.
180 ibid., p. 30.
181 ibid., p. 28.
182 Webb, 1951, p. 10.
183 McKenzie, 1976, p. 16.
184 Mountford, 1956, p. 40.
185 ibid., p. 43.
186 Bernardo, 1998, p. 123.
187 Evans, 1998.
188 Lantz et al, 1998, p. 1707.

189 Westin et al, 1988.
190 Westin et al, 1989.
191 Syme, 1997.
192 Kakadu Region Social Impact Study, June 1997, p.36.
193 Bodley, 1975, p. 152.
194 Stewart, 'The Sioux's Last Stand', *The Australian Magazine*, July 11-12, 1998, p.12.
195 Bodley, 1975. p. 152.
196 ibid., p. 152.
197 ibid., p. 152.
198 Cited in Hancock, 1985, p. 6.
199 *Official Journal of the European Communities* 1993, April 5. Council directive to facilitate the free movement of doctors and the recognition of their diplomas, certificate and other evidence of formal qualifications. 93/16/EEC.
200 United Nations International Covenant on Civil and Political Rights, 1996, Part III, Article 14.
201 See Australia Parliament, *A Matter of Survival*, 1992.
202 Harris, 1973.
203 Albee in Hancock, 1985, p. 6.
204 Freire, 1972, p. 68.
205 ibid., p. 68.
206 ibid., p. 28.
207 Airhihenbuwa, 1994, p. 352.
208 Most of this discussion occurred in Yolŋu Matha except where the children were quoting the English words of the teachers, 'free country' and so on.
209 There are many reasons why Aboriginal people like Yolŋu leave their land and go to live in Darwin. Some commentators say they feel these people come to Darwin to get grog. Though most do end up being alcoholics, I believe this is an incorrect assumption. I have talked to many of these people in Yolŋu Matha and asked them why they are in Darwin. There are a whole range of reasons, the most common being medical. I know of one whole family which is in Darwin because of its belief that it is being targeted by sorcery. Another family has a genetic defect leading to leukemia. Other individuals will say they are there to be close to Darwin hospital, and if you look back in their medical history you can find a time when they almost died. This gave them a big shock, so they want to be close to what they see as better medical services.
     I believe, with the education we are talking about here, that many people will be happy to return to their own country and will find a degree of security there, rather than becoming outcasts in the long grass of Darwin.
210 To show bacteria we placed ordinary water-born bacteria on the slides, as the handling of live Melioidosis is too dangerous. When the people understood the idea of bacteria in general, we showed them pictures of Melioidosis and told them that it was too dangerous to show them the real thing. To validate this information, we quoted from an encyclopaedia the number of laboratory workers who had died by contracting Melioidosis while handling it. The people were happy with this explanation.
211 *Case Study on AIDS Education,* Aboriginal Resource and Development Services Inc, 1995.
212 United Nations International Covenant on Civil and Political Rights 1996, Part 1, Article 1 (1).
213 Aboriginal Land Rights (Northern Territory) Act 1976.